A SIDEWAYS LAUNCH

Cover. Ship No. 2123 *Danby Cross* built for the Tees Towing Company. A spectacular sideways launch into Faversham Creek.

Frontispiece. Ship No. 2144 *Sun XXVII*, a tug supplied in 1968 to Alexanders for use on the Thames. From a drawing by Jack Salmon.

A SIDEWAYS LAUNCH

The Technical and Social History of James Pollock, Sons & Co. Ltd., Shipbuilders and Engineers of London and Faversham, 1875-1970

ANNE SALMON

MERESBOROUGH BOOKS
1992

Published by Meresborough Books, 17 Station Road, Rainham, Kent. ME8 7RS.

Meresborough Books is a specialist publisher of books on Kent with about one hundred books in print. In addition they publish a monthly magazine 'Bygone Kent' which covers all aspects of Kent history and was founded in 1979. A free sample of 'Bygone Kent' and a list of other books will be sent on request.

Books available include:

BARGE BUILDING AND BARGE BUILDERS OF THE SWALE by Don L. Sattin. The author was foreman shipwright of Whites in Conyer. Hardback £9.95.

OLD FAVERSHAM by Arthur Percival. An historic exploration of the town with 145 old photographs. Large format paperback. £4.95.

ISBN 0948193 68 9

PRINTED IN GREAT BRITAIN BY HEADLEY BROTHERS LTD THE INVICTA PRESS ASHFORD KENT AND LONDON

CONTENTS

ACKNOWLEDGEMENTS

Grateful thanks are extended to the many people who have helped in the writing of this book, and its illustration, including: John Andersen, Quay Lane Wharf; Mr R.S. Craig, St Margaret's Bay, Dover; Mr C. Downs, ex-loftsman at the shipyard; Mr P. Ellis, last managing director, Faversham shipyard; Mr H. Higgs, Sandhurst; Mr B. Hillsdon, Steam Boat Association of Great Britain; Captain M. Lee, Medway Pilot; Mr J.W. James, Faversham; Mr H.R. Long, Abbey Secretarial Services; Mr Stephen Lutman; M. McAloon, Naval Historical Section, MoD; Patricia O'Driscoll, Meresborough Books; Mr A. Percival, Faversham Society; R.H. Perks, Eastling; Mr B. Poulteney, Queen Elizabeth's School; Miss Daphne Pipe, Royal Brass Foundry, Woolwich; Cllr P.J. Salmon, my father; Mr W.F. Shields, ex Chief Engineer, Faversham shipyard; Mr and Mrs R. Smith, Faversham shipyard; Robert Weedon, Philip's Yard, Dartmouth.

Also, all the men and women who worked at the shipyard who shared their memories in words and photographs with me during the preparation of this book, some of whom will never see it in print.

The photographs in this volume are reproduced from the following sources: Mr S. Bushell, Mr G. Chambers, Mr C. Downs, Mr C. Godden, Mr P. Judges, Mr W. Hobbs, Mr C. Fowle, Mr C. Carter, Mr H. Lennard, Mr R. Smith, Mr J. Finn, Mr R. Flint, Mr S. Flowers, Mr W.F. Shields, Miss P. O'Driscoll, Mr P. Ellis, Mr P.J. Salmon, Mr E. Cripps, Mr Hills; also the author's collection and "Small Vessels", Walter Pollock 1946 and "Hot Bulb Oil Engines and Suitable Vessels", Walter Pollock 1918.

DEDICATION

This book is dedicated to all those who worked for the firm of James Pollock, Sons & Co. Ltd., and helped to make it great. Without them, it could not have been written.

Anne L. Salmon, BA, MCD, MRTPI, Faversham, 1990

FOREWORD . . .

Being an Island Nation our history and culture has by sheer necessity been closely allied to the sea and ships.

This book covers the true history of one small shipyard. The family behind the company had many historical links with the past.

They were coupled with great names like Rennie and Constant and many others, all part of that golden age of British shipbuilding.

Alas, like so many shipyards in Britain, the company and its yard have disappeared, a victim of the times.

The author has researched the subject in great depth and detail and presented a book well worth reading . . .

P. Ellis, MRINA, CEng
February 1990

James Pollock, 1838 – 1910

Walter Pollock, 1873 – 1947

Marshall B. Pollock, 1908 – 1966

Chapter 1
INTRODUCTION

The firm of James Pollock, Sons & Co. Ltd. was founded in London in 1875 and closed in 1970. It was a small firm, but its name was well known along the Thames estuary, and through its ships, all over the world. Shipbuilders and engineers, Pollocks were famed for the quality of their output. They were leaders in the popularisation of the internal combustion engine in shipping through their Bolinder agency, and contributed in a small but nevertheless important way to the war effort in both the World Wars of this twentieth century.

As shipbuilders, they became attached to the small town and port of Faversham, near the North Kent coast. Here, many people have memories of the firm and its ships, either as ex-employees of Pollocks or of other companies locally for whom Pollocks did repairs, or from whom they purchased components. The firm was for a long time the town's largest employer and as such was of major importance to the town's economy for a considerable part of this century.

I. The Pollocks' Engineering History

The founder of Pollocks, James, born in 1838, came from Glasgow. The Pollock family had already been involved in engineering for nearly a century. His grandfather, Walter (1753–1820), trained as a millwright in a firm which made sugar machinery, and gained both money and position in St Mary's, Jamaica, where he became a coroner and a Justice of the Peace. Walter's second son, Robert (1809–76), was born in Dumfries and became apprenticed to an engineer in Burntisland. A skilled engineer, Robert came down to London in 1835, where he made the steam omnibuses which ran on the road from London to Uxbridge. Unfortunately, one of these buses had a boiler explosion. Robert became involved in one of the earliest South-Eastern experiments in railways, joining the London & Greenwich Railway in 1836, and would willingly have worked for them even on Sundays, but his wife objected. His first involvement specifically with marine engineering was when he joined J. & A. Blyth, Engineers, of Limehouse. His grandson, Walter Pollock (1873–1947) states that Robert contributed significantly to mechanical engineering whilst working for them.

Robert Pollock had three sons, all of whom became involved in marine engineering. The second, also named Robert, born 1842, followed his father into the firm of J.& A. Blyth of 44 Fore Street, Limehouse, serving three years in the drawing office and four in the works. He became an engineer on several steamers; the *Jason* in 1861, for the London & East India Steamship Co., the *Vesta*, and on blockade runners in the American Civil War, the *Alliance* and the *Florence*. He departed for the Antipodes in 1873, where he became Superintendent Engineer of a New Zealand company, then Marine Superintendent at Mort's Dry Dock, Sydney, till 1879. Robert ended his career working for Lloyd's Register of Shipping, London, as a surveyor till 1912, and died in 1916.

The third son, Walter, born 1847, was in 1885 Chief Engineer on the *Dredger No. 121* steaming to Auckland, New Zealand.

It was the eldest son, however, who most distinguished himself in the field of marine engineering. James Pollock was born in 1838, and according to his son, Walter, had a rare knowledge of marine and other engineering, and was very popular in the City of London. James served his time from 1852–9 with J. & A. Blyth, four years ahead of his brother, Robert. As an engineering draughtsman, he was taught to colour plans and drawings, some of which took as much as a week to complete.

In 1859, at the age of twenty-one, James sailed on the wind-jammer *Orus* to Vladivostock on which was to be a major adventure. Aboard, in plates and angles was the tug *General Kharsakoff.* On arrival, in the dead of winter, the tug was re-assembled and steamed up the River Amur, the first ever steamer to do so. James was Chief Engineer, and in order that supplies be put aboard quickly, bribed a Russian storekeeper. He served in this position in Siberian and Mongolian waters for three years. In 1862, as James was returning overland on a horse droshki, he gave a young man a lift back to Moscow. The man turned out to be the son of the Russian Minister of Marine. James was offered in return the position of Chief Engineer to the Russian Navy, a position which he politely declined.

Having been Engineer on the New Zealand Shipping Co.'s *Ruahine* (a position in which he was succeeded by his brother, Robert), James crossed the Atlantic and entered a period of blockade-running in the American Civil War. The vessels involved included the *Don* built by Dudgeon's, and the *Atalanta*. The latter had eight names during her short career, 1862–69 when she was lost, of which the best known was the *Tallahassee*. This was whilst working for J. & W. Dudgeon, Engineers & Shipbuilders. Other work for the firm included installation of machinery for the Portuguese government in Lisbon and engineering on vessels of the North Sea service between London and Sweden.

Another post was offered to James in 1865, which he declined, after he had been successful as Chief Engineer in overcoming engine trouble on the s.s. *Mary* in the London–Gothenburg trade.

On 2nd January 1868, James married Emily Ethelinda Wiggins at St Alphege Church, Greenwich. He continued his varied experience of engineering, serving as draughtsman with Gilbert & Cooper of Hull, and there preparing drawings of treadmill wheels for Hull Borough Prison.

In 1870 he was aboard the *Italo Platense* as Chief Engineer, and saved the ship from loss en route from Italy to South America. The vessel was one of the Italian Mail Steamers running between Genoa and the River Plate. Over the period 1871–3, back in London, he worked as an engineer at Lewis & Stockwell's, Blackwall Reach.

James returned in 1874 to J. & A. Blyth as Designer, and there designed the *Rienzi* (114′×20′), a paddle tug with a single cylinder engine.

It was in 1875, at the age of thirty-seven, after wide experience in the engineering world, that James Pollock decided to set up in business as a Consulting Engineer and Naval Architect and founded the firm of 'James Pollock & Sons'. James was a member of the Institute of Mechanical Engineers, the Royal Institute of Naval Architects (1894) and the Institute of Marine Engineers. His death in February 1910 was reported in the Transactions of each of these institutions. The firm's history is described in subsequent chapters. James and his wife, Emily, had nine children, six of them boys. The eldest, Robert, born 1868, served part of his time in his father's office and the rest with Bow & McLachlan & Co. of Paisley. He gained a Chief Engineer's certificate and in 1890 was Chief Engineer aboard the China Mutual Steamship Co.'s *Kaisow*. Subsequently, he joined the General Steam Navigation Company. He later went to join his uncle in New Zealand, where he died in 1917. The second son, James (1870–1927), became a civil engineer, working first for the London & North-Western Railway and later as Assistant Engineer under Holman F. Stephens on the Tonbridge to Robertsbridge railway, which is, at the time of writing, being restored to partial use under the name Kent & East Sussex Railway. In 1904 James became a director of James Pollock, Sons & Co. Ltd., a position which he held until 1917.

Frederick (1872–1918) spent a short time in the paternal office, then went to Riley, Hargreaves & Co. Ltd. (Howarth Erskine) and became their Managing Director. This firm had associations with Singapore, hence Frederick enabled JPS & Co. to become buying agents for Howarth Erskine and sell vessels to Singapore. In 1909, Frederick Pollock married Gladys Erskine by whom he had three daughters.

Walter followed his father into the firm of James Pollock & Sons, becoming a partner in 1900, and continuing as Managing Director, then Chairman after the death of his father. Born on 25th March 1873, Walter was a weak boy and was not expected to be successful. At the age of nine, his father took him to see the ship models at a Naval Exhibition, and Walter's interest in marine engineering remained unabated throughout his life.

Walter joined his father's firm as an apprentice in 1887, and worked under him till 1892, when he became an Engineer and Naval Architect for the firm of Joseph Constant. Whilst working part-time for Joseph Constant, Walter was in succession Manager at Rutland Engine Works, Glasgow, in 1893–4 and Manager of Montrose Shipyard 1894–6. During his apprenticeship with his father, Walter's work included calculations and plans of marine engines up to 300 i.h.p. and plans of boilers, assisting at damage surveys and inspection of new craft. Evening classes three times per week included shorthand and typing. With Joseph Constant, Walter's experience was no less wide. There, he was designing and superintending the construction of steam tugs, coasters and other small craft.

Among his early design work were iron narrow boat steamers for Fellows, Morton & Clayton, and a number of Thames Sailing Barges. Of the latter, Walter Pollock designed thirty-seven between 1897 and 1903. The first of these was the 160-ton *Gloria*. A series of 180-tonners from Fay's Yard, Southampton, included *Briton, Saxon, Spartan* and *Scot*. Twenty-one more of that class were built at Southampton between 1898 and 1899 including the *Decima* which at the time of writing is based in Faversham Creek, owned by Dennis Wildish. Goldsmiths, pleased by the performance of the 180-tonners ordered a class of 250-tonners. They were built by J. Kievits & van Reede at Papendrecht, Holland, and by Otto & Zonen at Krympen d'Ysel in 1903–4. The large barges included the *Gothic, Teutonic, Oceanic, Servic, Doric, Britannic* which later served in the ballast trade, and *Germanic* which having been renamed *Lais* in the anti-German period around the First World War, came to Pollocks for conversion to motor in the 1930s. Three of these barges voyaged to the River Plate, South America, ketch-rigged.

In a particularly tiring period for Walter in 1895–1905, he was spending the day doing drawings and specifications for ships in London, travelling on the night train to Glasgow or Montrose, or sometimes to Holland. If Glasgow was his destination, his working day could last from 5.30 a.m. to 7.30 p.m. In Holland he supervised the building of the barges, sometimes going there twice a week. On one later occasion, only a cancelled booking prevented him travelling on the steamer *Berlin* on 21st February 1907 when she sank with great loss of life. Of the 141 passengers and crew of the liner, only fifteen were saved.

In 1898, Walter designed the chain and hopper gear of six large, towing barges, including the *Dromedary* built by Russell & Co. at Glasgow. These were not the only hopper barges he designed. One, for Gaselee's, later part of Alexander's tugs, who eventually joined Alexandra Towing, named *Herbert Gaselee*, had the hopper gear smashed as dock contractors dropped a 3½-ton piece of clay from 27 feet down its chute; needless to say, the contractors had to pay for the repairs. Walter himself narrowly escaped an unpleasant accident as an apprentice under his father, whilst aboard the *Dragon*, a tug for the River Thames designed by James Pollock & Sons. Having climbed through a 15″ × 11″ manhole, he was inside the boiler when another vessel collided with the 66′6″ × 7′0″ *Dragon*. Fortunately, she did not explode. Another risky venture in 1894 in which Walter was involved was the salvage of the tug *Prosper* off Arran. In a borrowed fishing boat, he went out in the middle of the night, pumped out the tug, sealed the hole and steamed her to Ardrossan. In the same year, to avoid a possible delay in the delivery of a vessel built at Montrose due to an industrial dispute, Walter himself took the tug *Northumbria* to Aberdeen for coal, sent a telegram to London to insure her and then steamed her to the owner who was waiting at Dover.

By 1900 Walter was working as a partner with his father at James Pollock, Sons & Co. of which he would be made a director in 1901, where his engineering experience and business sense were no doubt appreciated in the growing business. He continued also to work for Joseph Constant till 1905 by which time his now elderly father was willing to take a back seat to his able son.

George (1874–1923), fifth son of James Pollock, joined Parbury, Henty & Co. where he gained a broad knowledge of the export trade. He joined JPS & Co. to assist on the commercial side. He became Director in Charge of the Export Department dealing with Singapore and with Australia, to which he emigrated and where he married and had three sons, one of whom became an engineer.

Arthur (1876–1938) spent his time in JPS & Co. and then went to British Petroleum. In 1906 he rejoined James Pollock, Sons & Co. Ltd., where he became Secretary and later a director. He helped George in the Export Department, becoming head of the export business in 1923, and retiring in 1933 from the company to start one of his own, Arthur Pollock & Co. Ltd.

Of the three daughters of James Pollock — Emily, Alice and Margaret — one was to marry an engineer. Emily married H.P. Lawrence, who was apprenticed with her brother Walter to JPS & Co. from 1889–1892 and who later became Chief Engineer on a steamer to Siberia, and eventually made agricultural machinery in East Anglia.

The firm of James Pollock, Sons & Co. Ltd. through James's large family, in the early decades of the present century, had contacts spread across the globe and in useful firms from which they could expect to gain orders, added to the business contacts James had built up in the City of London and in the Institutes of Marine Engineering and of Mechanical Engineers.

To summarise, a family tree of the Pollocks involved in engineering.

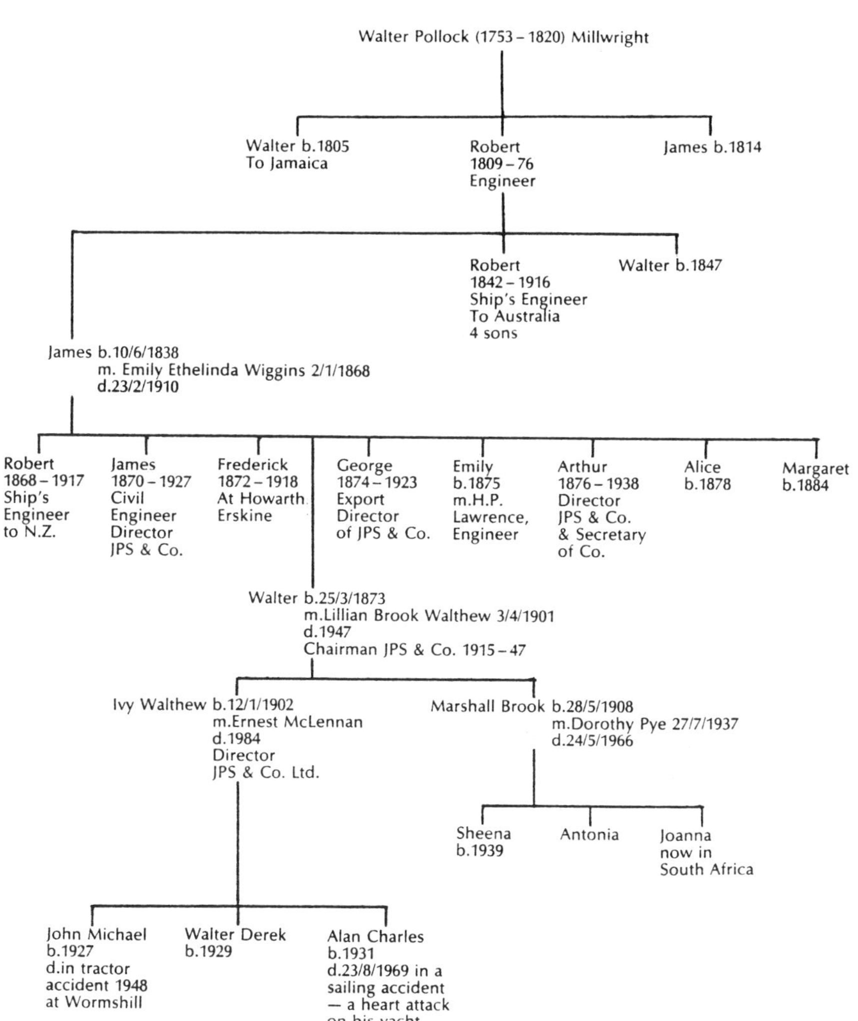

II. The shipping industry in the period 1875 – 1970

The period was one of great change in the shipping industry. At its start, sail tonnage was still greater than steam on the British register though mostly in the long sea trades to Australia and to the waters around South America where coaling stations were few and far between. According to Mitchell & Deane, steam did not overcome sail till 1883. Mild steel was only just becoming a viable material for the construction of shipping and of boilers, enabling greater cargo capacity because of its greater strength and lightness, and higher steam pressures. A model example of the new experiments in steel hulls and super-pressure steam from tubular boilers was the steamer *Anthracite* on which James Pollock based the design of a fast steamer, *Express*.

However, compound steam engines, which had become more common in large vessels in the 1860s – 70s, were also in widespread use for tugs in both British waters and abroad. Whilst in British waters screw had replaced paddle propulsion for most steam craft, the paddle steamer was still fairly common in the shallow tributaries of the Amazon especially for the ferrying of passengers and the development of the resources of the interior of South America.

In the Thames, the development of the enclosed dock system was continuing apace. The Albert Dock, opened in 1880, specialised in the frozen meat trade, and was followed in 1886 by Tilbury Docks, deeper and situated much further down river, having good links into the railway network. At the urgent request of the many shipping firms using the Thames, it had been dredged to a depth of 26 feet in 1888, but still no concerted effort to dredge the river was made till the Port of London Authority was formed in 1908.

A system of unloading of vessels onto lighters had developed, and a strong lobby of lightermen created who kept the system going despite the construction of the enclosed docks at which large vessels could unload directly onto a quay. The free water clause, a concession made by the Dock Companies to this lobby, under which lighters could continue to carry goods without paying dock dues in the enclosed docks was what kept the lighterage trade viable. Sailing barges under 45 tons were entitled to the same concession. Unpowered, the many lighters required the services of large numbers of tugs, each of which could pull six laden lighters, the maximum allowed by the PLA regulations then as now. Although efficiency in steam propulsion had increased, there was still room for a decrease in fuel costs, especially for tugs.

In Sweden, the firm of J. & C.G. Bolinder of Stockholm was one of the first to apply heavy-oil burning internal combustion engines to marine propulsion in the first decade of the twentieth century. Internal combustion engines in small vessels became a speciality of Pollocks, for they were Bolinder's British agents. Before the First World War, Bolinders had been applied to uses in fishing vessels, tugs, and in the barge trade on the canals, making it more competitive with the railways for bulk freight transport.

After the First World War, internal combustion engines made by various firms including Widdop, Allen, Kelvin and Mirrlees would become an almost ubiquitous means of marine propulsion.

The latest developments in construction and propulsion were increasingly being propagated in books or discussed academically at colleges such as Greenwich and South Kensington, so that mistakes in design could be overcome and

Ship No. 1131 *Caupolican*, a steam tug. The vessel is being fitted out alongside Standard House on the opposite side of the creek from the yard.

improvements made in a scientific manner. In this, Walter Pollock participated. (See programme of lectures in Chapter 5, made to conventions of marine and mechanical engineers.) Better machinery in shipyards meant that higher standards of accuracy could be achieved in the construction of ships.

In a period of change in the shipping world, early on Pollocks were leading the field, and in the bulk trades of the Thames and Medway, were unsurpassed, only finally being overtaken by events when the lighterage trade suddenly collapsed on the Thames in favour of road haulage and containerisation.

III. The advantages of London

London, where James Pollock had set up his business and to which his father had earlier come to develop the London and Greenwich Railway, was the focus of Britain's coasting and worldwide trade. At its heart was the City, containing the major commodity markets, the shipping intelligence and insurance facilities of Lloyd's, and offices of ships' brokers and agents. In the metropolis, then, all the necessary contacts for the development of a shipbuilding firm could be found. The metropolis itself was developing, so that there were opportunities for business in general engineering — indeed Pollocks were required as consultant engineers to assess the value of the property north of Aldwych before its replacement by Kingsway at the turn of the century. This property included the slum area of Wych Street and Holywell Street.

A popular man among his business colleagues in the City, and a keen linguist, James Pollock was well equipped to deal with the British and overseas customers he might obtain through having his business (later only its head office) in the world centre which London was and remains.

IV. The position of Faversham

The small town and port of Faversham, chosen by Walter Pollock for the location of his shipbuilding yard to build concrete coasters in 1916–17, is situated on a navigable creek. Four miles long, the narrow creek links the town to the Swale which lies between the north coast of Kent and the Isle of Sheppey.

FAVERSHAM SHIPYARD

The town had, throughout the previous century, and indeed before, been one whose economy rested both on agriculture and industry, early on being the major supplier to the country's arsenals of gunpowder. Of late, the main growth industry had been the exploitation of the large quantities of brick-earth which lay under and around the town.

Lying to the north of the main A2, and since 1858 being served by the railway to London from both Dover and Ramsgate, the town had good communications, a point which Water Pollock seldom failed to make in his leaflets advertising the shipyard.

Since the deepening and straightening of the creek in 1843, which eliminated the bends opposite Standard Wharf and round what became Crab Island, several shipbuilding yards had already been established on the creek. One of these, Goldfinch's yard at the lower end of Standard Wharf, had been building wooden spritsail barges and had built up a skilled workforce of shipwrights and carpenters. Another also building barges, was Dan's beyond the creek bridge on a site which was later to become the roller rink.

Timber, grain, bricks and coal were the main cargoes carried by the Thames barges, small ketches and schooners which plied the creek — its winding course requiring the use of tugs to assist vessels to reach the wharves to load and unload. Conveniently, to serve the wharves, the creek branch railway line extended across Whitstable Road via Iron Wharf, running parallel with the creek to Belvedere Road, enabling the raw materials which Pollocks would require to build ships to be brought to their doorstep, though they would still have to be fetched across the creek. The narrow waterway would allow only for sideways launches except for the very smallest of vessels, but this was a common practice among yards building small craft, other examples being at Beverley and Thorne. It created more splash, being much faster than the stern-first launches at yards with frontage to wider waterways.

No doubt, the town was pleased to receive a potentially important employer. The site they chose, adjacent to White's shipyard, had recently been exhausted as a brickfield and filled with the heavy remains of "rough-stuff" brought down from London to fire the bricks. This was an area which the town had wanted to see developed — the marsh adjacent was intended to be used for industry as well, hence a gasometer was placed on it. The development never came off, but the gasometer remained well into the 1920s. After this gasometer was half dismantled in the mid 1920s the shipyarders used to climb over the wall and swim in it in their lunchbreak.

On what must have been a fairly cheap site, with good communications to London and elsewhere, and with available skilled labour, Walter Pollock would develop from 1916 his shipyard which would remain a feature of the town for much of this century. The site's subsequent occupants, after the demise of Pollocks would be compared by Faversham people with James Pollock, Sons & Co.

A major local industry which not only employed many local people but also brought large numbers of workers into the town from Essex, from the North of England and from the West Country, the shipyard would affect not only the

Opposite: Aerial view of Pollocks' Shipyard in the 1920s, showing many vessels under construction.

The Carnival War Machine. This was one of Pollocks' floats built for Faversham's torchlight carnival in the 1930s.

town's economy but also its social life. By the 1930s, under the management of Marshall Pollock, Faversham Institute and the town's colourful, torchlight carnival would owe much to the efforts of the shipyarders, to their Social Club and not least to Marshall himself.

The creek, the artery on which the business depended, was kept well dredged to facilitate the launching of vessels and their passage. Marshall Pollock ensured this for himself by being on the Navigation Committee which he eventually chaired. Indeed, only after the firm's passing would it begin to silt up again.

V. Shipbuilding as an industry

Steel shipbuilding brought to Faversham the fine division of labour for which the industry nationally was infamous. Each group of craftsmen even within the Boilermakers' Society would be responsible for their own particular skill. A riveter, for example, could not do a burner's work, and to the craftsman, the non-unionised (till 1937) labourer would be definitely inferior, not having served the five-year apprenticeship required for all craftsmen. Perhaps the workers from outside brought it in, for early on they filled many of the posts in the plating and riveting departments. One North-Eastern shipwright quoted by Pagnamenta & Overy described the situation where he worked:

"It was all in the work. You had your shipwrights, you had your riveters, you had your engineers, you had your caulkers, your drillers, electricians, and many more small trades, and of course there was the labouring man. He was out of the question really." The pay structure at the yard throughout its history reflected this differentiation, the industrial aristocracy being the piecework platers and riveters.

A permanent feature of the town while the yard was running was the noise of the rivet hammers which rang across the Brents all day. The bell or hooter which called the men to work, and the swarm of bicycles which filled the Brents in the morning, at lunchtime and in the late afternoon would be missed when the yard closed, for in the years of its existence, they would have been regular enough to set any household clock by.

The following chapters document the history of the firm from its founding in the City in 1875, through the First World War to its purchase of the Faversham site. The development of the various crafts which went together to build ships and other machinery and the gradual modernisation of the yard is chronicled. From the 1930s, the involvement of the firm in the social life of Faversham becomes more important.

Through the Second World War, which brought to it a very busy period and in which it contributed to the war effort not only ships but men in the Home Guard and Rescue Party, the story continues. The 1950s brought some new machinery and men, but the 1960s brought mostly problems to a yard which, as it was becoming clear, had failed to diversify sufficiently to escape the effects of a change in bulk haulage which was taking place. Two untimely family deaths and the loss of valuable contacts through the closure of the London office sealed the fate of the firm in which potential customers still had faith till the end — faith enough for the firm to close with orders still on its books.

The photographs illustrate some of the wide variety of vessels and engines which the firm produced, mostly its output at Faversham; also the machine tools and the people who contributed to this output in the yard and buildings where they worked.

Sources

"Abstract of British Historical Sources". Mitchell & Deane.
"The Pollocks as Engineers". Walter Pollock, 1939.
"All Our Working Lives". Peter Pagnamenta & Richard Overy, 1984. BBC.
"A Couple of Bob on the Line". R. Dadson in Faversham Magazine Vol. 1, No. 2, 1966.
"Engineer", Vol. 109, March 1910.
Institute of Marine Engineers' Transactions. Vol. 52, 1910/11.
Institute of Mechanical Engineers' Proceedings. February 1910.

Chapter 2
JAMES POLLOCK, SONS & CO. LTD. — THE FIRM AND ITS SHIPS 1875–1915

The first forty years of the firm, founded by James Pollock in 1875 and originally based in Great Tower Street, London, saw it working largely as consultant engineers and Naval architects, contracting out the work of building ships to other firms in Britain and in Holland. As engineers, the firm was concerned to a limited extent with civil as well as marine engineering.

Through widespread advertising in various languages and many parts of the world, the firm soon built up contacts and could sell designs and finished vessels particularly in the Southern Hemisphere. Customers ranged from the railway ferry at Tilbury to harbour boards in South Africa and New Zealand and rubber plantation owners in the Amazon basin.

Many of the earlier vessels were steam-powered, either double or triple expansion engines. They ranged in size from 20′ launches to 350′ cargo vessels. Unpowered lighters of various types, canal barges and narrow boats were supplied in increasing numbers in the first few years of the twentieth century. Shortly before the First World War, the firm successfully propagated the use of Bolinder engines in a variety of vessels for the home market and for abroad.

Reflecting the gradual increase in the business of the firm, it moved into progressively larger premises, and came under the regulations of the Limited Liability Act in 1901. A board of directors was appointed and the founder, James Pollock received increasing help from them and from his son, Walter, who succeeded James on his death in 1910.

I. Pre 1900 — steamers for all over the world

One of the earliest ships designed by James Pollock, Naval architect, was the *Blosse Lynch* built for use on the Tigris by Rennies of Greenwich in 1876. She could still be seen there working forty years after her despatch to Basra in plates and angles. To facilitate engineering on subsequent vessels, James entered into a partnership with A.W. Robertson in his engine works and repair shop at Royal Albert Docks, a partnership which was to last till 1884. In 1877, an iron paddle tug *Her Majesty* was designed by James, and built at Allsop & Sons, Preston, for the Black Ball Line's use at Gravesend. 1879 saw the construction of *Gleam*, a fast launch with scantlings which were very small, the frames being only 1″ × 1″ × 3/16″ × 16″ apart, the smallest ever seen on a hull of this type. Powered by a loco boiler, she could achieve a speed of 13.94 miles per hour. In 1881, James Pollock began what would be a long-lasting connection with the Amazon, with the supply of a very strong launch with a non-condensing engine and loco boiler, the *Progresso*. Like many later vessels for the Amazon, she shipped out in plates and angles, a practice with which James had been familiar at Maudslay, Son & Field earlier in his career.

Ship No. 99 *Antonio Lemos*, a stern-wheel steamer built by Lobnitz, Renfrew, and supplied by Pollocks for use on the Amazon.

Closer to home, in 1883, he designed the ferry *Tilbury* to serve on the passenger link between Gravesend and Tilbury. A paddler, she remained in service for thirty-one years.

In 1894, James designed a 17-knot passenger and mail steamer for India, the *Puri* built at Dundee. Whilst he was superintending the construction of the vessel, James tapped one of the castings with the umbrella which he always carried. It went through the casting in one of the square, cast-iron columns, and it was later found out that the core box had moved in the foundry, leaving only a film of cast iron to carry the paint.

The firm's major commitment in the period immediately before the turn of the century was the continued design of vessels for the Amazon of various types. James Pollock & Sons were consulting engineers to the Amazon Steam Navigation Company. Among the craft were the cargo vessels *Marquesa de Saturnanca, Duquesa de Vista Hermosa* and the stern-wheeler *Antonio Lemos*, unusual in having solid instead of feathering floats. Orders from Amazon customers also included small launches and unpowered lighters.

From the start, the firm had made tugs a speciality. In 1883, they supplied a sea-tug *Awarua* to the Bluff Harbour Board in New Zealand, and in the 1890s the 115′ seagoing tug *Alert* to Table Bay, South Africa. Several were designed for use on the Thames, including the pair, *Dragon* and *Scorpion*, and one, *Conservator* for King's Lynn.

Four large (350′) cargo vessels were built at Sunderland for C. Howard & Sons, for whom Pollocks were consulting engineers, named *Oberon, Titania, Cymbeline* and *Imogen*. The last-named was not completed till 1905. Only a week elapsed between her launch and delivery, in which time she was completely fitted out including the bathroom for the master's stateroom, a remarkable feat. All four continued to be maintained by Pollocks till Howards sold them in 1911.

An established, profitable trade, the transport of coal required the design and supply of the flatiron collier *Battersea* for carrying coal up the Thames to the gasworks at Fulham and other industrial users, the vessel being designed to be able to pass under the many Thames bridges. The only vessel built for the Defence Vessels Construction Co., the *Bonaventura* was supplied to Erith in 1891.

II. The expanding company

By 1882, the firm had outgrown its birthplace in Great Tower Street and transferred all its offices to 5 & 7 Fenchurch Street. A second move, this time to 22 Billiter Street, EC3 took place in 1891. Eventually, in 1901, the firm moved to 3 Lloyds Avenue, to offices which it would occupy till the 1950s, before finally departing for a smaller suite in a building opposite.

James Pollock's firm became a private company on 1st January 1900, when a partnership between James and Walter Pollock was formed with capital of £700. Since that time, Walter stated in his history of the firm, it had paid out several hundreds of thousands of pounds in salaries, and by 1939, £149,000 in dividends. The firm had opened Civil Engineering and Machinery Export departments, and had arranged and carried out contracts for railways and public works in the East, in Africa and in South America.

On December 16th 1901 the firm became a Limited Liability Company. It had just two directors at first, but shortly afterwards more were elected. Walter Pollock became responsible for the firm of James Pollock, Sons & Co. Ltd. in 1905, and his business identity merged with that of the family firm, and he became Managing Director in 1910.

In 1898, the firm were so well-known as engineers that they were asked by someone in New York to design a 200′ rigid steel-plated airship. Designs were sent to the customer for the craft *Arabis* but Walter Pollock did not think it was ever built. Pollock himself declined to build it. He later wondered if its design had contributed in any way to the German advancement of the Zeppelin.

From 1903, the keen and able linguist, James Pollock, aided by his son, commenced the advertising of their many and varied products in illustrated catalogues, in Portuguese and other languages for the benefit of customers, enabling them to select the type most suited to their needs. A block printing process was adopted for the designs of vessels and plans were drawn to standard sizes. One of these catalogues was called "Tropical Vessels of Various Types". Another was that for vessels to the Amazon, described later in the chapter.

The firm was engaged not only to design new vessels, but also to survey existing vessels. One such was the unusual roller boat *Bazin* which had six roller wheels of 12′ diameter and 4′ wide in pairs, driven by a chain from a petrol engine, which achieved 8 knots despite its inventor's vain hopes that it would go at 50 knots.

Both Walter and his father were members of the Institutes of Marine Engineers, of Naval Architects and of Mechanical Engineers. In 1904, Walter became a member of the North-East Coast Institute of Engineers and Shipbuilders and in 1919, a member of the Institute of Metals.

III. 1900 – 1910. A variety of vessels

The firm began an association with lighterage on the Thames about 1905, with six 80′ swim-barges each with similar names with the prefix "Red", followed by others with "M" names and Dutch names. These may have been built in Holland, for Pollocks had already used the Dutch yard of Kloos & Son to build a dry dock for Sydney before the turn of the century. Canal barges for the Regents Canal were produced in half dozens, and swim-punts in similar quantities. Not only were unpowered craft designed and built for use in Britain, but towing lighters were despatched to Bangkok and Cochin China.

Launch frames and machinery including loco-type boilers, donkey boilers and engines were supplied to customers in Bangkok, India and South America.

A large number of tugs were designed for clients in all parts of the globe. Of one, the river tug *Constance* built in 1904, the following plans were kept:

Ship No. 106. Constance. Steam tug

Plan No.	Type	
13	Tracing	Sections
404	Tracing	Details
13447	Tracing	Tail shaft and engine
15334	Tracing	Surface condenser pumps
506	Tracing	Lines plan
292	Blue Print	Deck plan
291	Blue Print	Longitudinal sections
1394	Blue Print	Compound machine zonder condensate (Bolnes engine plan)
1390	Blue Print	Bolnes engine plan
1393-5	Blue Print	Engine plans
1391,1006	Blue Print	Engine plans

As well as the more common launch and barge tugs, Walter Pollock designed the steamer *Bheestie*, which combined the functions of freshwater boat, tug, salvage steamer, lifting lighter, mine and anchor laying vessel and despatch boat. The vessel's trials took place at Felixstowe in May 1910, and her qualities were reported in Lloyds Weekly List for 6th May 1910. She featured a special towing hook and Pollock Patent Stern Frame. Another unusual design was the ice-breaking tug for use in Boreal waters, the *Voevoda*, sent to Siberia in 1909.

The firm maintained a steady relationship with the Amazon, and also had customers in other parts of South America. Ships ranged from the small launches *Laju* and *Brani* to the 150′ sternwheeler steamer *Inca*. Notable were the hatched lighters, *Papagaio* and *Periquito*, and the large ferry-steamer *Guanabacoa* which was supplied with two small, steel tenders. The steamer, a double-ended Pennsylvania type, was powered by a Bablock & Wilcox engine which drove a continuous shaft with a propeller at each end. The speed specified by the purchasers had been 11 knots, and on her first trials, the *Guanabacoa* exceeded this figure by ¼ knot. The vessel, with her 80′ saloons, was put into service at Havana, Cuba, to carry passengers, carts, cattle and even trains. So well aware of the quality of Pollocks' vessels were customers in South America that one Chilean customer tore a page out of one of Pollocks' catalogues, sent it to the London office accompanied by a cheque, and requested that the firm build for him a vessel as in the illustration. The result of this unorthodox request was the launch *Arica* built in 1908.

In 1907, Walter was appointed technical adviser and consultant to the Thames Conservancy, forerunners of the Port of London Authority. From this association, Pollocks were able to gain a little work. The firm had already supplied two

Ship No. 183 *Darent*, a general purpose launch built by Ferguson and supplied to the Thames Conservancy in 1907.

lifting lighters to the Thames Conservancy in 1905. After 1907 and before the little boom ended with the formation of the PLA in 1908, Pollocks designed two more vessels. The first was a multi-purpose vessel, *Darent*, a combination of screw tug, tender, service vessel, salvage steamer, water boat and fire float; the second was a service and survey vessel, *Ravensbourne*, suitable for governments for survey and inspection work, harbour and river inspections, lighthouse, lightship and coast inspection work.

IV. Association with Bolinders

It was becoming apparent to Walter Pollock in the first years of this century that the internal combustion engine would be the ideal prime mover for small vessels. The first had been produced by Hornsby-Akroyd in 1894. In 1909, Walter visited the factory of J. & C.G. Bolinder in Stockholm, Sweden. The firm of Bolinders had been set up in 1844 to produce agricultural machinery. They later went on to produce oil engines in their Stockholm works, when under the dynamic management of Eric Aug. Bolinder. As Walter stated in his history of the firm of Bolinders, they were leaders in the construction of oil engines and their application. Over a five-year period, the oil engines proved to be 52% more efficient than steam engines in tugs; also there was less risk of explosion, and the cost of repairs was decreased. Since their first marine engines in 1902, developments took place, resulting by 1908 in the two-stroke vertical "E" type direct-reversible engine. This was produced in sizes ranging from 5-320 b.h.p. by 1912, including the useful 9 h.p. and 15 h.p. sizes suitable for canal boats. The 1914 "M" type had different gudgeon pins, a water-cooled cylinder and bearings, and combined fuel and air injection. This was the first model to be available in a size as large as 500 b.h.p.

Ship No. 527 *Ben Johnson* (ex *Ialine*) built at Vlaardigen and engined by Pollocks. She was used by National Benzole.

Walter began to use Bolinder engines from 1910 and his firm became the London representatives and agents for Bolinders, part of a network which spread to all corners of the globe. Pollocks held the UK agency for over twenty years. The engines were particularly well-suited for use in oil tankers, for they used the same fuel as the tankers carried. This would presumably save having separate storage capacity for two kinds of oil. A Bolinder engine was put into the 1912 tank-barge *Ialine* renamed *Ben Johnson* by National Benzole. This vessel was designed so that it filled to the draft line when it carried three tanks of light oil or two of heavier oil. She was still afloat in 1958 and paid a visit to the Exeter Ship Canal. Another tanker fitted with a Bolinder engine was the *Juniata* supplied to foreign buyers in 1916. Two coasters *Ila* and *Ife*, built 1913, had two 120 b.h.p. Bolinder engines each and were purchased for use in West Africa.

In fact, the first English vessel to be built with a Bolinder engine was the 70′ barge *Travers* in 1910, which with a 50 b.h.p. Bolinder safely made a voyage from Havana, Cuba, to Port of Spain, Trinidad, in very bad conditions.

Some remarkable feats were accomplished by early Bolinder vessels. One 65′ auxiliary vessel, the *Lingueta* with only a 30 b.h.p. engine sailed to Pernambuco in only fifty-three days. The tug *Bunga* (ex *Miri*) with two 80 b.h.p. Bolinders made a non-stop voyage to Sarawak (8,759 miles), the only spares required on this long trip being a few springs.

Some experimental vessels were powered by Bolinder engines, including the aerial-propelled tugs *Aerotug I* and *Aerotug II*. The engines were demonstrated in fishing vessels, for which Pollock stated they were especially suitable. The 1911 drifter *May Baby*, built by J. Weatherhead at Eyemouth made several tours of British fishing ports, the latter ones having aboard W.F. Shields as Chief Engineer. The herring fleet was at its zenith, there being as many as 1,006 vessels fishing out of Great Yarmouth in the bumper year of 1913. Several customers must have been impressed by the Bolinder demonstration fishing vessels, for

Ship No. 596 *Ila* was one of a pair of similar vessels built by Hawthorn, Leith, and engined by Pollocks. The pair were sent to West Africa.

Ship No. 566 *Bunga* (ex *Miri*). A small motor tug for use in Sarawak. This 91′ vessel made the long journey to Sarawak under her own power.

Pollocks supplied about half a dozen, including the *Present Help*, the *St Dympna* and the *Margaret*. One of their later herring drifters, the *Lerina*, with an 80 b.h.p. engine, was used as the lifeline between the island of Lundy and the Devon coast.

Cargo vessels did not miss out on the application of Bolinder engines. A group of four of the type, named *Innisdhu, Inniscroon, Innisagra* and *Inniskea*, were all constructed with the engines. However, most of the tugs constructed for customers in Britain and abroad, with the exception of the *Esperanza* for Montevideo, were steam-propelled. It was not until well into the First World War that oil engines would become more acceptable to tug users. Then, the tugs *Hector* and the much more powerful *Grove Place* to be used on the Thames were built.

Bolinder engines were soon proving useful on the English canal network. A dozen canal barges were supplied, each with a 15 b.h.p. engine to the Grand

Ship No. 611 *Speedwell* built by Walker Bros. This was one of many narrow boats for use on the canals for which Pollocks supplied Bolinder engines.

Ship No. 585 *Atair*. An auxiliary yacht, described in "Amazon Vessels" as a useful pleasure vessel. Note the similarity to vessels designed by G.L. Watson in the same period, c.1912.

Canal Carrying Co. in 1912, and many more to the largest of the canal carriers, Fellows, Morton & Clayton in 1912, including the *Lupin*, one of a set of twenty narrow boats designed by Walter Pollock. To tow the pre-existing unpowered canal boats, double-ended tugs named *George* and *Dudley* were bought by the Birmingham Canal Company. Still, it was the use of engines in canal barges which would revolutionise the canal trade in both Britain and Ireland, making it faster, and more competitive with railways in the carriage of bulk cargoes.

A number of sailing yachts and a barque were built with auxiliary engines. Among them was the elegant *Atair* built in 1913 to a design which had already been about for thirty years and to which, in other vessels of the type, steam auxiliaries had been fitted. A large, beautiful yacht, *Fantome II* had a 240 b.h.p. auxiliary engine. The much smaller rigged motor lighter, *Fort York* with an 80 b.h.p. engine, was built for use by the Hudson Bay Company. Other auxiliary vessels included the *Ronaki* and *Ilen*, both built in the 1920s.

Of the coasters which were designed with Bolinder engines, the *Indorita* and *Eldorita* both originally had twin 160 b.h.p. engines. Later, *Eldorita* was single screw as may *Indorita* have been; the three in the period 1917–20, of the "Miramar" class are described in more detail in Chapter 5.

Thus, by the end of the First World War, the engines had been shown to be suitable for a wide variety of uses. Not only were the engines supplied built into vessels, but as agents, Pollocks provided both the British and French Admiralty with a number of engines alone throughout the war.

V. The Amazon rubber boom

The firm were fortunate enough to be able to supply a large number of vessels of various types to the Amazon during the rubber boom and opening up of the interior of South America which took place in 1910–12. A copiously illustrated catalogue was produced, showing a range of ship designs suited for use in the shallow waters of the river and its tributaries. It was written in English and Portuguese. In 1910 alone, there were orders for six vessels in just a few days, accompanied by three cable drafts for £5,000, £4,000 and £1,200 in a single day. The boom was to last till a sharp increase in the price of the best Para rubber to 12/3d in Liverpool in 1912. In these two years, Pollocks had supplied 120 passenger vessels, tugs, launches and lighters for the Amazon, more than the sum of their competitors.

Types illustrated in the catalogue included steamers for carrying cattle, or fresh meat or fish in Tropical climates, or for the transport of passengers. Tugs which the firm had successfully sold to customers in various parts of the world were shown, among them *The Collector*, for a harbour board in Karachi, and the *Resource* for India, which had been shipped there with its machinery on board complete, and had been at work since 1909. The example used of a seagoing tug was the *Romano* which, whilst having a similar hull design to *Resource*, had wooden decks and was of a general design aimed at ensuring the rapidity of handling. It could be supplied with salvage gear and fire pumps should the customer so wish. Smaller launch tugs could be built with or without deck cabins. Typically, these would have awnings fore and aft and open engine rooms. One such was the *Senador Flexa*, which was sent to the Amazon in 1907.

A range of designs of launches to suit customers' varying needs was set out, with photographs instead of plans of any of them which the firm had built for earlier customers. These included the launch tug *Maracaru*, the 30′ launch, *Guiomar* and the tiny, open launch tug suitable to be used as a tender to a large steamer, the *Sentinella*. Even the smallest of these launches, the catalogue stated, could carry about a ton of rubber. The boiler was usually of the vertical tube type, and a full outfit including mooring lines, lamp, spanners and even a mop would be supplied. Adaptations to meet a specific requirement of the customer could be requested through a complicated system of telegraphic codes.

Stern-wheel steamers were still the most popular method of transporting passengers and cargoes up the river network, and a range of these was shown; the *Inca*, the *Antonio Lemos* designed for river or lake cargo and passenger service where very light draft and large deadweight capacity are essential, and the smaller *Lassance Cunha*.

Customers were urged to switch from sailing pilot vessels to more modern oil-engined ones. These, said the catalogue, could be supplied in various sizes and speeds, and could be delivered under their own power to any part of the world and finished complete. The oil motors used crude oil and although of an expensive make, were reliable and economical to work. (They were, no doubt, Bolinders.)

The auxiliary yacht *Atair* mentioned earlier in the chapter was given as one of the examples of useful pleasure vessels, on which the accommodation could be arranged for Tropical work or for general all-round use in any part of the world. Motor yachts were in vogue at the time, and Pollocks had a number of up to date vessels available.

Selected examples of up to date fishing vessels, the larger ones suited for use as carriers, were illustrated. These could be sent with a fish and ice room fitted and fishing gear to the customer's requirements. Those advertised to the Amazon customers were mostly steam, and could be worked economically for a small initial cost.

Service vessels were shown, for example the teak motor launch *Smith's Dock No. 2* which Pollocks had designed and constructed as a service vessel and tug for use at Middlesboro', fitted with a 40 b.h.p. Bolinder engine. Cargo ships were also featured, the motor barge *Travers* being given as an example, its 1,200-mile trip relying only on its small motor being quoted. *Travers* was in service as a cargo carrier in Trinidad.

Elegant house lighters with engines, in a variety of designs were described, again with photographs or plans of each different type. Examples of these were the *Acuria, Acacia* and the much earlier *Natal*. Cargo lighters, with or without rolling hatch covers, could be supplied in plates and angles, or if the customer wished, could be towed out to the River Amazon complete.

In addition, floating docks could be supplied, either single or double sided, in which the many vessels sent out could be kept in a good state of repair. Should fortunes look like being made in another commodity, gold dredgers could be built, and a special pamphlet on gold dredging sent out.

For investors whose stocks were about to go up in flames, self-propelled fire floats were available, with fire pumps connected to both sea and deck. To coal the many steamers using the ports of the basin, coaling barges of a type largely used in England for coaling steamers quickly could be sent out. Steel ships' boats were illustrated which unlike wooden ones, did not shrink with the sun or leak if they struck anything. They were built of Siemens-Martin steel plates and angles, and the firm usually held some in stock.

Engines and boilers could be supplied separately should the customer wish, and a selection was shown. Triple expansion and compound surface condensing engines were described as being of high quality, to Lloyds' rules, of the best materials and suitable for passengers and cargo steamers, and in sizes from 50 – 300 i.h.p. Smaller, outboard condensing engines for use in fast launches were illustrated. Of the boilers shown, all gave a maximum of heating surface, and were arranged for good water circulation and easy cleaning. Locomotive type boilers, the catalogue explained, were especially suited for use in light draft vessels, for example stern-wheelers, as their evaporating qualities were very good, and their weight per i.h.p. small.

Two different types of steam-driven ice-making machinery could be installed either just to make ice, or to both make it and cool an insulated chamber.

A standard agreement for construction and delivery was set out, detailing the timetable required by the firm for the payment of instalments of the cost of the vessel. Suggestions indicating how to make cables clear when ordering a vessel or requesting alterations were made, as follows:

"Orders — code word in cable implies one article only. No other word necessary except client's name, remittance for 1st instalment, unless special instructions have to be given.
Enquiries — code can be used to enquire re prices (+ other codes). Use code word before any enquiry. Give own code word if none suitable in book for ease of reference in quoting prices etc. and cheaper for client. Clients should quote their codes used.
Time for construction — important to know maximum time. Longer can mean cheaper. Usually have about 20 vessels ready for delivery. See stock and delivery sheet (monthly) 12 – 14 weeks for launches and small vessels, 20 – 24 for larger if new construction. Longer if galvanised hull. In every case from date of receipt of first instalment in London.
Shipping — clients should indicate if urgent delivery required, or if cheapest freight will be preferred — if no construction, will despatch promptly by cargo steamer as economically as possible.
Cargo Capacity — all figures in book refer to total amount of cargo including bunker and coal fuel. Capacities taken on drafts mentioned under ordinary working conditions and without heavy spare gear or special stores.
Volumes or packages — no definite number per ton — any figures on basis of 40 per ton or ½ cwt (25 kilos) each.
Speeds — speed decrease means decreased price or deadweight increased. Purchasers should not insist on greater speed than is necessary. A better commercial job can be done at an economic figure.
Delivery — prices in UK are f.a.s. London or Liverpool. In the case of small vessels to be carried on deck, delivery is free alongside export steamer.
Packing — prices include packing where needed — if not, this is charged extra at nett cost. For small vessels to be lifted on deck of an export steamer — sometimes slings provided — if not, purchasers should bear cost. Our CIF prices include all these.
Remittances — if no arrangement with clients, they should arrange for cash credit in GB to cover full cost.
Instalments — (these were set out in the Contract to build).
Agreement — could be varied to suit circumstances."

The code by which customers could briefly request vessel types or changes in design was very detailed. Such telegraphic codes were in common use well into the 1920s, and would later be replaced by the telex. Just the codes for specifications of the ice-making machinery ran to twelve lines, as folllows:

Babusedfas	cable cost ice-making plant for 5 cwts per day
Babusedfet	cable cost ice-making plant for 10 cwts per day
Babusedfil	cable cost ice-making plant for 20 cwts per day
Babusedfom	arrange to fit + supply at lowest cost plant able to make — cwts a day
Babusedgon	fit ice-making plant as per your cable quotation
Babusedgup	cable cost ice-making plant with cooling chamber — cu.ft. + necess. coils
Babusedjin	cost ice-making plant as per inquiry is £_____
Babusedjop	cost ice-making plant with cooling chamber as per inquiry is £_____

Babusedjur supply ice-making plant with cooling chamber
Babusedlab ice-making plant not necessary
Babusedlen ice-making plant to make transparent ice
Babusedlip ice-making plant to make opaque ice.

VI. Other pre-war craft

In addition to their Bolinder vessels and the many supplied to the Amazon basin in the rubber boom, the firm designed a number of tugs and lighters of note in the years immediately leading up to their involvement in the First World War. One was the steam tug *Dreadful* for British Columbia. There being no Panama Canal at the date of her delivery, she reached Vancouver by the treacherous Cape Horn route, and once there, had trials with a timber raft in Vancouver Bay. A very powerful tug, the *Dreadful* was requisitioned by the Royal Navy for war work in 1917. *Dreadful* was later given to Watkins to replace the tug *Oceana* which they had lost at Scapa Flow in 1918. Another steam tug, *Lola*, built in 1911 was delivered complete to Antofagasta, Chile on a steamer's deck. The tug was unloaded by being slid over the side of the ship off baulks of timber into the water. She came up from this strange baptism undamaged and her trials were reported in a contemporary edition of the "Shipping Gazette Weekly Supplement".

The lighters included a set for Maranhao, in North-East Brazil. These, named *Olga, Carmen, Coroala* and *Codo*, were 93 feet long, had a draft of only 2′6″ and could float lightly laden in 4 inches of water. They were designed without the usual hatchways and hold, and the deck formed the upper member of a girder, whilst the bottom plating formed the bottom member. Great rigidity and strength with the lightest possible weight were obtained by a series of lattice girder longitudinal bulkheads for the full length of the lighters.

There was also a second collier for the Thames coal trade, named the *Fulgens* built in 1913. At the close of 1914, Pollocks, like many other shipbuilding firms, began to design and construct vessels to assist Britain's effort in the First World War. The firm's contribution would culminate in the concrete coasters for the construction of which, they would lay out the yard at Faversham. The great engineering talents of Walter Pollock were also put to use in the war doing army work on the East Coast defences at Saxmundham.

VII. Other engineering interests

The firm specialised in the valuation of machinery, and their first contract in this line was at Barclay, Perkins & Company's brewery. In 1909 Walter Pollock valued the machinery at Cook's Soap Works. The largest of the contracts was the valuation of the buildings pulled down by the London County Council when Kingsway was opened up between Holborn and the Aldwych. In order to keep the values private, a code was devised from the word 'WORKMANSHIP'; W would represent £1, O = £2, and P = 10/-.

Walter's engineering interests led him to set up a number of specialist companies, most of whose offices were run from Pollock's premises at 3 Lloyds Avenue, which occupied areas on two floors of the building. He was chairman of the following companies: The Marine & Mechanical Electric Welding Co. Ltd., The Marine & Mechanical Electric Welding Co. (Cardiff) Ltd., The Belgian Marine

Ship No. 436 *Dreadful*, a powerful tug built by Hepple, she voyaged under her own power via Cape Horn to Vancouver, Canada.

& Mechanical Electric Welding Co. of Antwerp, The British Brazing Co. Ltd., The Rapidal Paint Co. Ltd., The Thames Deep Water Wharf Ltd., as well as The Star Contra Propeller Co. mentioned in Chapter 5.

As early as 1903, Walter had written his first book on ship designs, entitled "Vessels of Various Types", which volume was on Lord Fisher's desk when he sent for Walter in 1915 to design the Dardanelles landing craft known as "beetles". A number of biographical articles appeared in various papers, including "The Shipping & Mercantile Gazette", on 3rd September 1914.

For recreation, Water was a keen motorist. One of his cars, an Armstrong Siddeley, he kept for six years. He travelled widely, to Holland, France, Belgium, Denmark, Norway, Switzerland and several visits to his friend, Eric Bolinder in Stockholm, Sweden. Like his father, Walter must have built up a working knowledge of a number of languages through his travels.

Sources

"James Pollock, Sons & Co. Ltd." in "Ship and Boat Builder", May 1955.
"The Bolinder Book". Walter Pollock, 1930.
"The Past Afloat". Anthony Burton, 1981. BBC.
"The Pollocks as Engineers". Walter Pollock, 1939.
"Amazon Vessels of Various Types". Walter Pollock, c.1911.
Footnote on "The Exeter Canal". Kenneth Clew — review in "Ships Monthly", February 1985.

Chapter 3
CONCRETE COASTERS

The expertise which the firm of James Pollock, Sons & Co. Ltd. had shown in the design of steam and diesel vessels in the period leading up to the First World War led to recognition by the First Sea Lord, Lord Fisher, when specialised vessels were needed for the war effort. It was the war which was the direct cause of the setting up of the yard on a site at Faversham by the recently-elected Chairman, Walter Pollock. Earlier in the war, Pollock had designed landing-craft in the form of shallow X-class lighters, otherwise known as "Black Beetles". These were mostly 105′6″ in length, with engines of various powers and makes, including Skandia, Avance and Bolinder. Seventeen Z-class launches were supplied to the Admiralty, most of 28′ or 32′. Of the lighters, several were still afloat in the 1970s. One of the smaller class was the 98′ beetle m.v. *Doddles*, built at Dobson's, Newcastle, which spent most of her life in the East Coast sand and gravel trade, another the Horlocks coaster *Spithead*, in the estuary ballast trade having previously been trading dry cargoes. Others still afloat included J. Prior's *Sidney P, Colin P* and *Peter P*. Lighter *X100* was renamed *British Toiler*, and spent much of her career with Shell-Mex & BP Ltd. and has only recently been sold for demolition.

Eight 170′ monitors were built elsewhere in 1915, each of which had 9″ guns and were supplied with Bolinder engines just after Fisher and Churchill resigned over Gallipoli. The culmination of Pollocks wartime production followed the suggestion by Lord Fisher, First Sea Lord and Winston Churchill to Walter Pollock that the firm should build ships of war in the "government town" of Faversham. By the time the yard was set up the war was nearly over and a steel shortage led the yard to build its first two vessels of concrete. The work was to be the foundation of a successful shipbuilding business at Faversham in the yard which in the war had been known as Admiralty Shipyard extension No. 15.

I. The site and its layout

The 5¼ acre site which was chosen by Walter Pollock already had a 600′ long wharf as it had been a brickyard used by Perry's. It seems part of the site adjacent was used as a boatyard before by White's for building wooden ships. All around the site, areas were still used for grazing stock, some of which was owned by George Gregory's father, and ducks were kept close by Quarrington's house on the Front Brents.

A shed for plating was put up, with a track running into it from the creek bank, on which the bogies would run carrying plates between operations. Belt-driven machinery was installed, some new and some second-hand from a shipyard at King's Lynn or the guncotton factory. A small workshop was equipped for the use of the carpenters and joiners, again with belt-driven machinery, and a range of buildings including a fitting shop and Bolinder display area erected.

The layout of the yard

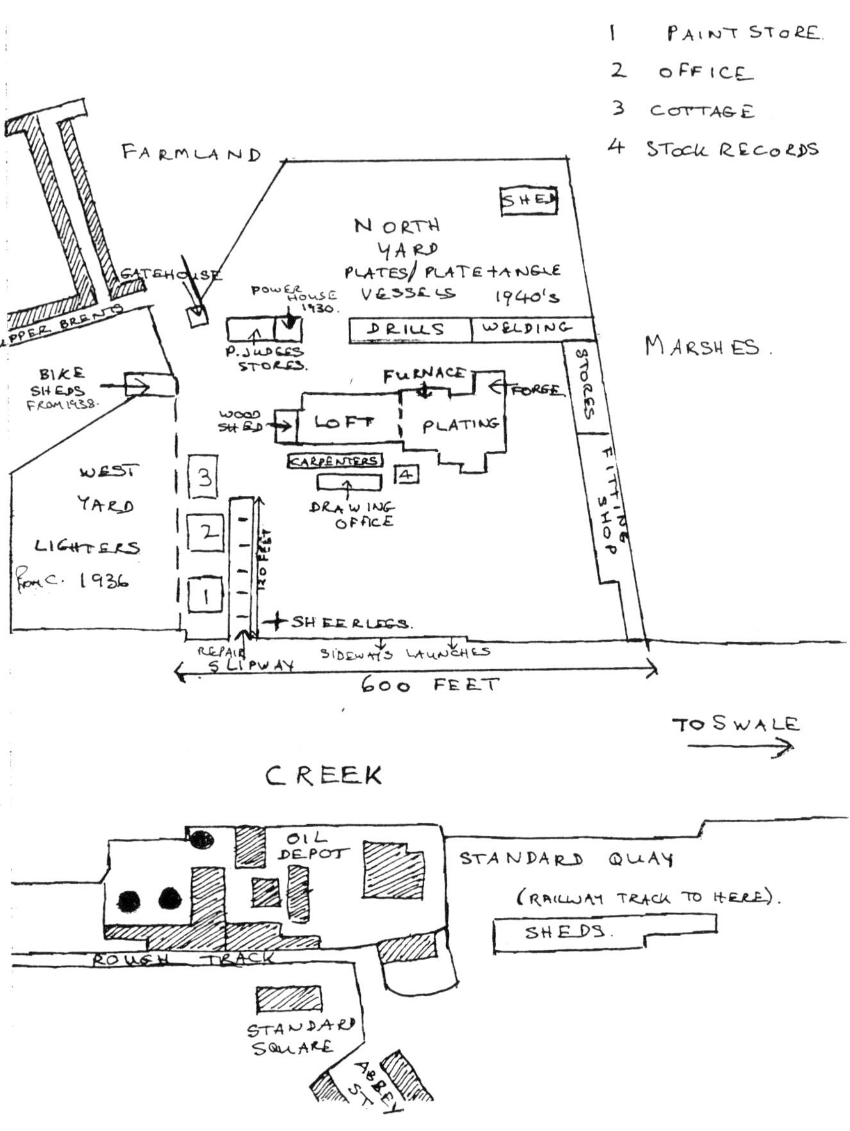

II. Earlier concrete coasters

The idea of constructing ships out of concrete had been around since 1848 but, as Robert Simper states, it was the steel shortage of the First World War which led to the commercial adoption of ferro-cement hulls. Robert Simper cites the case of concrete vessels built at Queenborough also around the First World War designed by a Mr Courtney. As Patricia O'Driscoll explained in an article in "East Coast Digest", the first seagoing concrete ship, the *Nansenfjord*, was patented in 1910 by the Norwegian, Fougner. This was a 200-ton vessel, 84'×20'×11'6", and like those Pollock designed, was propelled by Bolinder engines. Other concrete ships were built by the Ferro-Cement Ship Construction Company in Barrow, whose craft *Armistice* traded across the Atlantic with potatoes.

III. Walter Pollock's design

The two concrete coasters designed by Walter Pollock were ship numbers 889 and 891. O'Driscoll was told by Philip Ellis that ship number 890 was a 400-ton wooden coaster which was never built but had been destined for Bolinders in New York. Walter described the design of his concrete ships in his own book, "Hot Bulb Oil Engines and Suitable Vessels", published in 1918, as follows:

"A straight-lined vessel was introduced by the author in July 1917. It is a reinforced concrete auxiliary coaster, dimensions 125'×25'×11'9", and a coefficient of 0.72, which will carry 300 tons of cargo on 10' draft. Curved work is dispensed with in connection with the reinforced concrete, the vertical sections consisting of a series of straight lines: this reduces the cost of construction, and makes it easier to keep the steel rods for reinforcements in their correct position. Horizontally, the straight lines have the corners rounded off. Reinforced concrete construction is also specially suitable for tugs and lighters."

Unlike concrete ships designed for the North Atlantic run, which Simper said had 6" thick concrete hulls, the two designed by Pollock had thinner concrete. Theirs was only 3" thick, at a weight of 143 pounds per cubic foot. The coasters had a loaded displacement of 640 tons, with a hold capacity of 17,320 cubic feet. The bare hull weighed 290 tons and the ratio of deadweight to displacement was 44.5%.

As the design shows, the vessels were rigged as three-masted schooners with gaff and boom sails with no tops'ls. Only the *Molliette* had a fixed bowsprit and could set a fores'l and jib, which O'Driscoll argued from first hand experience would have been a hindrance rather than a help in enclosed docks.

Both vessels had 120 b.h.p., two-cylinder M-type Bolinder engines. The engines were centrally situated and ran at 225–250 r.p.m., and there was also a bilge pump. These engines would typically take twenty to thirty minutes to start, and involve the heating of bulbs by a paraffin blow-lamp, the coils first being pre-heated by methylated spirit.

The motor winch abaft the foremast was a 5 or 8 b.h.p. Bolinder Reid single cylinder engine which drove the windlass with a messenger chain. The fuel oil was carried in two circular tanks, one each side of the engine room, resting in built-in cradles about 5' in diameter and 10' long, holding about 1,200 gallons each. Lubricating oil and paraffin were carried in square fifty gallon tanks, while about 250 gallons of fresh water was carried in a tank on deck between the two hatchways. The crew quarters were forward in the forecastle, which had pipe-cots, a wooden table and two forms, a washbasin, a water can and a food and

MOLLIETTE

Inside the joiners' shop during the preparation of the wooden framework of the two concrete ships, 1918.

clothes locker for each man. Four or five men would live in these quarters with an additional three officers aft in a wooden deck-house bolted to the concrete deck. These each had separate cabins with a bunk, folding washbasin, locker, wardrobe, water bottle and glasses on a rack. The mess room had a table, locker and was heated by a Tortoise stove. There was in addition a galley, lamp room and WC aft. The wheelhouse, on deck, was open with bridge wings, with boats carried either side of the deckhouse launched by davits, one of these lifeboats being a jolly-boat, the other a double-ended lifeboat which could not easily be sculled. Neither of the flat-bottomed coasters had leeboards, but *Violette* had a brail winch to raise the gaff or for working a cargo boom.

As Lloyds List for 18th January 1918 explained, the concrete vessels were so built because of the steel shortage, and were of a similar design to the earlier Pollock-designed coaster, *Lee-Lee*. Load line regulations in respect of concrete vessels were set out in Lloyds List for 30th January 1918.

IV. The construction

For the construction of the two concrete coasters, Walter Pollock took on a number of carpenters who were supervised by Mr Jeffery, who was the landlord of the Market Inn. Among the men who worked in the newly-erected carpenters' shop were Percy Dadson and Tommy Beer. A foreman shipwright was taken on, Charlie Carter, who had already worked as a shipwright at Cremer's of Hollowshore and for W.F. White Ltd. at their Conyer barge yard. The craftsmen constructed the wooden framework of the vessels. This construction must have been a complicated business, since it took nearly two

Opposite: Ship No. 889 *Molliette*. The first of two concrete vessels built at the yard. She is seen airing her sails in the creek alongside the yard.

In the fitting shop, 1st June 1918, during the construction of the concrete ships.

years from the time the yard was opened for the framework to be ready for concreting.

Work was also going on in the fitting shop, of which the foreman was named by Charlie Godden as Mr Bellinger. The fitting shop men included a young W.F. (Bill) Shields, only sixteen when he began work at the yard in 1918, who had learnt basic engineering making bicycles. Another was one Captain Smith, formerly of Goldfinch's barge-building yard on the opposite bank of the creek; also there as an apprentice was Percy Wass, who would later work mostly with Bolinder engines, accompanied by his father and brother.

Riveting the steel reinforcements by hand, among others was Charlie Godden, who had been sent to the yard by his father to learn a trade. He was one of the first few apprentices to be taken on at the yard on the meagre wage of five shillings per week, and had to cycle in from Selling to work every day for the first few years. Another of the first group of apprentices was Jim Weaver, taken on at the age of fourteen in 1918, and who was to serve the firm for the rest of his working life except for two years in Sydney.

As Charlie Godden remembered, it was George Ledner who gave him the nickname "China", which he bore throughout the remainder of his career at the yard, on account of his slant eyes. This feature was to be the cause of a joke at Godden's expense when two Chinese men came in on a vessel in the 1920s, that Godden would feel at home.

Helping the craftsmen were labourers from two families who were to be involved with the yard for a long time, the aforementioned George Ledner, uncle of Harry and Chris Sunley, and Austin Cornelius, whose son, Bill, would later run the Power House.

Opposite: the people who built the two concrete ships. Much of the concreting was done by the women, who included Millie Epps, Edie and Ida Wade and May Post. Also included in the photo are Captain Smith, Charles Carter, Joe Wade and Jim Weaver.

Ship No. 889 *Molliette*, showing the construction of the wooden framework of the vessel from the inside.

Ship No. 889 *Molliette* on the blocks prior to launching. The use of wooden trestles as scaffolding can be clearly seen.

Ship No. 889 *Molliette*. A sideways launch into the creek on 19th November 1918.

According to O'Driscoll, the hull work on *Molliette* began on 2nd September 1918, and by 6th November she had been concreted. The concreting was done by a gang of women which included Ida and Edie Wade, May Post, Mrs Skipper, whose future son-in-law was the shipwright Clarence Fowle, Millie Epps and Mrs Heyland, under the supervision of one Mr Farmer of contractors, Bradfords. The concrete was put on to the requisite three inches over a framework of steel mesh put on by Mrs Skipper, to a weight of 143 lb per cubic foot.

V. Launching the first concrete ship

The launch of the first of the pair of concrete ships took place on Tuesday 19th November 1918. As Richard Dadson described it, the launch was an unusual one, the vessel being so heavy as to need drag chains when being launched, a practice not apparently used since. The engine was put into the *Molliette* on 21st November, and she performed sea trials on 17th January 1919, and subsequently on 10th February of the same year.

Molliette's sister-ship, named the *Violette* was begun on 14th March 1919 and completed on 10th April. Her launch was watched by Ernie Cripps, shortly to start work at the yard as a riveter, from the coal-yard opposite which would later become an oil depot. It was photographed, as had the launch been of *Molliette,* by local photographer, William Hargrave. *Violette* had her engine installed on 16th May and she went on her sea trials with Bill Shields aboard as engineer and Alf Smith as skipper on 5th August.

VI. The vessels' subsequent history

Both vessels were involved in the coasting trade, and in the 1920s were amongst the most difficult vessels to handle. Bill Shields called them "Sluggish, when under sail". Simper states that *Molliette* "got a shave" once or twice, and once hit Tower Bridge and some shipping in the Thames at the same time. The concrete ship was not damaged. The engine was removed early in *Molliette*'s career, and she became a night-club near Clacton, Essex. She was later run down on the River Colne and is currently lying off West Mersea, marked by a beacon,

VIOLETTE

Ship No. 891 *Violette* immediately after launch. The boys on the left are standing on a coal wharf. The launch took place on 16th May 1919.

after having been used as a bombing target in the Second World War, and is only visible at Low Water Springs.

Violette was not accepted by her owners following the six months of sea trials on which Shields had accompanied her. Instead, she traded hard-core up river to Cory's Wharf at Erith, and laid at anchor till sometime in September. Then she sailed for Rochester, proceeding via the Swale, with a stop at Harty Ferry. This is an unusual route as it is shallow water for much of the journey. The usual route would be via Sea Reach, the Nore Swatch Grain Spit and up the Medway, using the flood tide to get from Grain Spit to Rochester.

Violette was unfortunate enough in 1921 to collide with Southend Pier. On 18th January, under Captain Knott, she had been en route from Antwerp to London with a cargo of 241 tons of iron girders and logs of wood. It was very bad weather, and she was in difficulty for eighteen hours. She had progressed only thirty-seven miles despite running her engines at full speed. The story of the collision, reported in the "Southend Standard" included the following description:

"While off Southend, the vessel became unmanageable, and was driven furiously against the west side of the pier."

She dragged her anchor while laying above the pier because there was no one on anchor watch. It had been such a bad passage that the Captain and all aboard had turned in, and the anchor was a stockless type with less holding power than a traditional one. 160 feet of piles along the pier were broken and the decking and tramway destroyed, but of the crew, only the Captain was hurt. The damage to the pier was so great that the pier-keeper was marooned and had to receive supplies by boat. The hold filled up with water to a depth of six feet and *Violette* had to be pumped out by the salvage vessel, *Refloater*. The damage to the pier

Opposite: Ship No. 891 *Violette* seen at work in the London Docks.

cost £5,540 and the *Violette* was declared a total loss. Pollocks bought the wreck and brought it back to Faversham on 23rd April. Her engine was used in the oil tanker *Stourgate* and the hull left off Seasalter before the Second World War, and bathers would swim out to her. She was then taken to Chatham, fitted with tanks and used as a refuelling lighter for the New Medway Steam Packet Company's craft. By 1975, *Violette* had been moved to Hoo. She no longer had any deckhouse, and was in use as a mooring barge.

Since the two concrete hulls had remained resistant to the many collisions in which they had caused so much damage to other craft, it was clear that it was not the material but the design which was at fault in the Faversham vessels. The use of concrete as a shipbuilding medium has continued, the particular type of concrete most often used being known as *Seacrete*.

VII. About the firm; its offices

When the yard was first laid out at Faversham, all the preparatory drawings were done in an office which was housed, along with a shipping office and a cashier's office at 3 Lloyds Avenue, London. These offices occupied one and a half floors of the building. At one time, apparently, the firm had used all four floors and had design work done at their 24 Chapel Street, Liverpool office as well. The London drawing office staff included Mr Henry Lamputt as Naval Architect and Senior Designer, and Walter Pollock himself was still closely involved. At this time, Walter began the practice of daily correspondence with the small office at his Faversham yard, a practice which would last till shortly before his death. The office at Faversham was only a general office.

To take account of the new circumstances occasioned by the firm having a shipyard of its own, a revised standard Contract to Build was drawn up as follows:

"AGREEMENT FOR CONSTRUCTION AND DELIVERY OF A__________

1. AN AGREEMENT entered into this ____ day of ______ 19__ between ________ hereinafter called the Shipbuilders of the one part and ________ hereinafter called the Purchasers of the other part.
2. Dimensions: The Shipbuilders will build for the Purchasers of the best materials and workmanship, a ______ vessel

   Length O A ______
   Breadth Mld ______
   Depth Mld ______
   Draft, about ______

   having ______ Engine(s) developing __ H.P. when running at ____ R.P.M. Speed of vessel to be about ____ Statute miles per hour on the measured mile, near the Shipbuilder's yard. Other particulars to be in accordance with Specification No. ______ and Plan No. ______
3. Payments: The Purchasers shall pay the Shipbuilders for the vessel a sum of £______ (____ Thousand ____ Hundred Pounds Sterling) delivered at ______ in the following manner:
   First instalment on signing the agreement 30%
   Second instalment one month after signing this agreement 30%
   Third instalment, balance of purchase price, after trial trip and one week prior to leaving the Shipbuilder's yard.

4. Delivery: The Shipbuilders will do their utmost to deliver the vessel in the river or dock at ______ alongside export steamer ____ months from receipt of first instalment in London. The Shipbuilders undertake to do everything in their power to obtain delivery at the port of ______ at the earliest possible time after completion in the United Kingdom.
5. Construction: The Shipbuilders shall be allowed an extension of time in the event of any strike or lockout of workmen or other circumstances beyond their control, interfering with the construction or delivery of the vessel.
6. Replacement: Should the vessel be lost or destroyed the Shipbuilders have the option to replace the vessel as soon as possible, always providing they have insured and obtained the insurance money.
7. Alterations: The Purchasers shall be at liberty to require any alterations or additions to be made, during construction, to the vessel and machinery, providing they do so by cable, and confirm in writing; an addition to the purchase price and extra time being allowed.
8. Trial Trip: A trial trip shall take place in the United Kingdom near the Shipbuilder's yard before the vessel is delivered and the Purchasers or their representatives shall have permission to be present and satisfy themselves that the vessel has been built in accordance with agreement, plan and specification. If satisfactory a certificate to be given to the Shipbuilders to that effect.
9. Delay in Payment: In the event of any instalment remaining unpaid for ten days after due, the Purchasers will pay the Shipbuilders 1% per month on the instalments unpaid, and if any instalments remain unpaid for thirty days, the Shipbuilders shall be at liberty to sell the vessel as she may lie, or may complete her and sell her after completion, and any loss on such resale shall be made good by the Purchasers.
10. Arbitration: All disputes, if any, to be submitted to the London Court of Arbitration.

    Witness to the ______ For and on behalf of ______

    Signature of: ______

    Note – The responsibility and risk of delivery should be made clear, and whether the builders or the owners are to pay insurance costs should be agreed beforehand."

Sources

"A Couple of Bob on the Line". R. Dadson in "Faversham Magazine" Vol. 1 No. 2.
"The Deepsea Man". W.F. Shields in "Coast & Country" Vol. 10 No. 6.
"Indestructible Ships". Patricia O'Driscoll in "East Coast Digest" Vol. 5 No. 1.
Postscript re *Molliette* and *Violette*. P. O'Driscoll in "East Coast Digest" Vol. 5 No. 2.
"Concrete goes to Sea". Robert Simper in "East Coast Digest" Vol. 4. No. 5.
"Britain's Maritime Heritage". Robert Simper, 1982.
"Small Vessels". Walter Pollock, 1946.
"The Case of the Concrete Coasters". P. O'Driscoll, "Concrete", August 1976.
"Wavelength". Laurence Dunn in "Ships Monthly", November 1988.

Chapter 4
DEVELOPMENT OF WORKING PRACTICES

Over the fifty-four years Pollocks' shipyard was in existence in Faversham, necessarily working practices gradually changed. Labour-intensive hand methods were gradually supplanted by some new machinery and a few men had to learn new skills, others to adapt those they already had to newer technology. This was one of the factors which contributed to varying demand for labour at the yard.

I. Riveting

There were very few men locally who had the skills required to build steel ships, and thus many of the men who worked at the yard as riveters were recruited from the North of England or more commonly from Wivenhoe Shipyard, Essex, over the period 1920–3, among them Micky Bloom, Charlie Pritchard, Wally Service and Ginger Woodward. These men were skilled in the craft of hand riveting, a practice which involved heating rivets till white hot with tongs whilst also pumping a charcoal brazier to keep them hot; the rivet would be thrown into a box with a wet rag in to avoid it bouncing out (though it still sometimes did). The rivet would then be put in by a holder-up and hit alternately by a left and a right handed riveter. Five men were employed in these early rivet gangs. The hammers used were heavy ball hammers. The riveters were responsible for paying their helpers out of their pay, which was paid piece-work — and when imported men came in who would accept lower piece rates, life was made harder for the heaters and holders-up. They would have to do more before a decent income was achieved for the riveter, and he could afford to pay them out.

Between 1923 and 1925, new machinery came in which was to both reduce the size of the rivet gang and speed up the work. The machinery was pneumatic running on air supplied by pipe from a compressor in the fitting shop. The compressor, by the mid 1920s also alleviated the need to hand pump the bellows to heat the rivets four at a time in the brazier, which would sometimes be put inside the partly-built ship for convenience. A few of the Northern men would heat their rivets in an iron rack as had been the practice in their yards. The holder-up would be annoyed if the rivet thrown to him was burnt at the end for it was useless, or if it was the wrong size. If there was a liner to fill the gap between two plates, long rivets (2″) would be needed, then standard rivets (1½″). The use of liners, which had been supplied by Semark's of West Street, Faversham (now a filling station) was gradually phased out in favour of joggling plates.

With the pneumatic machinery, only one riveter would be required, but at first, the riveters would often injure their hands on the heavy tool. A modification to this tool was introduced by "China" Godden — a brass steadier, an idea

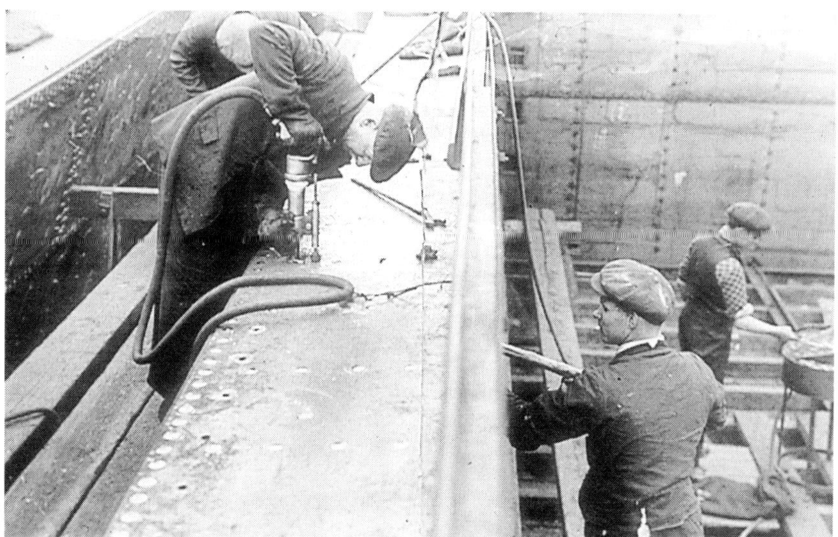

A rivet gang at work. The rivets were heated up in a brazier. The riveters include Ernie Cripps.

which originally came from Wivenhoe. Gradually, others copied it. Some of the riveters who had worked with the hand equipment kept on with the new, for example Wally Service and Reg Bottle. Others, including Cripps and Godden himself became burners. Bloom just went labouring in the heavy gang.

The pneumatic pipes which fed the rivet hammers and also caulking tools needed a considerable amount of maintenance, especially as the bogies which trundled about the yard on rails carrying plates had iron wheels. The pipes were laid out in 60′ lengths which, joined end to end, at maximum could reach half a mile. When they were punctured, as was frequently the case, they would be mended with a piece of copper pipe and tied together. They would only be replaced when considered too bad to be repaired. The job of pipe maintenance required one labourer practically full-time, to mend pipes which had either been punctured or sheared by accident when they trailed across the shears. A succession of men did the job; Swaffer, Cremer, Bill Lennard and Horace Lennard, who left in 1958 and was not replaced. The job was done instead by a fitting shop apprentice. The windy-man's job must have been a busy one in the 1920s and 1930s when twelve or more squads of riveters were at work, as well as caulkers.

The work of the three members of the rivet gang was not easy. If riveting was required in a double-bottom, the holder-up and riveter would have to crawl between the plates. Extra money was paid for this confined space work as it was very dangerous. The heater had to ensure that he (or she, during the war) had the right length of rivet ready for the riveter. This was quite a skilful job; some of the rivet heaters later became riveters themselves, for example Tom Jordan, while others remained labourers. Engine seating would need more care with riveting and was carefully inspected by tapping to see if a seal had been made. If not, the rivet had to be burnt out and re-done or else caulked. The foreman, at the end of the day, would count the rivets done by marking them with chalk, or sometimes, the stores man, Featherstone, would count rivets and to delay him, someone would rub out the marks he had made with his chalk. The record for one man in a day was 900 rivets, achieved by Jim Weaver. Micky Bloom and Jack Burford were almost as efficient. Riveting was a noisy, arduous business, and in order to get some brief respite from the deafening noise, the heater might sometimes throw a few rivets in the creek so the gang had to wait while some more heated up.

Riveting could not easily be done in rain, so the riveters were frequently sent home with no work and no pay. Yet on the barges in the 1930s, riveters might even have to come in on Sundays and were not paid at any higher rate. A typical rate pre-war was 6/3d for 100 × ⅝″ rivets and often 3,000 a week would be put into previously countersunk holes, tooled with a heavy, revolving machine by Riley or Willis. To line up mis-aligned rivet holes, a reamering tool was used. By 1930, a riveter on piece-work could expect to earn £4 – £5 before he paid out his two helpers. The piece-work system would last well into the 1950s before finally being replaced by day wages.

In 1949, rates were as shown in the table:

Faversham Shipyard 13th May 1949
Section — Riveters
Price list for barge work
The undermentioned prices are to be plus 25%; war bonus to be extra.

	Rivet Dia.	**Rate per 100**
Hold and swim bottom	⅝″	8/3d
Hold sides; stringer and end decks	⅝″	8/6d
Bulkheads	⅝″	8/6d
Hatch coaming sides	⅝″	7/9d
Battens, wedges and cleats	⅝″	7/9d
Hold frame feet	⅝″	8/-
Hold brackets before erection	⅝″	6/9d
Hold brackets after erection	⅝″	8/6d
Keelsons	⅝″	8/-
Bulkhead frames	⅝″	9/-
Bottoms in way	⅝″	9/-
H C foundations and angles	⅝″	9/6d
Cleats, battens and wedges if done without H C	⅝″	15/-
Hatch coaming ends	⅝″	9/6d
Swim ends	⅝″	9/9d
Budget	⅝″	9/-
Footrails	⅝″	10/-
Cabin rails	⅝″	10/-
Bowboards	⅝″	13/6d
Swim ends (inside work)	⅝″	13/6d
Mooring rings & windlass pawls	¾″	22/6d
Stern post	¾″	20/-
Fenders	¾″	22/6d
Strong beams	¾″	9/6d

¾″ dia. rivets — above prices plus 1/6d per 100
½″ dia. rivets — above prices less 1/3d per 100
Sundry jobs to be paid at 5/- per hour per squad. Max. deduction for rivet heater 30/- per 47 hour week, 28/- per 44 hour week.

Most riveters and holders-up were in the Boilermakers' Society, and it was through this body that they served their apprenticeships. On entry to an apprenticeship, a document like the one below would be signed:

United Society of Boilermakers and Iron Shipbuilders

This is to certify
that Thomas H. Jordan has been accepted by this society as an apprentice, and he agrees with his employer, Messrs James Pollock, Sons & Co. Ltd., to serve an apprenticeship for the term of 5 years to commence on the 26th day of May 1925 at the age of 15 years. In witness whereof we have subscribed our names and affixed the seal of our branch Faversham on the 22nd day of June 1928.
C.J. Taylor President
H. Packman Secretary

II. Caulking

This was, in fact, one of the last jobs to be done on a vessel's hull. As with riveting, most of the caulkers who worked at the yard were brought from elsewhere, with one notable exception, Jimmy Jordan. Fred Bolt and Sam Joliffe both came from up North and Jim Snowball from there also, while Bill Shead came from Wivenhoe.

Caulking also began as hand work, done with a heavy hammer and chisel. When the pneumatic machinery came in for riveting in 1925, new caulking hammers were introduced. One of the first men to use these was Jim Snowball, brother of the Foreman Plater, Jack. Like the riveters, caulkers were members of the Boilermakers' Society, serving a five-year apprenticeship. Experienced caulkers such as Jordan would work piece-work and could earn relatively good wages. As well as sealing the joints between plates, the caulker would cut the name in the side of the ship ready for the loftsman to paint it, and mark the Plimsoll Line and certifications in the fuel and ballast tanks. In addition, he would chamfer the edges of the plates so that the welders could make a deep weld. Some of the "new" caulking machinery was second-hand Ingersolls, while later additions were made by Holman's. This job, like riveting, was very noisy and tended to make its regular practitioners deaf. Some, including Reg Shead also recognised the problem of arc-eye, as the welders who were working nearby with bright torches would wear goggles and the caulkers none. Caulking would be tested by Lloyd's, whose surveyor at one time was Mr Chisholm. When caulking was paid piece-rate, the yard was the unit for calculation of pay. Alex Featherstone would draw a wavy line of chalk, it being clearer than a straight line, and measure how many yards had been done so that the wages could be worked out. A characteristic of Pollocks' vessels was a nick in the top of the angle bars when caulked as the yard had no facilities for cutting off their rounded tops.

Other types of sealing were used on wood decks by shipwrights. These share the name of caulking, but not its methods.

Machinery in the plating shop. The picture shows the lifting tackle. The plates were transported from the shop into the yard on bogies.

Working in the angle furnace. The group includes Jack Finn, Reuben Lennard and Frank Ward.

III. Drilling and plating

As with many of the riveters and caulkers, many of the platers were imports either from the North, as the early foreman, Jack Snowball, or from Wivenhoe; for example Fred Ribbans, or, in the 1930s, a few from Dartmouth.

Early on, there were some quarrels between the platers and the shipwrights. Such quarrels, Bill Poole explained, were over platers taking on what the shipwrights argued should have been their work. Most platers were in the Boilermakers' Society, but a few were non-union.

As regards equipment for plating, much of this was second-hand when the yard was first laid out in 1916–17 and was never replaced. Inside the platers' shop were a number of punches down one side and a set of mangles which once took Fred Ribbans' toe off as he stood on a moving plate. There were benches down the other side of the plating shed. The guillotine to cut the plates, which at one time was worked by Ernie Shead, was out in the yard and unguarded, although it was quite sharp enough to cause injuries, and did so on several occasions, mainly lost fingers. To cut the plates, they would be lifted onto trestles. Between the mostly belt-driven machines, the plates would be moved on bogies on a track.

The furnace, situated at the end of the platers' shop, in which plates would be heated for bending, was worked in the 1920s by the skilful team of ex-Wivenhoe men, Albert and Dick Simons, and was originally fired by coke, later oil. It was 30′ long but much narrower. To beat the ½″ or ⅝″ thick plates into shape, hammers ranging in size from 7 lb to 28 lb would be swung by hand. Four to six men would thus be employed regularly. One of the worst jobs was the bending of boss-plates to fit round propeller shafts, which required considerable amounts of heavy labour. The furnaces were also used to bend angle-irons by use of holes in the floor.

It was in the late 1920s that the furnace was converted to oil, which did not make the work any less heavy or demanding. Frequently, the furnacemen would come home soaked with sweat and filthy. It would still also take a long time to get the furnace hot, usually at least half an hour. Frank Ward described the difficulties of lighting a second burner when the first was already alight. One or other would usually go out, causing thick, choking fumes. Similarly, if the Power House shut down for any reason, fumes would fill the furnace. These fumes were an industrial hazard whose effects are still noticed by ex-furnacemen.

Especially in the 1930s, when the yard was busy, the pace of work in the furnace was fast and few could stand it. Under a hard taskmaster, Bob Johnson, the men would turn out vast numbers of hull-frames for swim-barges for very little extra pay than the outside labourers, only 37/6d a week in the 1930s. However, when work was scarce, so that labourers could otherwise get sent home, even heavy work in the furnace was preferable to poverty. Machine tools for use in the furnace were made in the yard's forge by Fred Liddle.

As with the furnace, drilling required a lot of repetitive work when there was preparation for swim-barges. Till the late 1930s, there was only one radial drill, so that in order to complete the work quickly, much night work was required. Labourers, among them Chris Tyler, brought in stacks of plates on a bogie and clamped them onto the bench to be drilled. The drill would be worked by Fred Shepherd or George Moore and could do up to a dozen plates at once. Thus,

Plates for standard orders such as lighters were drilled twenty at a time. The bogie on its track ran under the drilling machine.

Horace Lennard using a hydraulic buffer on the hull of a vessel. The pipes to these machines were laid out in 60′ lengths.

By the 1950s tubular scaffolding was in use at the yard. The scaffold shown is for the stern of Ship No. 2129 *Capacity*.

Tyler said, in three weeks, plates for four lighters could be done by one drill. A new drill shop was erected in 1939 which contained three radial drills and eliminated the need for night shifts.

Once drilled and countersunk, the plates would be taken, still on the bogie, down the tracks to the building blocks. This was the main hazard to the hydraulic pipes as the bogies had solid, iron wheels. At the blocks, the erectors, for example, Joe Groom and Albert Lines, each with the help of two labourers, of which "Totsy" Bones and Alec Gamble were examples, would start to erect the ship. The plates at this stage would be held together with service bolts which could later be removed and re-used. These would be put in by Bill Weaver. The lifting of plates for erection was not easy before the arrival of cranes. The plates would be lifted with a block and tackle, and the operation was quite labour-intensive. It could occupy up to twelve labourers, and it was not till during the war that much better cranes arrived, paid for by the Admiralty. If a plate failed to fit when it was put in, it would be heated to white hot and doused with water, or beaten. "China" Godden, the burner, would sometimes do this, though the foreman, Harry Packman, doubted the safety of this method; he feared that the plate would snap.

The platers were paid piece-work, and like the riveters would pay their helpers out of their wage. The most experienced of them, Ben Jones, on a good week as marker-off in the 1930s could take home up to £9 for his 47-hour week, though a more usual wage was £4 – £5, with labourers taking home 36/8d per week, being paid at 10d per hour, with the same rate for overtime.

The plating thus was completed in three main processes; cutting; countersinking and erecting, and each process would be done by different men. Rough edges of plates would be buffed with either an electric or a hydraulic tool. An experimental hydraulic tool was tested by Horace Lennard.

Necessarily for riveting or plating, scaffolding had to be erected. In the early days, the greater part of this comprised planks resting on trestles, a method which the riveters felt, even after the tubular scaffolding came in, did not get in their way. An alternative to trestles was wooden poles tied with wire rope and wedged in tubs of earth, which could be moved along the ship as needed. This, Frank Sagrott stated, was still in use in the 1940s, and was worked with by his predecessor and co-worker, Harry Coleman. In the late 1940s, Marshall Pollock invested in some second-hand tubular scaffolding from Canterbury. New cranes also came during the war, which were to considerably aid the work in erection and reduce its previously extravagant demands for labour.

After the war, then, although conditions for the erectors improved, those in the platers' shop and furnace were much the same. The wage of a plater had risen to an average of £7–£10, while their labourers would earn about £4. The plater's wage would be presented to him with a slip like the one below for 1962:

Platers Piece-work bill — Faversham Shipyard
Name: Newman — W.E. 16th Sept 1962
Check Nos: 42
Time: 42½

Ship No. or Job No.	Description of work	Quantity	Rate	Amount
61/3	Sundry platers work			11 9 0
	less credit			2 9
				11 6 3
	N. Ins.			10 7
				10 15 8
	Sick fund etc.			1 2
				10 14 6
	G. pension			2 0
				10 12 6
	I. Tax			12 0
				£10 0 6

Signed: A. Stroud & checked by F. Parfect

IV. Engineering and fitting

When the yard first opened, Walter Pollock drew on the local engineering firm of Semark's for some of his fitters and turners, among them Pat Hudson who came to the yard in 1923.

Some of the machinery in the fitting shop was bought second-hand when the yard was laid out, and much of it saw out the whole of the yard's history. Like that in the platers' shop, most of the machinery was belt-driven. It included a large, 20′ lathe, smaller lathes, a radial drill, grinders and pipe-benders. One lathe, which came in the late 1930s, was metric and very accurate. Much of the machinery was along one side of the fitting shop under the windows, with a compressor and benches on the other side and a saw for steel pipes. Above the fitting shop was an office used mostly by W.F. Shields, from which he could see into both sides of the building.

The closure of the Bolinder stores at the yard in 1934 enabled new stores to be opened in which to keep the requirements of the fitting shop and yard. They had much more space than those used previously, some of which were in the gatehouse.

The 1940s saw the addition to the fitting shop machinery of an electric pipe-threading machine, a new emery-wheel grinder and an electric drill. A new lathe came in the 1950s. By 1957, Pollocks could advertise that their "modern"

Machinery in the fitting shop. Some of the machinery was second-hand when the yard first opened.

machinery in the engine shops could cope with vessels up to 1,000 tons dry weight.

The fitting shop occupied 24–36 men. In the 1940s the distribution was as follows: six lathe turners, one radial driller (Bob Punyer), two working on Sureal winches (Bud Wensley and George Partis), two electricians (Chas. Marshall and Jimmy Eames) and other fitters and labourers. Of these, some would be in the AUEW. As with the other skilled trades, apprenticeships were for five years, and it was usual for two evenings per week to be spent at classes to learn technical skills. Several apprentices trained by Pollocks' fitters and turners went on to have excellent jobs elsewhere, among them Dominic Nacci, who went on the *Cunard Countess*, and Geoff Athawes. Many were easily tempted away, as the money was not good at Pollocks; 7/6d as an apprentice fitter aged 14 in the 1930s, rising to about £3 full pay. By the 1940s this had reached £5, and £9 in the 1950s. Drillers in the 1930s would be on about £2 per week.

V. Welding

Welding was a method whereby scantlings could be reduced, and it was partly for this reason that its acceptance by Lloyd's was slow, yet in the 1930s welded ships were common in the USA and Germany. Still, there had been some spectacular accidents in which welds fractured and ships broke in two.

However, in 1936, Pollocks constructed a welded bulkhead and displayed it at the yard. The welded section was tested and the weld proved more resistant than the plate. Customers were not much impressed. Throughout the 1930s, welding was used on some trawlers, especially in the area where the otter doors came up the vessels' sides when the gear was hauled, so that they slid over a smooth surface.

Charlie Carter, the foreman shipwright, working with the carpenters on the deck of a vessel.

Welding, at first, was only used on butt-straps. In liaison with "Murex", in 1939 a welded barge was constructed, much of the welding being done by Bert Crockford Snr, this being a standby job for the electric welders. Its sides were welded on the ground and lifted into place by crane. The barge, *Irwell*, of 170 tons, required 44 tons of steel, 11% less than a similar-sized riveted barge with scantlings of the same strength. It worked successfully on the Thames in the 1940s.

Till the 1950s, welding was used in conjunction with riveting, not as a complete replacement, as Lloyd's were still reluctant to class welded ships A-1. The 1950s and 1960s saw a major expansion in the use of fixed and portable welding units. A group of welders including Colin Frake, Brian Boorman and Peter Maxey were trained. New welding equipment including CO2 gear came in 1959–60 for work on the *Broadness* and *Stoneness*, these being some of the earliest all-welded powered craft at the yard. Into the 1960s, many of the lighters were all-welded including two for a coal company, but tugs still had riveted frames. Gradually, riveting was being eliminated by welding. About six welders would be employed in the 1960s on c.£10 per week. The early welding of the 1930s used no flux, but later, new equipment came in. The welders would work in a shed next to the electricians' one.

The final contribution to the yard's output made by the welders were two 500-ton barges, *Greybear* and *Greyfox*.

VI. Burning

Only a few burners were employed at the yard, the two most familiar being Harry Packman and Charlie Godden. Both had previously been riveters. Harry was also the Secretary of the Boilermakers' Union and a shop steward. Owing to the restrictive practices of the Boilermakers' Union, the burner had to be waited for whenever any burning wanted doing, for example, if a rivet had not sealed properly and had to be burnt out. Godden described how the burners would have to crawl under the engines of vessels to acetylene burn rivets, or burn out the holes for anchor cables or skylights over engines, or the portholes. The work was dangerous, but even the necessary gloves had to be supplied by the workers themselves before the war.

At first, burning was done with pyro-gas which had a tendency to poison men with its fumes, as it was produced by dripping water onto coke. Later, acetylene from cylinders was used, and it was this equipment on which Ernie Cripps learnt the trade from Godden. Copper nozzles had to be used when burning wartime treated steel plates.

Like the majority of craftsmen, the burner would frequently work with a mate, whom he would pay out of his earnings. By the late 1950s, the wage of the burner had reached £10 a week, for the arduous task of removing typically ten or eleven plates each with 200 rivets, or rough cutting large numbers of plates for shearing.

VII. Shipwrights and carpenters

Many of the shipwrights and carpenters were local men, for these crafts had already been prevalent in Faversham for some time. The skill was passed on by means of five-year apprenticeships in the Shipwrights' Union, later part of the Boilermakers. Among the early men were Charlie Dane and Clarence "Chick"

Fowle, Bert Diamond and Percy Dadson. From Cremer's at Hollowshore came Charlie Carter, the foreman. When many of the old men retired in the 1950s a new generation of shipwrights and carpenters took their place.

The shipwrights' work included the setting up of the framework of ships and the laying of slipways. Before the ships could be built, keel blocks had to be laid, then a wooden or metal framework of the ship erected and a ribband put through the frame to keep the ribs the correct distance apart. When wooden decks were laid, it would fall to the shipwrights to caulk the seams with oakum and pay them with pitch.

The most vital part of the shipwrights' work was the laying of slipways down which the vessels would ultimately reach the water. Sideways launching required great precision in the construction of slips as it was very fast, the speed required to stop the vessel rolling back on the quay:

Fixed launchways are 12′×12″ pine with a ribbing of 12′×3″ pine, which are bolted to the 12′×12″ with ¾″ bolts with a 3″×3″ angle at the ribbing side, the bolts are 3′ apart.

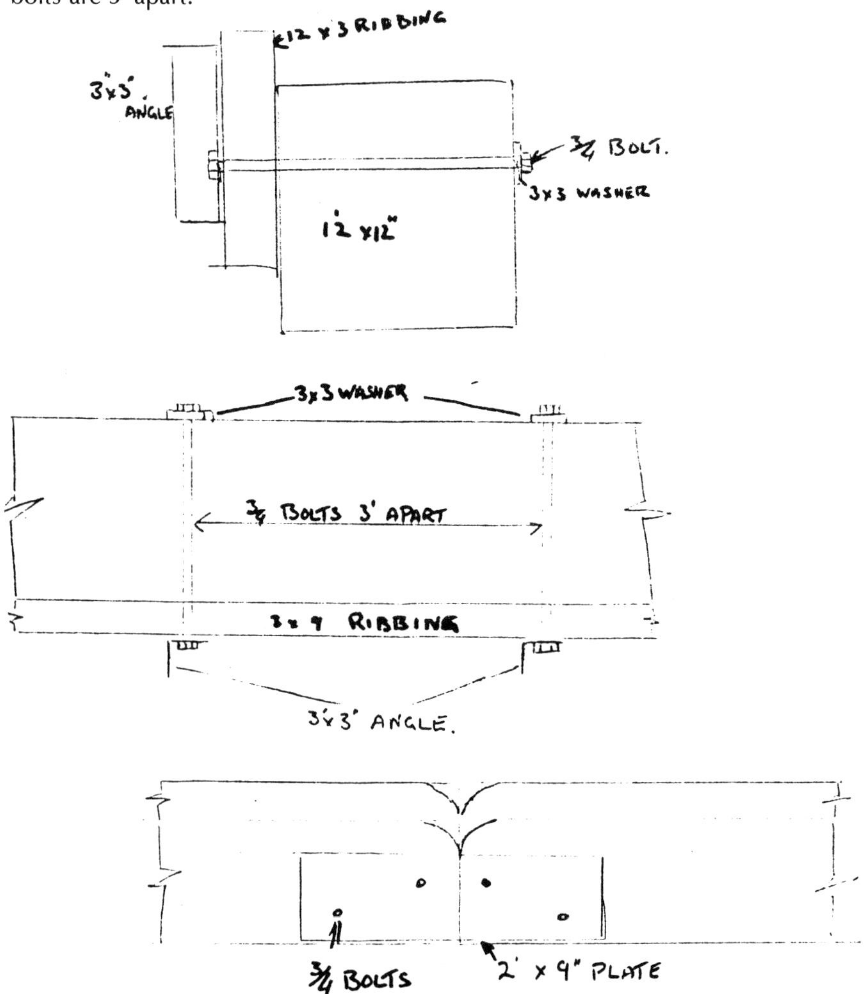

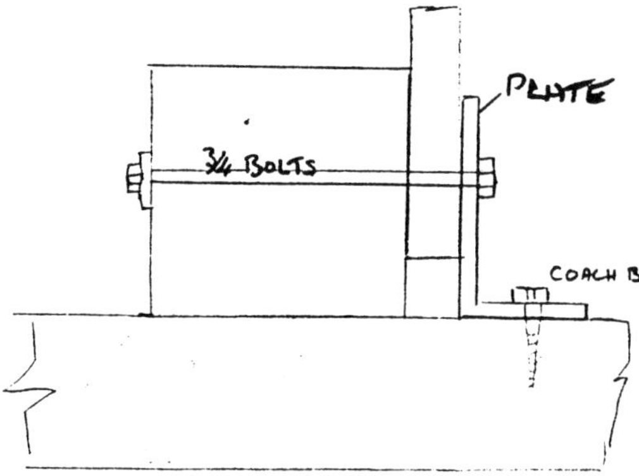

PLATE

3/4 BOLTS

COACH BOLTS

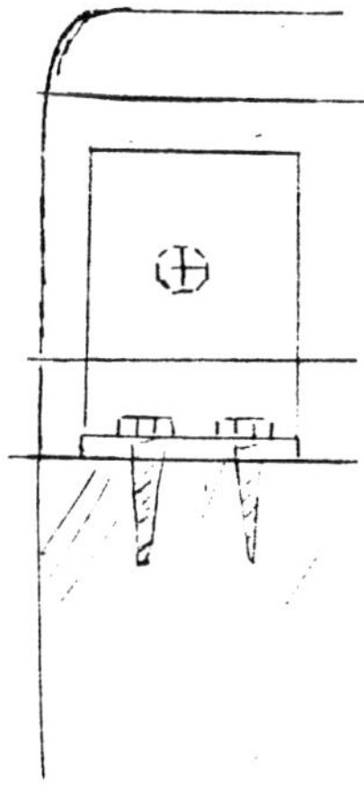

Launchways are set up in 2.4.6.

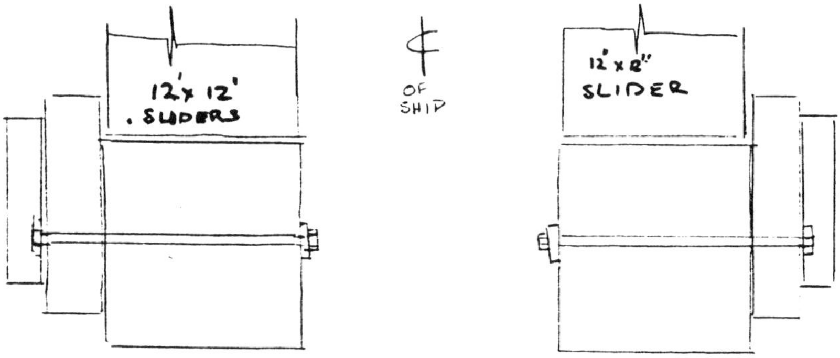

12' x 12'
SLIDERS

℄
OF
SHIP

12' x 12"
SLIDER

THE SET UP FOR A FLAT BOTTOM SHIP

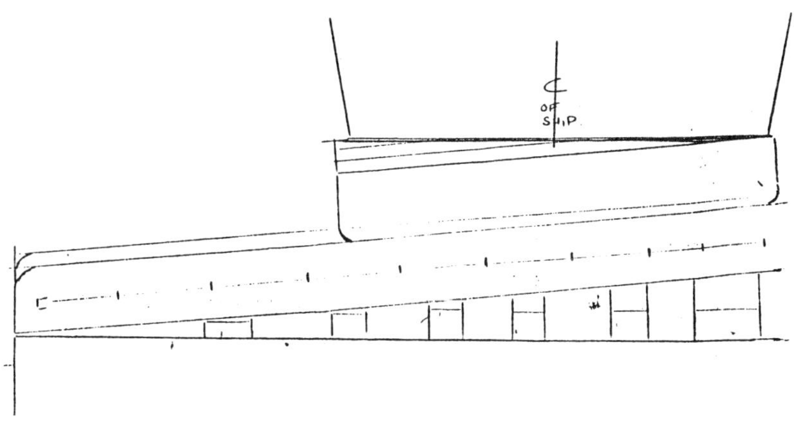

Charlie Godden with a cylinder of acetylene gas used for burning out rivets or the holes for anchor cables.

The "basekote" was applied with mops, followed by the Dutch "slidekote" applied by hand by the labourers of the heavy gang.

The shipwrights' foreman, Charlie Carter, would launch the vessel by cutting a rope, releasing two or more launch-triggers, the blocks having previously been knocked out by "Chick" Fowle, and if sufficient grease had been applied, the ship would rush down the slipway of declivity 1½" per foot into the creek. Only on a very few occasions did the method fail to work; once when the grease dried out at a launch and again when there was a splinter of metal on the slip. The latter incident was recalled by Bill Weaver:

"It was a double launch. George Hunter, who was an experienced member of the launch-preparation gang, who did not normally watch, saw it. I said, 'There goes the first one.' It floated away. Hunter said, 'Let me know when they take the blocks out for the second.' The second barge went three parts down the slip and fell off. In fact, the first had toppled in and fouled the slipway. The shipwrights had regreased, but a sliver caught on the second lighter and it came off."

Nine or ten shipwrights would be employed at the yard in the busy 1920s and 1930s at a rate of £2 10s when fully-qualified, or four men in slack periods. The wage rate rose to £12 in the 1950s, and for the most skilled men to £18 in the last few years of the yard.

Whilst the shipwrights' work was largely outside, the carpenters and joiners had the use of a "shop" containing a circular saw, band saw, grindstone and a cross-cut saw which all originally ran off a belt, but later were individually

The mechanism of the launching trip which was released when the rope was cut to launch the vessel.

powered. They could, on account of these facilities, quote for outside joinery work.

The carpenters had a separate foreman from the shipwrights. In this position, Charlie Dane was succeeded by Joe Moat. Finally, as the yard began to decline, the two trade groups were combined, and in the 60s their foreman was the aforementioned Joe Moat. Carpenters would be involved with vessels at the initial stages and when cabins were being fitted out.

VIII. Electrical work

For much of the history of the yard, two electricians were employed, though this was increased to three during the war, with the addition of Jimmy Eames to the regular team of Edgar Bulley and Chas. Marshall.

The electricians did very little of the wiring of vessels, but might put lighting into double bottoms. Outside contractors did the more complicated work, for example McKays, who wired up the *Ripon* and the *Seafox*.

The yard electricians early in the war would de-magnetise ships by running wires round and creating a magnetic field. Later, ships were taken to Tilbury for this degaussing process, accompanied by W.F. Shields.

The main rôle of the electrical team would be to supply lead lamps, look after motors and the high-cycle drills (110 volts) which could be plugged into the power supply from the Power House. Other electrical equipment included reamering tools, the high-cycle countersinker in the plating shop and buffers to smooth down the edges of bored holes. All the machinery was d.c. except the drills, which were a.c. and needed a converter.

Should a flood occur, the first job of the electricians would be to hose down the electrical equipment to remove mud and salt before letting it dry out.

Bill Jacobs applying "Slidekote" to a launching way. This was applied by hand, cold.

Inside the power house. The engine shown is an Allen Diesel. The power house provided all the power for drilling and welding.

The electricians came under W.F. Shields as foreman, and to get an annual rise in their pay when apprentices, would have to see Shields and tell him that it was his birthday, Edgar Bulley recalled. When fully qualified, in the 1940s, an electrician could earn £3 – £4 per week, sometimes rising to £7 if he did a great deal of overtime.

IX. Gangs of labourers

The number of labourers varied widely as the amount of work at the yard rose and fell. One gang, under Tommy Mallion, was responsible for painting the insides of vessels. This was frequently unpleasant work as the fumes from the paint, sometimes red lead, would affect the lungs and necessitate continually coming out of the confined spaces to get a breath of air. The gang usually comprised about eight men, in the 1930s including spray painters Tim Tyler and Bill Towells, together with Jim Glass, Charlie Hill and Jim Ellis. Of these, some had left by the 1950s to be replaced by Bill Jacobs, Bert Beeton, who also worked on the wall round the North yard, and Fred Buffee. Associated with this gang was Clem Ware, the charge-hand who had been a master rigger. He would supply labour for the shipwrights on launch preparation. Charlie Hart, Ivo Lloyd and Ted Hunt were frequently on this job and knew it well. Bill Jacobs, of the paint gang, also slidekoted the slipways.

Work on wire-brushing of hulls to remove rust was done by a gang of up to twelve men. This was demanding work for the men (or women during the war) who performed it, and there was no bonus for doing it quicker. The labourers who worked under a craftsman could sometimes collect a tip of 2/6d for speeding the skilled man's work.

X. Comment

Though new innovations and machinery were fairly slow to come in to replace old methods, by the late 1950s and early 1960s, the yard had gained labour-saving devices in erection; welding had almost replaced riveting, taking away the possibility of boosting earnings on piece-work, for it was the riveters who were the last to adhere to this practice. Work was less labour-intensive. It was still noisy, and to be heard, shipyarders would talk directly into each other's ears. This, or sign language, was common all over the country in shipyards and is described in Pagnamenta & Overy by a shipwright:

"You came out of the job you were working on to where it was more open to get a bit of relief. About about three weeks, it didn't seem quite so bad. Then when you'd been there two months you said, 'It's getting great, I can stand that noise now'. And when it got to years it sounded quieter still. Until one day you were talking to your wife and she would say, 'Don't shout'. And I said, 'I am not shouting'. And she said, 'You are. And I am shouting to you so you can hear'. You didn't realise you were deaf."

In some respects, the yard and its practices scarcely altered. Much of the machinery left at the close in February 1970 was original and was only removed after this date.

Sources

"All Our Working Lives". Peter Pagnamenta & Richard Overy, 1984. BBC.
"Small Vessels". Walter Pollock, 1946.

Ship No. 928 *Rene*, a small launch tug with a 20 b.h.p. Bolinder engine.

Ship No. 1035 *Mary*, one of a group of three 78′ swim barges delivered to London in February 1923.

Ship No. 1350 *Magdalena*, a cattle lighter supplied by F.N. Roman, in Puntarenas, Chile.

Chapter 5
1918 – 29
MOSTLY A PERIOD OF EXPANSION

This period was one when the yard was being developed with large numbers of men being taken on and technical changes taking place, especially the introduction of pneumatic machinery mentioned in the previous chapter. A wide variety of craft were being built, some still steam, more now oil-engined. Of these, a significant number were for abroad, especially South America. In addition, many tugs and lighters were supplied for the mundane but no less important, bulk trade on the Thames, and barges for the canals. Till the bad winter of 1929, work at the yard was fairly plentiful, but still continuity of employment could not be ensured.

I. Non-Faversham ships

Whilst the yard at Faversham was busy constructing the two concrete coasters, three tugs of different types had been designed and were built elsewhere; the *Albion*, a stern-wheel tug; the *Florida*, a launch tug. and the *Stentor*, a canal tug for Chance-Hunt at Oldbury. A ketch, *Mountsfield* (99′3″ × 23′5″ × 8′3″), was fitted with a Bolinder engine, and a Petter winch supplied for a sailing vessel, the *Portugal*. A launch tug, the *Rene*, came up to Faversham to have an engine fitted.

In 1920 – 1 a number of Bolinder engines were supplied to the Argentine Steam Navigation Company. The New Zealand schooner, *Ronaki*, was fitted with auxiliary Bolinder engines and journeyed to the Antipodes under her own power. Similarly, in 1923 the 110′ brigantine, *Dolphin*, was supplied with auxiliary engines. In this same year, a steam barge-tug, *Ulco*, was built for Union Lighterage and was used on the Thames.

A vessel of note which Pollocks designed was the auxiliary sailing vessel *Ilen*, a small craft with only a 24 b.h.p. engine, but which made a voyage under her own power to the Falkland Islands.

Continuing the use of Bolinder engines in fishing boats which had been introduced in the second decade of the twentieth century, a trawler, *Lilias*, was built in 1926 for Grimsby. Its trawl winch was unusually geared to the 350 b.h.p. main engine. *Lilias*' main claim to fame was that her Chief Engineer was Jim Wells, who was subsequently to be employed as engineer's draughtsman first at 3 Lloyd's Avenue and later at Faversham. Another fishing vessel was the *Lindfar* (1927) of Lowestoft, capable of competing admirably with the largest steam or sail herring drifters in the port, with her 60 b.h.p. Bolinder engine.

With specifications like the canal barge *Bolford*, built for APCM at Faversham, the 73′ *Cromford* was fitted with a 100 b.h.p. Kromhaut engine. *Bolford* had a Bolinder. Both names were derived from the engine make.

The *Quitador*, a large and very powerful 600 b.h.p. tug was supplied to the River Plate in winter, crossing the Atlantic in very bad weather. It was built by Crichton's, Saltney, whose other two shipyards were at Turku, Finland, and Antwerp.

A Maldon-built ketch barge, *Record Reign*, was fitted with twin 30 b.h.p. Bolinders. When the vessel went aground on the Dutch coast, Bill Shields was sent for to repair her engines.

Motor winches were put into the schooner *Ryelands* and Everards racing barge *Veronica*.

II. Faversham output

As agents in Britain for Bolinder's, in the 1920s Pollocks were to supply several land-engines of various powers, among them, one to the Eastern Smelting company.

At the yard, regular orders were being placed throughout the decade for Bolinders for canal barges in sets of six or twelve for a variety of firms. Many of the canal craft were for Fellows, Morton & Clayton, largest of the English canal carriers, for whom Walter had designed the narrow boats which were built at Yarwood's, Northwich. A sharp drop in the supply in 1923 reflects trouble Fellows, M & C were having with their employees. A strike for higher freight rates temporarily crippled the trade. Once the dispute was over, the supply resumed on a regular basis. A lesser number of narrow boats were built and engined at Pollocks' own yard for the same company.

As before the war, Pollocks were also supplying swim-barges for the Thames. It must have been extremely difficult for any owner to think of names for these unpowered, unattractive craft, but sets were named after birds, or had girls' names or place names. Some had more fanciful names such as *Gondola*. Most of the swim-barges were built in sets of six or twelve, with all the plates being drilled together for stock sizes of 160 or 200 tons. Working in the swim-ends of these lighters regularly caused problems, especially in the days of hand-riveting.

For a customer in Puntarenas, Chile, in 1929 a specialist cattle-barge, the only one of its type to be built by Pollocks, was supplied. Named the *Magdalena*, her dimensions were 85′×17′×6′. More on the lines of Thames sailing barges were five motor barges, named *Lagopet M.B.1* etc. up to *M.B.5;* they would be registered in Venezuela. Having been riveted by Chris Sunley and others, they were floated to London and shipped aboard a steamer to the Dutch West Indies, off the Venezuelan coast. Each had twin 30 b.h.p. Bolinders.

More unusual were two stern-wheel towing barges, un-named and supplied to the Colombian Government in 1926, and the tropical-style barge *Patricia* for the island of Fernando Po, off West Africa. A speciality of the yard were tank barges for which there were frequently to be seen a number of spirit tanks lined up waiting to be lifted aboard. One of the early customers for the tank barges was the South Metropolitan Gas Company whose first order for one came in 1922.

Pollocks' programme of coasters continued with the *Linton* ex-*Admiral Vernon,* built 1919–20 on similar lines to the *Lee-Lee* which had been commenced in 1915. *Admiral Vernon* was sold to W. Vernon of Liverpool. My grandfather, Arthur Salmon, worked on the *Linton* which was delivered in May 1921. *Linton* was repurchased and managed by Pollocks under their subsidiary "Miramar Coasters" as had been the *Lee-Lee* and *Lutona*, but all three were soon sold as the firm did not want to compete with potential clients. Whilst *Lee-Lee* was managed by Pollocks, Bert Collins and Fred Flory were engineers on board, on voyages between Antwerp and Norwich via Yarmouth. *Lee-Lee* was later sold to Everard's, and became the *Annuity*.

Ship No. 933 *Linton* (later *Admiral Vernon*), one of three "Miramar" class coasters which were owned and managed by Pollocks in the early 1920s.

A coaster with which the young engineer Bill Shields was closely connected, was the *Ben Truman* (1919), Bolinder-engined but with steadying sails. Built for Truman, Hanbury & Buxton's brewery, whenever the regular engineer was absent Shields would run the vessel instead. She was registered at Chatham. The vessel later became the River Weaver Navigation Trust's *River Weaver*.

The coaster *Ferrocrete* was being built throughout the strike of 1926 for the Thames and Medway trade in cement. She was launched in September 1927 and whilst being fitted out, suffered a fire in her engine room. Subsequent to her delivery to APCM, *Ferrocrete* paid several return visits to the yard for repairs. The vessel was still afloat fifty years later, being used as a committee boat for barge matches.

The 1927 coaster *Don Lorenzo* which sailed on a Friday, having been fitted out beside the coalyard on the ex-BP site, lived up to the superstition of bad luck associated with Friday sailing felt by the sailors. She was lost at sea off Torbay and never reached her intended destination in Venezuela.

Three coasters were built in 1928–9, the last of which was for Goldsmith's and named the *Goldace*. She would be followed in 1932 by *Goldbell, Goldcrown, Golddrift* and *Goldeve* to the same firm, and by the *Goldhind* and *Goldlynx* after the war. Another coaster, the *Geoffrey Stanley*, was built for the War Department, and in the 1960s she was being operated out of Woolwich Arsenal by H.R. Mitchell, who also operated the *Vawdrey, Katharine Mitchell* and *Redoubtable*.

The first influx of workers from the North of England, Jimmy Jordan said, came as early as 1919 to work on two 75′ tugs, the *Flanchford* and the *Rocott*. The first voyage of *Rocott* was a crowded affair and she steamed down the creek with flags flying. Both tugs were destined for the Thames. The Northern men proved expensive and some were replaced shortly by men from Wivenhoe, Essex, whom some of the Faversham people, among them Les Jacobs, thought of as sneaky. This Wivenhoe influx came in 1920–3 as a result of the closure of

Ship No. 940 *Rocott*, a 75′ tug seen with a large crowd on board for her trial trip.

Wivenhoe yard by its new owners, Shipbuilders Securities, who were buying up yards and closing them to reduce surplus shipbuilding capacity.

Still, in 1923, some customers preferred steam propulsion for their tugs. The 65′×15′3″×8′ *Malcralph* had steam machinery, as did the 1924 69′ tug *Caupolican*, which, like a number of other ships, was fitted out on the opposite side of the creek in front of the attractive, weatherboarded stores on Standard Wharf. *Caupolican* was taken by Shields to London and put aboard the steamer *La Paz* bound for Valparaiso, Chile.

Often, tugs were built for stock account. One such was *Jolly Tar*, on which Shields did the entire installation with the help of only one labourer. It was purchased by a firm at Charlton Wharf, Anchor & Hope Lane, London.

One of only a very few Pollocks vessels to bear Faversham registry was the 1925-built *Noni*. She was designed for use on the creek for towing barges, and for her size was very powerful. Only 54′ long, she could pull six fully-laden Thames barges, a total weight of nearly 1,000 tons. A very valuable asset on the creek, after duties with the South Atlantic Command in 1942 and as United Africa Co.'s *Tunku* in 1947, this tug was sold to Australia for more than she cost to build.

Ship No. 1131 *Caupolican*, a tug, being lifted aboard the steamer *La Paz* for transport to Chile in 1924.

It was unusual to see a vessel on her sea trials without already having a name painted on her bows, but this was how the tug *Pasto* destined eventually for Colombia made her first trip down the creek. Other tugs which followed swiftly after *Pasto* were the *Laybay* and the *Dart*. An unusually-designed tug, with an awning for use in tropical climates was the Widdop-engined *Vulture*, sent out with two hopper-barges to Sierra Leone, all three being launched in July 1927.

By 1928 Walter Pollock had begun a programme of standard tug designs. *Laybay (Eastwick)* was to be the prototype for a specific class of tugs, and *Barking* began the *Lonie* type. *Scottie* was the first of a class of barge-tugs which were very economical to run and well-suited to river and harbour use. The second of this class of 270 b.h.p. tugs was the *Tat*. She was supplied to Tester Brothers at Greenhithe for towing swim-barges in March 1930.

The earliest post World War I tanker *(Stourgate)* to be built at Faversham in 1923 had, as mentioned in Chapter Three, the engine which had been taken out of the *Violette*. For *Stourgate*'s launch, a big reception was held. An incident in the history of the vessel was described by Captain A.V. West in "East Coast Digest". Captain West joined the Anglo-American Oil Company's *Stourgate* in 1928. The firm always used the suffix "gate" in the names of tankers. On the Calder, they ran the tanker *Caldergate*. Captain West's description follows:

"The *Stourgate* had several unusual features. She was a single-skinned ship, with no wooden rubbing band, although this feature was normal with a petrol-carrying vessel. Her Bolinder engine was started via pressure blow-lamp, and

Ship No. 1270 *Scottie* at work towing lighters on the Thames. She was the first of a class of powerful tugs used for river and harbour work.

Ship No. 1073 *Stourgate* (later *Harriet Spearing*). This tanker, fitted with the engine formerly in Violette was supplied to the Anglo-American Oil Company.

constant vigilance was imperative, after discharge or loading that the engine-room was gas-free. Great care had to be taken that you gave no heavy knocks to the hull for fear of creating a spark. Apart from the fact that a rivet out was some cargo out.

"She was very powerful, being capable of towing two laden spirit barges down over the tide from the war-time installation at Walton-on-Thames and saving her water onto the berths at Fulham or down to Silvertown. Although her wheel-house could be halved on hinges, she was still a tight fit in some places. On the Medway, for instance, she had to lock through at Allington and belt down thro' Aylesford Bridge. It was always a near thing and I think my grey hairs dated from then.

"Her duties included keeping up stock of aviation spirit at Faversham and Sandwich depots. She was the first ship to load spirit in the war, in 1939. Painted slate-grey during the war, she had no distinguishing marks.

"I was taken by car up to the Admiralty to get my official routeing as our cargo of motor-spirit was for Sandwich. My route was down the North Edinboro' Channel, so I pointed out to the officer that he was putting many miles on my journey, and suggested that the Prince's Channel, the Queen's Channel, or the "overland route" south of the Margate Hook would be better. He asked me to indicate my suggested course and when I showed him, he said 'Go ahead your way. You are more likely to be knocked down by a lorry than torpedoed!'

"After this voyage, the acoustic mine made it imperative that we kept to the swept channels.

"To ease the tanker traffic using the Channel and the Estuary, the Petroleum Board opened a pipe-line from Avonmouth to Walton-on-Thames. The residents of the homes and houseboats in this sheltered part of the river hardly knew that there was a war on, but it was about to come to them. I well remember having groped up through the London bridges, towing two tank barges in poor visibility, when a launch about a quarter of the size of *Stourgate* appeared. It had a large Naval Reserve crew, and was commanded by a man who turned out to be A.P. Herbert. Through his loud hailer he called, 'You tanker people are a menace, disturbing sleeping people in their houseboats.' Fortunately distance prevented any repartee, bar telling him that there was a war on down in the Estuary.

"It was most fortunate that we got to Walton that way, because the river was in flood, and a small tug with two spirit-laden barges had gone athwart the Sunbury lock weir. With our greater power, we were able to tow them clear. This was so appreciated by the Petroleum Board that they gave myself and my crew a financial reward. Two nights after that was the first air raid of Richmond locks — the war had at last come to the Upper Thames and the poor houseboat residents were to be disturbed for many nights to come.

"Among the additional hazards of wartime was the extinguishing of lit buoys etc. around the coast. On the Thames, the two orange lights alongside each other marking the working arches of bridges were also blacked out and how badly they were missed.

"Pre-war, the PLA regulations were exceedingly strict. All petrol traffic loaded or empty, had to stop at sunset and not recommence till daylight. The war did away with these bye-laws, and now the night traffic of petrol-laden self-propelled vessels greatly exceeds all other traffic."

Ship No. 1104 *Presidente Ospina*, a suction and grab dredger built for use in Colombia.

During the vessel's time afloat, she paid several visits to Faversham for repairs. She ended up at Rochester as the *Harriet Spearing* before being broken up.

A specialised vessel for carrying oil in bulk was the 94′ tanker *British Maiden*, built for Shell-Mex/BP. She had a Gardner engine. *British Maiden* was slightly smaller than a tanker built two years later named *Lido*.

A particularly unusual vessel to be built alongside the fitting shop and subsequently marked to be sent out in plates and angles was the steam-powered suction and grab-dredger *Presidente Ospina*. She had a very big bulkhead and a strangely shaped stem, and was nicknamed *Stonewaller* by some of the men. Perks described her as having a stem like a Thames dredger and a stern like a Mississippi river boat. When she was completed, the fitter, Harry Smith, who had worked at Goldfinch's yard across the creek, went away with her. The multi-purpose vessel was landed in Puerto Colombia and was transported by rail to Barranquilla on the Magdalena River to be re-erected under the supervision of Harry Smith. Within two years of the contract being signed, the craft made her trial trip in Colombia, having been built, taken apart and rebuilt.

The next year, 1925, a vessel was commenced whose launch was to bring a number of notable people to Walter Pollock's Faversham shipyard. It was a yacht for the Rajah of Sarawak, Charles Vyner de Windt Brooke. In 1923 the Rajah had used his former yacht to make a journey up river in Sarawak to preside over a reconciliation ceremony which virtually ended the troubles of the interior. He decided to have the yacht replaced with one which was very luxurious for its time, and had teak decks. With all the fittings for the galley and furniture for the dining room and other accommodation made at the yard, she provided a lot of work. She was the largest vessel constructed at the yard by 1925. Among those who worked on her were shipwright "Chick" Fowle and labourer Jim Speed. A detailed description of the fittings and accommodation of HHMY *Maimunah* was given in the Sarawak Gazette dated 1st March 1926.

Amongst those at the launch of the 500-ton vessel in October 1925 were His Highness, the Tuan Bunsu of Sarawak, Captain Harry Brooke; Mr C. Willes Johnson, legal advisor to the Sarawak Government; Mr J.A. Smith, the Rajah's Secretary; and Dr Charles Hose, a member of the Government Council. The vessel, named *Maimunah*, was launched by the mother of the Rajah, Margaret

Ship No. 1198 *Maimunah*. The vessel was a cargo and passenger carrier for the Rajah of Sarawak. The launch by the Ranee, Margaret Brooke, was a grand occasion attended by several of the Sarawak Government as well as Pollock directors.

de Windt Brooke. The launch was watched on the far bank of the creek by Alf Stroud, a future chief cashier at the yard, who ran down from school to see it, and in the yard anxiously by Mrs Walter Pollock and by directors of James Pollock, Sons & Co. Ltd., including Arthur Pollock, J.M. Scott and J. Mackley, also a Lloyd's surveyor, James Dalgleish. At 2 p.m., on a none-too-high tide, *Maimunah* hit the water, flying the Sarawak flag, the rope being cut by the axe of Charles Carter, foreman shipwright, under the supervision of yard manager, George Johnson. J.M. Scott subsequently presented Ranee Margaret with a silver bowl at a reception in Pollocks' offices.

Maimunah was fitted with a 350 b.h.p. ME 11 Bolinder engine, and on her first trip to London was accompanied by engineer, Pat Hudson. Two Pollock engineers, Bert Collins and Jack Wheeler, accompanied her on the voyage via Suez to Sarawak. Able to achieve 9.75 knots, she made the journey to Kuching in 54 days, arriving on 27th February 1926, having travelled 8,804 miles and using 65.04 tons of fuel. She was to be used in the development of the business of the Sarawak Government as a cargo and passenger vessel and as a pleasure craft until she sank.

Of some who were at the launch of the *Maimunah* or associated with her, the resting-place is known. Whilst in England, the Brookes had used a house at Burrator, Devon. In the nearby churchyard at Sheepstor, Margaret Brooke and her son, Charles Vyner Brooke lie in the family vault.

One of several launches for abroad was the *Ichabod*, made alongside the fitting shop almost entirely by a plater called Jones, helped by Fred Fox. 32′ long and steam-propelled, she was despatched to West Africa for use on a river. A slightly later launch, in 1927, for the same area was *Senchi*, 70′×14′×5′6″.

Overall, Pollocks maintained healthy business with firms both at home and abroad. For abroad, the method of shipment in plates and angles proved particularly convenient to many customers, but in order that the parts being sent out did not rust in transit, they were treated with linseed oil. Necessarily, the pieces had to be carefully marked and supplied with an adequate number of rivets. The Thames lighter trade was at its zenith and was to continue to be flourishing for at least another twenty years.

III. The yard

The overall decline in the shipping industry, however, made it necessary before the end of the decade to consolidate shipbuilding operations at Faversham, rather than Pollocks-designed ships being built in other yards elsewhere. The Faversham yard itself was no longer as busy by 1929 as it had been just a few years earlier. The weather in the winter of 1929 cannot have helped, for it was very cold. The insecurity of work in this period cannot have made life easy for the men who relied on piece-work to earn their wages. Frequently in rain, the manager, George Johnson, had been known to send men home rather than let them wait till the rain stopped and then carry on working. When work was slack, as was widespread in the shipbuilding industry, men were frequently laid off, and in 1929 there were few men actually working in the yard. Not only was there little job security, but wages were very low.

These general conditions had led to a strike, part of the General Strike in 1926 in which some members of the Boilermakers' Society took part, but few of the apprentices. They continued to work on the *Ferrocrete*. At least one of the apprentices would not have been able to strike even if he had wanted to. Les Jacobs was a bound apprentice through the Caslock Charity, the indenture being worded as follows:

"This indenture witnesseth that Leslie Cyril Jacobs of number 10 Menfield Street Faversham in the County of Kent the son of Maud Mary Jacobs of the same address widow (hereinafter called "the Apprentice") with the consent of the said Maud Mary Jacobs doth place and bind himself Apprentice to James Pollock, Sons and Company Limited carrying on a business or trade of Shipbuilders and Engineers at the Shipyard Faversham aforesaid (hereinafter called "The Masters") to learn their art and with them after the manner of an Apprentice to serve from the Ninth day of May One thousand nine hundred and twenty two for the term of five years during all which term the Apprentice shall faithfully diligently and honestly serve them the Masters and obey and perform all their lawful and reasonable demands and requirements and shall not do any damage or injury to the Masters or knowingly suffer the same to be done without acquainting them therewith but shall in all things conduct and acquit himself as an honest and faithful Apprentice ought to do and in consideration of the sum of Eight Pounds by the Municipal Trustees of the Charities of the Borough of Faversham ordered to be paid for the use of the Apprentice out of the Public Charity bequeathed by the Will of John Caslock . . . Gentleman for aid towards placing out poor children of Faversham aforesaid Apprentices namely Four Pounds in binding and providing clothes for the Apprentice and Four Pounds in providing clothes for the Apprentice on the Ninth day of November One Thousand nine hundred and twenty four and also in consideration of the services of the Apprentice to be done and performed to or for the

Masters they the Masters at the request of the said Maud Mary Jacobs and with the consent of the Apprentice testified by their executing these presents do hereby covenant and agree with the said Maud Mary Jacobs and also with the Apprentice in the manner following that is to say that they the Masters will take and receive the Apprentice during the term aforesaid and will also during the said term to the best of their power knowledge and ability instruct the Apprentice in the trade or business of a Shipbuilder and in all things incident or relating thereto in such manner as they the Masters do now or shall hereafter during the said term use or practice the same and will pay to the Apprentice (except in the case of illness or neglecting his work) during the first year of the Apprenticeship the sum of Ten Shillings per week during the second year of the Apprenticeship the sum of Twelve Shillings per week during the third year of the Apprenticeship the sum of Sixteen Shillings per week during the fourth year of the Apprenticeship the sum of Nineteen Shillings per week during the fifth year of the Apprenticeship such a sum (not less than Twenty Shillings per week) as shall be agreed upon between the Masters and the said Maud Mary Jacobs and also the Apprentice in accordance with the individual ability and workmanship of the Apprentice and the said Maud Mary Jacobs doth hereby covenant and agree with the Masters that she or her executors or administrators will at her or their own expense provide the Apprentice with good and sufficient board lodging clothing washing medicine and medical attendance and all other necessaries during the said term in witness whereof the said Leslie Cyril Jacobs and the said Maud Mary Jacobs have hereunto set their hands and seals and the said James Pollock, Sons and Company Limited have hereunto caused their Common Seal to be affixed this tenth day of October One thousand nine hundred and twenty three."

Signed by Leslie C. Jacobs, Maud Mary Jacobs, and by Walter Pollock, J.M. Scott and Arthur Pollock, who was Company Secretary. It bears an embossed company seal.

Early in his apprenticeship, Les had proved most helpful when in the drought of 1923, he kept the riveters at work by plying them with drinks containing oatmeal and water. It appears he was the only apprentice at the yard aided by the Caslock Charity.

CASLOCKS CHARITY

INDENTURE of APPRENTICESHIP

of

LESLIE CYRIL JACOBS

with

JAMES POLLOCK SONS & Co. Ltd.

Dated 10th October 1923

This is to certify that LESLIE CYRIL JACOBS has completed his apprenticeship to our satisfaction, from 9th May 1922 until 9th May 192

Signed George Johnson
Local Manager

JAMES POLLOCK, SONS & CO. Ltd
UPPER BRENTS
FAVERSHAM. KENT

In the Bolinder showroom. The showroom displayed a range of Bolinder cookers and domestic appliances.

IV. Bolinders at the yard

Throughout the 1920s Pollocks maintained a close connection with the Swedish firm of Bolinder's, an interest which was looked after by director, J.M. Scott. Within the yard at Faversham was a large showroom displaying a variety of their rapidly developing engines. This was managed by Alec Challice, later of the London Office. By 1924 these included a lightweight model so that owners could have an auxiliary set running on the same fuel as the main engine. Models could be supplied with one, two or four cylinders generating respectively 6–7 b.h.p., 12–15 b.h.p. and 20–30 b.h.p.

Replacing the need for the time-consuming process of trying to get a Bolinder to heat up using a blow-lamp, 1926 saw the commercial application of Petter's quick starting method for Bolinder engines. This could guarantee a two minute start even in winter and proved a great asset to customers who often found it difficult to keep the engines running at idling speed without the pressure lamp having to be continually relit. Reverse gearboxes were introduced in 1927. The culmination of these developments came in 1930, with the cold-starting Bolinder, again patented by Petter, of up to 400 b.h.p. for use in tugs. By the same year, 1930, there were forty-eight British coasters with Bolinders, thirty-seven British tugs and two hundred and forty barges so equipped, most of the engines being supplied by Pollocks as agents for Bolinder. In all, about a thousand vessels were supplied with Bolinder engines by Pollocks. Bolinders set up a separate company, Bolinders of London Ltd in 1932, and kept stocks at Faversham until 1934.

The stores in which the Bolinders were displayed were the particular province of Percy Judges in the early part of his career at Pollocks. They also contained a range of Bolinder cookers and domestic appliances. Percy later worked in the main office and as Chief Storekeeper.

Having begun the programme of stock tugs, coasters and launches, the firm of Bolinder's, keen to market their products, commissioned Walter Pollock to write volumes on their engines of various types and on the types of vessels in which they might be used. These appeared at "Hot Bulb Oil Engines and Suitable Vessels" published as early as 1917, which sold nearly 1,000 copies at £2 2s each before 1939; and as "Designs of Small oil-engined vessels" which proved a useful medium for advising clients of the suitability of Bolinder engines in a variety of trades. Walter also wrote up the history of the firm of J. & C.G. Bolinder, which was published in 1930, from which much of this section is drawn.

V. New designs in fittings

Walter Pollock was a considerable innovator in the design of aids to propulsion and to cargo handling. One was the Pollock patent stern frame, which had a horizontal arch-piece inside the counter plating to increase the efficiency of the propeller and to assist steering. For the benefit of workers on the decks of cargo vessels, an absolutely flush manhole cover was introduced. Walter described it as follows:

"A hole is cut in the steel or wood deck, or tank top the outer size of the cover and then a ring is riveted or welded underneath the steel deck or tank top for the cover to rest on. With a joint of hard rubber, or insertion (covered with graphite to prevent sticking) an absolutely flush and watertight joint is made. It is not necessary for the nut to come off the bolt that holds the 'dog'. A cut in the bolt enables the end of the spanner to turn the 'dog' after the nut is slackened back, the door complete can then be lifted out.

"A stop is fitted under the deck to keep the 'dog' in the correct thwartship position when the nut is being screwed up. The cover or manhole door is fitted with two flush handles for lifting. The cover is also useful for fuel and oil tanks, fresh water tanks and for access to watertight compartments in peaks and sides of hopper barges."

Pollocks also used a unique arrangement of twin rudders for canal barges with the screw propeller immediately forward, which prevented the banks of the canal being washed away by the action of the propeller.

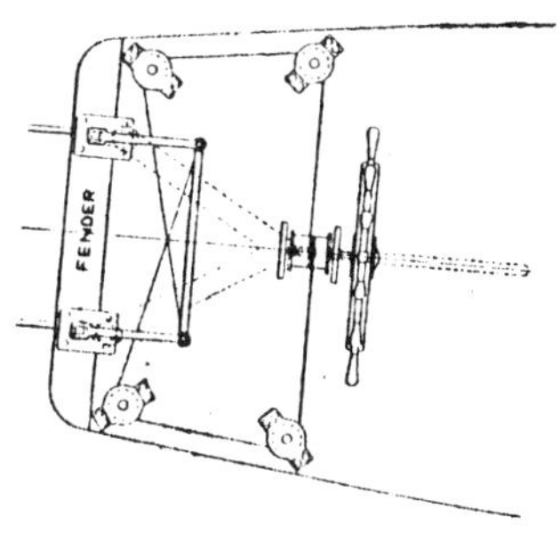

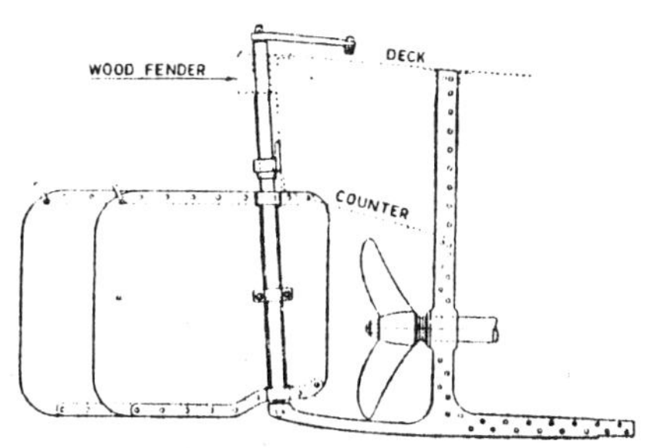

Continuing his association with the Star-Contra Propeller Co., which he had founded, Walter presented a paper to the Institute of Naval Architects of which he was a member. The paper was entitled "The Star-Contra Propeller" and was preceded by one on methods of increasing the efficiency of the screw-propeller. The same two papers were also presented to Walter's fellows in the North-East Coast Institute of Engineers and Shipbuilders. The star-contra propeller was designed to increase speed and decrease fuel consumption at an economical initial cost.

Always a keen writer on developments in marine propulsion and an advocate of the efficiency of oil-engines, the use of which he had pioneered, Walter had in 1921 also presented to his colleagues in the Institute of Marine Engineers a series of papers entitled "Internal Combustion Engine Gearing", "Internal Combustion Engine Installation" and "Internal Combustion Engine Auxiliaries" on 4th January, 8th February and 22nd March respectively. Walter also presented two papers to the Royal Institute of Naval Architects, the first in 1918 on "Reinforced Concrete Vessels", the second in 1925 entitled "A suggested method of increasing the efficiency of the screw propeller".

VI. Publicity

In a liaison with the firm of J. Stone & Co. Ltd. of Deptford, Pollocks publicised the "Stone–Pollock scuttle clip". An undated paper describes it as follows:

"The Stone–Pollock scuttle clip provides a quick-acting easily adjustable fastener for most types of ships' scuttles and portlights. The clip is made of high-quality Brass or Gunmetal and is provided with a special cam. When fastening the light this cam quickly brings the glass frame into contact with the rubber or other joint, and, by means of a decrease in the angle of the cam increases the pressure on the joint as required. The reverse action takes place when opening the light.

"With ordinary clips, four or five turns of the nut or handle are necessay to secure or release the fastening. With the Stone–Pollock clip, less than half a turn is sufficient. Any desired degree of pressure can be obtained. Stops on the cams prevent the application of excessive pressure. The position of the handle can be determined as required by the adjustments of the cam and locking nut.

Advantages

1. Scuttles can be opened or closed almost simultaneously.
2. Straining of frame and the consequent breaking of glasses prevented.
3. Easily installed — No necessity for any alteration to existing scuttles.
4. The very simplicity of the clip constitutes its reliability. There is no possibility of its jamming or getting out of order. This is a decided advantage in the case of scuttles which are only occasionally operated.

"There are many other purposes, where quick action and security are desired, to which this clip can be applied; in fact wherever a clamp or butterfly nut is at present used."

Advertising catalogues continued to be produced, showing a selection of vessels produced by the yard, one such being the eight-page leaflet called "Light Draft Vessels" produced in 1929. It detailed the codes currently being used by the firm as: A1, A.B.C.4th & 5th edition, Engineering, Western Union, Pollocks Private Codes, and Bentleys. The leaflet pictured the yard and a variety of coasters, tugs, launches, tank vessels, stern-wheelers and towing lighters at various stages of construction and at work. It explained that these could be built and delivered to any port in the world. The leaflet was designed to "help purchasers in their selection and enable them to detail their enquiries in such a manner that will ensure the firm tendering for what is actually required at a competitive price." It also refers them to the aforementioned book, "Designs of small oil-engined vessels", published by Constable & Co. Ltd. of 10/12 Orange Street, London.

More specific leaflets detailed a wider variety of motor tugs, of barges and of coasters, all to a standard format for ease of reference.

VII. Summary

Thus, with good publicity and by the consolidation of shipbuilding operations at Faversham, Pollocks' yard remained fairly busy till almost the close of the 1920s. The London office was large, comprising a shipping department, the drawing office and a cashier's office. At Faversham, the office was being run by Bessie Luckhurst, with office-boy, Harold Jacobs. A branch office in Liverpool had by now been closed.

Admittedly, for the workers, there were the problems of adapting to new methods in the caulking and riveting departments, and the eternal and widespread problem of lack of security of employment. These problems were minor compared with those encountered in the North as a result of the decline of the shipbuilding industry there, and which had caused the second influx of workers from the Sunderland area in the late 1920s.

Despite the bad winter of 1929 and the general shipping depression, the firm entered the 1930s with a degree of optimism that their products would continue to sell. Walter Pollock's son, Marshall Brook Pollock (born 1908) had reached the age of twenty-one. Having spent the previous five years learning the methods used in a variety of crafts at the yard, Marshall came down to live in the room above the wages office, from which he would soon apply a new style of management to the yard.

Sources

"Thames Petrol Trade". Captain A.V. West, in "East Coast Digest" Vol. 1 No. 2.
"Hot Bulb Oil Engines". E. Sargent in "East Coast Digest" Vol. 6 No. 3.
"The Bolinder Book". Walter Pollock, 1930.
"Canal People". Harry Hanson, 1978.
"The Pollocks as Engineers". Walter Pollock, 1939.
"Reflections in Steam". R.H. Perks in "East Coast Digest" Vol. 6 No. 1.
"Small Vessels". Walter Pollock, 1946.
"The Sarawak Gazette", 1st March 1926.

CHRISTEN SMITH
BELJEANNE

Chapter 6
THE DEVELOPMENT OF STANDARD TYPES IN THE 1930s

Following the brief period of slack working in the late 1920s, work began to build up slowly and rose to a peak by the mid 1930s, when it was said that the yard was producing a swim-barge a week. The workforce was more stable due to a new management policy of not laying off men as soon as the weather or trade grew bad. Lay-offs had lost the yard several good craftsmen. A little new machinery arrived and another influx of men.

A major change was the dissociation with Bolinders. This period saw the main development of standard types of tugs and coasters and a sharp decline in the number of vessels built for abroad. It appeared that most of Pollocks' South American customers had followed the implied advice in a remark by Sir James Lithgow, quoted by Pagnamenta & Overy about the introduction of modern machinery:

"The real fact is that the invention of pneumatic tools has been a blow to British Shipbuilding looked at from an insular standpoint. It has converted many operations in which our men were specially skilled into purely unskilled jobs, for which all our foreign rivals have an ample supply of suitable labour."

The trade had gone elsewhere.

Outside the yard, the new Managing Director, Marshall Pollock (who took on this responsibility in 1935), was keen to become involved in the life of the town, and contributed to the carnival and the Institute, and was instrumental in setting up what became a very lively Social Club.

I. Various types of barges

The trade which had built up gradually in the 1920s in swim-barges by the 1930s became the backbone of the yard's work. Several hundreds more of these craft were built, the plates being drilled by the dozen on a single radial drill which by the mid 1930s was running night and day. A typical swim-barge, *Cyclops*, of 250 tons had labour costs of £510 7s 8d. Almost all were for use on the Thames, many for regular customers, Everard's or Braithwaite's. A barge of this class, *Gulliver*, was used to transport an 80 ton oil-cracking apparatus through Yantlet Creek to the Isle of Grain, where three râilway tenders were needed to move it to its final location.

Canal barges of various sizes, usually supplied in sets of six or twelve, were another important but repetitive element of Pollocks' work. On 5th September 1931, the "East Kent Gazette" reported the following:

"Two craft were launched lashed together at the Shipyard last Monday for service on the English canals. This is a novel launch in as much as it is the first of its kind at Messrs. Pollocks' yard and it is believed to be without precedent anywhere. It was highly successful. The two craft were built apart, and the day

Opposite: Ship No. 1385 *Itaca III* being loaded aboard the Christen-Smith heavy-lift vessel *Beljeanne*. She went out with a cargo of locomotive destined for the Argentine Railways.

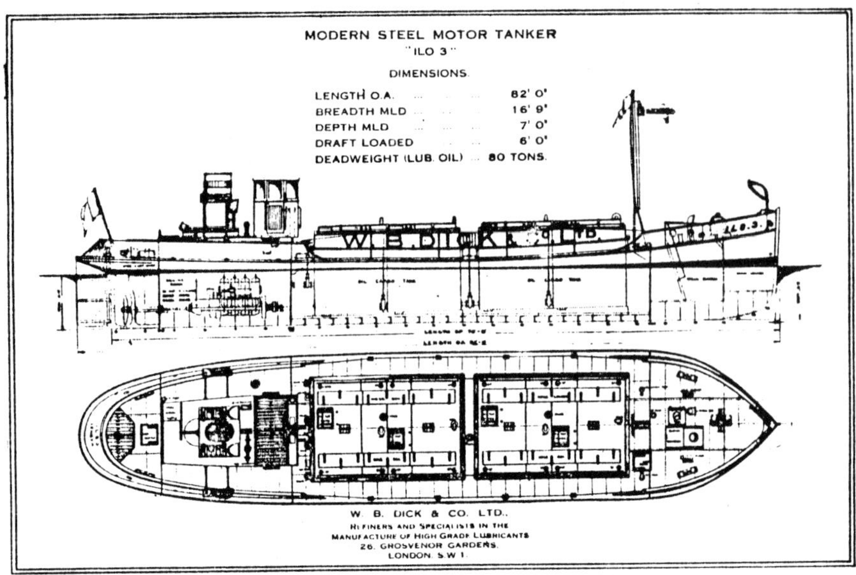

Ship No. 1477 *Ilo 3*, a motor tank barge. She was the first Pollock vessel to be fitted with a Petter-patent cold-start Bolinder.

previous to launching were brought together and lashed with wire ropes on the same sliding ways. They were then launched in the same way as a single craft."

The vessels described were *Henry* and *Prince* for Associated Canal Carriers and were delivered by Bill Shields to Watford. *Prince* was still afloat carrying coal in 1982.

The tank barge which was the first to have a Petter-patent cold-start Bolinder was the *Ilo 3*, designed for W.B. Dick & Co. to carry oil. Whilst the engine was being put in by Swedish men, none of the yard men were allowed below. *Ilo 3* was the latest of three tank barges for W.B. Dick.

Another motor tank barge, of a totally different design, was the 91′ Bolinder-engined *Itaca III*, launched in October 1930. Perhaps the most notable event which happened to this vessel was its loading aboard the "Bel" ship, *Beljeanne*, one of several of this type. The *Beljeanne*, built in 1926 by Armstrong Whitworth

Ship Nos. 1399 – 1400 *Henry* and *Prince*. A pair of canal narrow boats. This was said to have been the first time a pair of barges had been launched together.

on the Tyne, was one of the largest lifting vessels afloat, and had been designed by Christen-Smith. In November 1930, with *Itaca III* aboard, she sailed for Buenos Aires. Also on board were a consignment of railway locomotives and rolling stock, and a pair of tugs, the *Pato Overo* and *Pato Picazo* built at Philip's yard, Dartmouth, which were loaded at Torquay. The consignment was for the construction of the Argentine railway network. When *Itaca III* was put aboard, the son of Christen-Smith was present and met Marshall Pollock and Bill Shields, by now Chief Engineer at the yard.

In 1931 four motor barges or coastal lighters of the *Goldcrown* class each with twin Bolinders were built. Named *Goldbell, Goldcrown, Golddrift* and *Goldeve,* they were all destined for the firm of Goldsmith's. The latter two were later sold to new owners and respectively named *Suleskjaer* and *Leaspray*. Refitted with a Crossley diesel engine, as *Leaspray*, the *Goldeve* traded for the firm of Sully's at Bridgwater in the early 1960s, and was sold and renamed *Warlight* in 1966.

Concurrent with the programme of building motor barges, twelve of Goldsmith's sprits'l barges which Walter Pollock had designed over the period 1897 – 1903 returned to their designer's yard to have engines fitted in order to guarantee delivery times of cargoes, the work being done by Bill Shields over the period 1930 – 4. They included the *Servic, Maymon* (ex *Teutonic*) and the *Lais* (ex *Germanic*). Another was the *Runic*, which, as the *Gazelle*, was one of the last barges trading in 1981. The cost of the repairs to bring *Lais* up to Board of Trade requirements included labour costs of £428 7s 11d. During her repairs in 1934, she caught fire, and the fire brigade had to be called to put out tins of burning paint. The yard at the time was being supervised by Alec Featherstone in the interregnum between J.M. Scott and Marshall Pollock.

The smack *Emma* was similarly converted to motor, and the engine put in, a Bolinder, ran well into the 1970s.

Ship Nos. 1406–1409 *Goldbell, Goldcrown, Golddrift* and *Goldeve* seen under construction.

II. Tug development

Of the tugs built over the period 1930–9, several were for Knight's, a Rochester firm, for use on the Medway. It was a policy of Knight's to begin the names of their tugs with "K", which letter they also bore in stainless steel on the funnel. Thus, one of a class of barge-tugs launched as *Landay* in March 1935, was renamed *Kara*, and this is the name she bore when she revisited the yard for repairs in 1945. Originally built for stock account, the costs in the initial stages of construction of labour on *Landay* were as follows:

Ship 1438
STOCK TUG
Commenced W.E. 5/9/33

	5/9/33	12/9/33	19/9/33	26/9/33	3/10/33	10/10/33	C.F.
Loft	5 5			8 11	14 7	16 11	2 5 10
U. Steel	2 11 4	1 6 3		14 6			4 12 1
Shipwrights			1 0				1 0
Sundries				2 6		2 6	5 0
Fitters					5		5
Platers Frm					6 9	9 2	15 11
Furnaceman						4 6	4 6
Platers						17 6	17 6
Burners						2 8	22 8
	£2 16 9	£1 6 3	£ 1 0	£1 5 11	£1 1 9	£2 13 3	£9 4 11

The total labour cost for the tug which was built over a period of four years was about £1,130.

Another of Knight's tugs built at Pollocks' was *Kawara*, reputed to be the strongest tug afloat in 1934, the year of her launch.

By the mid 1930s the Widdop engine was increasingly adopted instead of Bolinders in launch tugs. 60 b.h.p. Widdops powered a number of 41′ vessels of this class, named *Jubilee* on account of their first example being launched in 1935. *Jubilee* was followed later in 1935 by two tugs named *Jaymar* and *Swift* and more in 1936–7, *Varlet, Vassal* and *Swallow*. These tugs, well-suited to towing

Ship No. 1449 *Kawara*, a tug fitted with an Atlas Polar engine, she was supplied to Knights at Rochester.

Ship No. 1512 *Jubilee* (ex *Widdop*), a launch tug with a Widdop engine. She was launched in 1935, hence the name.

one, two or occasionally more barges short distances on the Thames at a lower cost of crew and fuel than larger tugs, continued to attract customers in Britain and abroad till the late 1940s. Of the basic *Jubilee* type, other examples included *Samaden* and *Luka* laid down for stock in 1938–9, built by Bob Johnson, Bill Weaver and Frank Ward, and after the war, *Kofi* and *Kwami* for the United Africa Co. at Takoradi in 1948.

Subsequently Pollocks advertised for sale their remaining Widdop engine sets. A letter was circulated for this purpose, worded as follows:

"FOR SALE

New and Unused as received from Engine Makers

'EMX 3' TYPE WIDDOP TWO CYCLE VERTICAL THREE CYLINDER COLD STARTING MARINE DIESEL ENGINE, developing 90 S.H.P. when operating at a speed of approx. 400 r.p.m.

The Engine is arranged for direct reversing by compressed air and is complete with three steel air receivers, with valves and pressure gauges; automatic starting air valves, and air compressor driven by the main engine.

The Engine is complete with disc flywheel, plunger type, gunmetal fitted, water circulating and bilge pumps, high pressure fuel pumps and injectors, centrifugal variable admission governor, speed control and water cooled silencer. Exhaust outlet is at the forward end of the exhaust manifold.

The Engine has direct pump pressure lubrication to crankshaft and connecting rod bearings. The lubricating oil sump, from which the oil circulates, is a separate tank.

An oil cooler is included.

The Engine has a heavy duty ball type thrust bearing mounted on the after end of the engine baseplate, complete with an expanding type clutch, embodied in the engine assembly, with compressed air operated engaging and disengaging motion.

The Engine is complete with the Maker's standard tools and accessories.

OFFERS INVITED

The above engine can be inspected during normal working hours at:
James Pollock, Sons & Co. Ltd., The Shipyard, Faversham, Kent."

A small narrow tug, again powered by a Widdop engine, was built and launched in 1936 for use on the Grand Union Canal in London. Named *Ruislip,*

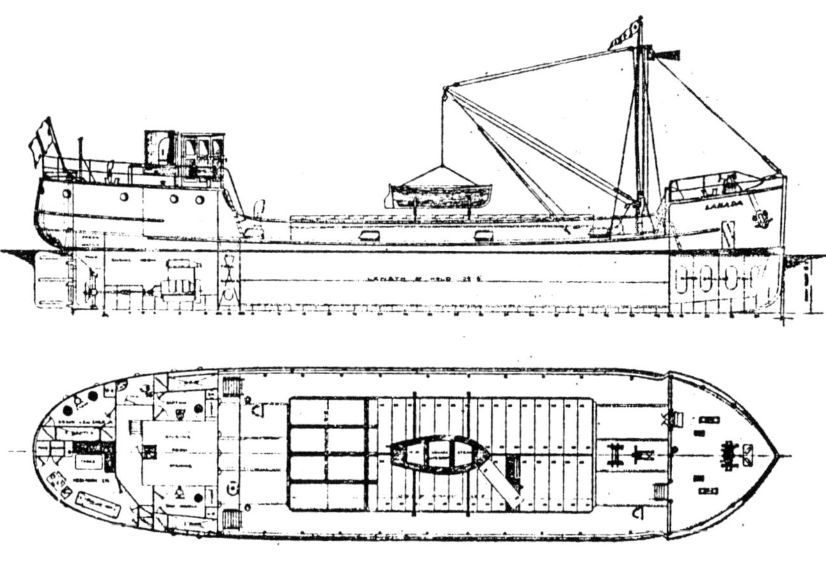

The group of visitors at the yard for the launch of Ship No. 1515 *Lady Stella* in the office at the yard.

her dimensions were 31′6″ × 6′9″ × 4′3″. A slightly larger one, named *Tring* for the same destination, was launched in February 1937.

Larger than the "Jubilee" tugs, with the added benefit of a cabin, were the Crossley-engined *Tommy Lee* and *Duckett*, both 1937, of the "Coronation" type, an extended "Jubilee". These latter bore a resemblance to the later tugs *Silverdash* and *Silverdot*.

III. Standard coasters

In order to compete with the increasing competition from Dutch craft in the coasting trade, Walter Pollock designed new types of motor coaster including the "Lanada" and "Landina" types. The "Lanada" type, with twin screw, and a short engine, for maximum cargo capacity was begun with the *Lady Sheila* with twin Allen engines. In the plan, as the pioneer of her class she is shown as *Lanada*. After a career in the coasting trade, she finally sunk in the Channel. Another of the same class, *Lady Stella,* was built the following year. A reception was held after her launch, in the yard office, hosted by Walter and Marshall, who was by then Managing Director. *Lady Stella* later changed hands and was renamed *Glas Island*. As such, she was still afloat working for Palmer's of Gravesend in the 1960s.

Of the larger "Landina" type, single screw, with a large water ballast capacity for voyages lightly laden, were *Camroux I* and *Camroux II*. These were built in 1934 with Allen engines, but were later fitted with Deutz, and were supplied to the Newcastle Coal & Shipping Company to work to Rosebank Wharf, Fulham. They were the largest vessels built at Faversham by 1934, and some of the biggest steel mercantile vessels ever built in Kent. At the launch of *Camroux I* in October 1934, Pollocks charged admission to enclosures arranged in the yard for a close-up view, the money so raised being given to the Cottage Hospital.

Opposite: Ship No. 1465 *Camroux I* (later *The Marquis*). A record of the launch was kept on film. The camera can be seen at the right of the picture.

Only slightly bigger than the "Lanada" class was the "Loreta" type coaster *Lady Sophia*, built in 1937 for stock. Single screw and with no double bottom, she was suited for special trading and entering very restricted ports round the coast which only very shallow vessels could enter. The crowd at her launch on 12th August 1938, at 4 p.m., included Mrs Claringbold, the wife of a rivet-heater. In 1944, a customer who had been offered the vessel and refused it was forced to regret his decision when she saved his life. Till then, he had been unaware of the splendid seagoing qualities of the standard Pollocks coaster. *Lady Sophia* was still afloat in 1955 when she was seen at Countess Wear on the Exeter Canal.

Another of the "Loreta" type was the *Dominence*, which was slightly larger than *Lady Sophia*, and was supplied to London & Rochester Trading Co., now Crescent Shipping. She was a familiar sight on the Medway, hence she is immortalised as a model in the Medway Heritage Centre. *Dominence* sea trials were on the Maplin measured mile rather than the usual Harty Ferry or Gravesend, during which she had trouble with her engines. These were discussed in the regular letters which passed between Walter and Marshall Pollock. Dennis Wildish said that his cousin as skipper of the *Dominence* was using her to run supplies to the Channel Islands in the early 1940s. It would have been possible to have made several such trips before the islands came under Nazi occupation in July 1940.

On an advertising leaflet for coasters, several other types were named: the "Laurel" of which the 1911 *Fitzroy* was an example — she was supplied to Australia painted deep green; the "Lomola", described as a very economical type and a solution to owners changing from sail to powered vessels. *Ferrocrete* was quoted as a typical example. The "Lindsay" and "Laguna" types were mentioned, but no examples were given.

Ship Nos. 1631–1633 *Roc I, Roc II, Roc III* were three tank launches for the Anglo-Iranian Oil Company in Sharjah.

IV. Unusual vessels

Although Pollocks had lost some of the business which they previously had in South America, they still had customers in Africa and the Middle East. A launch of 55′ with an Atlantic engine, the *El Motahir* (1930) was another of the vessels to be shipped out on the deck of a steamer, this time to Alexandria. There she was used on the River Nile. Earlier in the same year, a larger launch, *Awunaga*, had been despatched in the same way to Ada in West Africa where her sister-ship *Senchi* had been at work since 1927.

To service the growing number of flying-boats in the 1930s, three small refuelling launches named *Roc I, Roc II* and *Roc III* were built and launched in 1936–7 for Anglo-Iranian Oil. Fitted with 66 b.h.p. Allen engines, they were destined for Sharjah, now in the United Arab Emirates. There, with their fairly shallow draft, they made short trips out to sea or down-river to refuel flying boats with aviation spirit and put on or take off crew members.

Closer to home, a small but important specialist vessel was the *Alfred Robertson*. 54′3″ long, she combined the functions of harbour and service vessel with the role of medical launch. Her equipment included a small doctor's surgery. She was used by the Corporation of the City of London on the River Thames.

V. The yard and engineering

In the early 1930s, Pollocks ended what had been a long-standing arrangement with Bolinder's to display and market their engines. From 1931, in fact, only a very few of their engines were being installed in Pollock-built vessels, Widdops or Allens being used instead. Walter was pleased in 1934 to see Bolinder's leave the shipyard as he wanted the space in their showroom for new stores for the fitting shop. His son was equally adamant that the Bolinder showroom and spares should stay, and told Bill Shields so. Walter and Marshall discussed the matter amicably, and Bolinder's left, taking with them Pollocks' Managing Director, J.M. Scott.

Pollocks marketed winches in 10, 20 and 30 cwt ratings, for use on vessels to drive windlasses and other machinery. They were sold under the trade name "Sureal".

Tanks and gritters were a speciality of the yard. The vehicle fitted with gritting equipment shown belonged to Farnham Urban District Council.

As Chairman of the Faversham Creek Navigation Commission, Marshall Pollock was keen to see the sluices of the creek bridge were kept in good repair. They were iced up in the winter of 1963.

Around the same time, as part of the fittings of the "Lanada" class coaster *Lady Sheila*, some winches were brought in and Marshall Pollock asked Bill Shields what he thought of them. Shields responded by building two winches himself for the next vessel which needed them. The winches traded under the name of "Sureal" and their production kept one turner and a fitter, plus one apprentice, constantly employed. The castings for them would be ordered regularly in batches of six from Seagers, where one of the workers was the father of Charlie Godden of the yard. The "Sureal" winch as produced by Pollocks from 1935 weighed under a ton and could lift 15 cwt in a single purchase at 80 feet per minute and 30 cwt in double purchase at 40 feet per minute. It was available in 10, 20 and 30 cwt S.P. ratings. Installed on a vessel, it could be used to drive the windlass by means of a messenger chain. This mechanism was also produced in the fitting shop at the yard. The winch would run on the same heavy oil as the main engine of the vessel on which it was installed. Later winches were fitted with a Lister engine which ran on light oil.

Pollocks' services as engineers proved useful to a number of local firms including the breweries and the bone factory. Trusses were built for Weston Works (Doyles) and hoppers made and kept in good order for Faversham Gasworks by the platers and riveters. It was quite common for the yard to make and more often to repair agricultural machinery for John Scutt and other farmers. The firm used to advertise these services at the Kent Show at Mote Park, Maidstone.

Tanks and gritters were another speciality which were produced in significant numbers and a variety of sizes. The tanks were supplied to Shepherd Neame's brewery and other firms. The gritters were mostly made for Johnson Brothers of Aylesford, or for local authorities, one such being Farnham Rural District Council.

Regularly, gangs of shipyard riveters would be sent to work on cement kilns sometimes as far away as Humberside. For this, in addition to their pay, the men would receive £1 per night "Out of Pocket" expenses. Among them were Bill Jemmett, riveter, and Reuben Lennard, labourer, who regularly acted as a holder-up. At the Gravesend firm of Priestley's, work would often take place over a weekend, and owing to the pace worked at by riveters from Faversham, the work they had been contracted to do over three days would only take one day. So fast was the pace that Priestley's regular workers would not work with the Pollocks' men. Although their job had been completed in just one day, the men would still gratefully accept pay for the whole three days. Riveters from Pollocks were responsible for the gasometers at Herne Bay and Whitstable.

More locally, they often repaired the creek bridge, especially after Marshall Pollock was elected Chairman of Faversham Creek Navigation Commission, which was responsible for the maintenance of the creek, its dredging and the bridge.

A sample of the customers which the firm regularly supplied can be seen in a page from the Marine Sales Journal for July 1937.

"Marine Sales Journal No. 2 page 16–17
July 1937

		Brought forward	Brought forward	Yard Job	Customer
		2	£4,075 16 4		
Jul	19	13 8	14 6	48/645	Eloys Transport
July	21	19 12	12 0	146/1	Dover Industries Ltd.
—	—	19 7	21 16	48/647	Folkestone Fishermen's Society
Jul	22	9 5	13 18	48/648	Lambert's Laundries
	23	5 10	691 13 4	Ship 1638	F.J. Everard
	"	24 9	2,722 0 0	Ships 1631-3	British Tanker Co. Ltd.
	26	6 6	17 4	48/650	S. Kingham
	27	2 4	1,100 0 0	32/1	W.H. Allen & Son
	28	8 1	80 0 0	Ships 1575-8	Perkins & Homer
	"	5 10	36 5	Ships 1561-2	Greenhithe Lighterage Co.
	"	2 9	31 0 0	Ship 1526	R.G. Odell
	"	8	42 0 0	Ships 1488-9	R.G. Odell
	"	6 4	60 0 0	Ship 1306	W.J. Earnell, Sons & Pocock
	31	4 6	15 9	88/24	Societie des Etab Utard
	"	3 7	300 0 0	Ship 1409	E.J. & W. Goldsmith
	30	4 0	5 6	Yard job 58/118	H.S. Tett & Co.
	"	8 11	14 14 4	10/3	A.J. McLennan
	3	6 0	8 0	Redline Glico Ltd	Yard petty cash
	26	0	1 11 0	Cardox Ltd	Yard petty cash
	17	9 8	1 6	Yard job 146	A.T. Burbridge
Apl	30	6 4	13 18 1	Yard job 146	Shipyard petty cash
	"	11 1	153 10 1	Shipyard petty cash	Shipyard stock

"	9 4	2 11 8	"	Shipyard stationery
May 31	6 6	16 6 1	Yard job 146/1	Newcastle Coal & Shipping Company
"	12 3	45 0 0	Shipyard petty cash	Shipyard stock
"	11 2	203 17 6	Shipyard petty cash	Shipyard stationery
"	9 1	5 4	"	Shipyard petty cash
Jun 30	6 9	8 12 7	Yard job 146	"
"	12 4	60 0 0	Shipyard petty cash	Newcastle Coal & Shipping Co.
"	11 11	65 2 4	"	Shipyard stock

VI. Working conditions

The shipyarders were relieved to find that management techniques changed slightly when Marshall Pollock became closely connected with the running of the yard. Unlike George Johnson, he was not as quick to lay off people as soon as work became slack, since because of lay-offs, good men had been lost to other firms. Marshall also realised that much productivity was being lost to illicit smoking in the toilets since it had been banned in the yard. To remedy this loss, he permitted smoking everywhere except in the carpenters' shop and took out extra insurance to cover any possible risk of fire as a result.

He set about increasing general productivity, introducing some overhead cranes to lift plates onto and off bogies and reduce the amount of manhandling. Almost too late for the 1930s swim-barge boom, new radial drills were brought in. Had they come before June 1939, they would have made for far less of the night work which went on to complete barge orders in the mid 1930s. The sheer numbers of barges had required a 1¾ acre extension to be laid out in 1936, known as the West Yard.

The yard's most significant development in the 1930s was the construction of the Power House. This important building was equipped with three Bolinders and an Allen engine, and was run by a single man. It was the power source for all the electrical machinery for drilling and welding, and contained a compressor for the air supply to the many hydraulic riveting and caulking hammers. It would be regularly started at 7.30 every morning.

The Boilermakers' Society members in the early 1930s continued to be dissatisfied with their piece-rates and 1931 saw a second strike by those in that union at the yard, among them Harry Stockwell. One foreman plater, Fred Ribbans, explained to most of the labourers that there would as a result be little work, but one, Bill Poole, he told to wait in the dynamo box till called to do odd jobs for Ribbans. The strike only lasted a few days. It had come in the wake of a slack period which had lasted since 1929, in which the loftsman, Frank Pepper, had been forced to leave. Marshall Pollock did the work for a short time himself, then Tom Nell, a Tyneside Naval Architect, lofted out two vessels. Soon after, Charlie Downs took over in the loft, where he remained till the yard closed. In the same slack period, the undermanager, Charlie Hadlow, also left and went to the Grand Union Canal Co.

BOILER-MAKERS SUPPER, SWAN INN, FAVERSHAM
NOVEMBER 23, 1934. (PHOTO: BARBER, FAVERSHAM)

By 1932, with a general recession in the shipbuilding industry, Pollocks were lucky to be able to offer work to a group of men from Dartmouth, who had been employed at Philip's yard there. At that time, the Dart was mostly being used to lay up unused vessels. A connection had been forged between the two yards when the loftsman at Faversham in the 1920s, Billy Adams, a Dartmouth man, had married Chief Typist, Bessie Luckhurst. The men from Dartmouth were mostly members of the Boilermakers' Society, and included the Porter brothers, a skilled plater named Sid Henderson, and a riveter who had already been in a shipyard at Barrow-in-Furness before going to Dartmouth, named Charlie Weedon, whose son became yard manager at Philip's. Also, a coppersmith came, Ralph Coker, who would work under Bill Shields in the fitting shop. Apparently, the recession at Dartmouth was short-lived, for by 1935 most of the men went back.

Till the mid-1930s it had only been the skilled craftsmen who were unionised, and they had been very protective in not letting non-union men do their work. In 1937 Percy Wells, later to become Member of Parliament for Faversham, held a public meeting in the Fleur de Lis public house to begin a branch of the Transport & General Workers' Union, for the benefit of the stagers, painters and labourers. Within a year, a success had been achieved; the first paid holidays in 1938. Before that, these men, especially the labourers on only 36/8d, had dreaded the short weeks at Christmas and Easter, and to augment their meagre pay for these weeks, would "sub" 10/- at the office to bring their money up in the bad weeks from 19/1d to 29/1d, but then had to suffer four more weeks when their wage would be 2/6d less than usual to make up the 10/-. With a week's paid holiday in July, the men would often go cherry picking and actually improve their income.

The Union in other respects had few successes and was not apparently well-liked by Marshall Pollock. However, one of the benefits which was offered by the unions was sick pay at a rate of 5/- per week. The non-union men either joined the National Deposit Friendly Society or, after 1937, the Social Club Sick Fund.

There had been a large number of labourers and craftsmen employed in the 1930s — Ron Dron said that in 1934 there were twelve squads of riveters and Fowle that at the same time there were nine or ten shipwrights and carpenters. However, by the end of the decade, just before the onset of World War II, work was again very slack, and a number of men left and went to Bristol. As Alf Willis remembers, he was one of only a few dozen men left. The iron fighters were stood off. Most men who remained were in finishing trades. The yard could have been forced to close if the war had not come along. Yet in 1937–8 it was the political uncertainty surrounding Neville Chamberlain's visit to Germany which had caused orders to decline to the state they were just before the onset of war.

VII. Social activity

For the benefit of the men outside their working hours, a new development was under way. In 1937 a Social Club had been formed by the men which had met at

Opposite: suppers for the boilermakers were held in local pubs. The supper shown is in the Swan on 23rd November 1934.

the Market Inn or the Limes. Encouraged by Gilbert Smith, a few years later Marshall Pollock purchased for the club the former Liberal Club in East Street, which had a bar and facilities for darts, billiards and table tennis. At the inception of the Social Club, the chairman was Charlie Carter, the foreman shipwright. The club ran a football team which included Jack Finn, and a cricket team which used a ground below Dark Hill owned by Mr Streatfield. The cricket team was captained by Charlie Downs and included Harry Smith, Sid Smith, Bert Crockford, Jack Finn, Jack Ribbans and George Nicholson. The umpire was plater's help, Alec Gamble.

As treasurer of the Social Club, Downs also ran its sick fund and a savings club for people to put money away for Christmas.

A few of the shipyard workers were in the town's famed roller-hockey team whose rink was situated on the west bank of the creek in front of Doyles. The team was captained by yard riveter, Wilfred "Cush" Moon who, in 1930, carried home from Switzerland the Cup of Nations. Another of the team members on this illustrious occasion was Bill "Podge" Betty, a holder-up.

The large numbers of members which the Boilermakers' Union had at the yard made it possible to run successful outings to a variety of places which included Brighton and Southend. Once, an outing to Boulogne was arranged, which Jimmy Jordan remembered as costing 13/6d return.

Annually, the Union would hold a dinner at the Swan Inn or later the Brents Tavern, and through the photographs of these events, it would be possible to trace the varying strengths of the Union, which encompassed most of the skilled men except the fitters.

Marshall Pollock involved himself and his men in local activities in the 1930s which included the Carnival, then held on a Thursday afternoon, for which he would give participants a half-day off, and once "China" Godden entered as Old Mother Riley. Shortly before the war, a grand float entitled "The Carnival War Machine" was entered which blew out a hundredweight of confetti. It had taken up much of the spare time of the shipwrights and carpenters to build this spectacular entry.

At the Institute, in which Marshall also got involved, men from the yard laid the maple floor and sandpapered it.

1937 saw a major event in the life of Marshall Pollock. Having courted Dorothy Pye, daughter of the owner of Tett's hardware firm, for more than two years, he decided to marry her. A grand wedding was held at Kippington Church on 27th July, to which Bill Shields among others was invited. A party was held at the Limes at which all the shipyarders were given a set of six silver spoons. A more long-term pledge of a pension scheme was made, but never came about. The marriage, to Marshall's everlasting disappointment produced no son, only three daughters, Sheena, Antonia and Joanna. Earlier in the century Walter Pollock had made sure that his daughter, Ivy, learnt enough about engineering to at least maintain a car before he would buy her one. Marshall could have gone a stage further and involved his daughters in the business. The wedding at least gave Marshall the hope of a successor, and thus was cause for celebration.

Pollocks' cricket team, captained by Charlie Downs, played on a ground owned by Mr Streatfield at the bottom of Dark Hill, Faversham.

VIII. Walter Pollock

Walter Pollock continued to be a respected figure in the shipping world. By the end of the decade, he was a liveryman of the Worshipful Company of Shipwrights. As his role in the family firm was now mainly that of a figurehead, he began to spend a great deal of time writing up the history of the firm which he had helped so much to develop. The first result of these labours was "The Pollocks as Engineers" which told the story of his family and the ships they had built before 1939, explaining their origins and ancestry in the Glasgow area. He continued with a four-volume autobiography.

A keen motorist, Walter paid occasional visits to the Faversham yard, but on his arrival, many of the shipyarders expected at least one person to be sacked, so they did not look forward to his coming. Nevertheless, such was his concern for his workforce that he purchased houses on the Upper Brents for his key workmen and encouraged his workers to devote a few hours to the running of the social and welfare side of the business.

IX. Summary

The 1930s marked a far-reaching establishment of the firm of Pollocks in the local economy and community which would last for the rest of their existence at Faversham. They had adapted their work to meet the new challenge of Dutch competition in the coasting trade and retained their share of the market for Thames lighters. They had lost some of the overseas customers whom they had supplied in the previous decade. Their new designs of tugs and the "Lanada" and "Landina" coasters were found by customers to be very reliable. The tugs went all over the world and the coasters found markets mainly in British ports.

However, the sharp fall in work which took place in 1938 might have been fatal had the war not come along with its concomitant increase in demand for shipping. Being on the Admiralty list which had been kept from the end of the First World War, Pollocks knew that they would again be called upon to help with the war effort.

Sources

"50 Years Ago Column". "Faversham News", 12.10.84.
"East Kent Gazette", 5.9.31.
"Faversham News", 24.1.85.
"Small Vessels". Walter Pollock, 1946.
"Ship Sales". Laurence Dunn in "Ships Monthly", May 1985.
"All Our Working Lives". Peter Pagnamenta & Richard Overy, 1984. BBC.

Chapter 7
THE EFFECT OF THE SECOND WORLD WAR ON THE YARD

The war was to effect major economic and environmental changes at the yard. Other factors were to enhance Pollocks' prestige both nationally and locally. Walter Pollock's standing in the shipping world reached a high point when as Master of the Worshipful Company of Shipwrights, he organised a major exhibition just before his death in 1947. Marshall Pollock used the profits from the war to make new investments in property in and around Faversham, but at the yard it appears he did not invest to any great extent. The war can thus be seen either as a turning point in the history of the firm or merely as a temporary reprieve from their struggles in the latter part of the 1930s. The onset of war was a boon to the yard, for order books had been almost empty and many workers had been laid off. Not only did previous customers order new vessels, but as in the First World War, the yard was to earn money by building ships for the Admiralty and become very busy. The yard came under the direct control of the Admiralty, and Marshall Pollock attended quarterly meetings on production. At these meetings, other yards requested additional machinery; Marshall requested little, if any.

I. Machine tools

The fact that business had been slack in the years immediately before the Second World War had perhaps contributed to at least one piece of machinery not being able to stand up to any extra use. Bill Cornelius described an accident involving one of the old Bolinder engines in the Power House which had been second-hand in the first instance. Some wires on the engine came loose and began flailing around wildly. Bill tried frantically to stop it, and afterwards needed treatment for shock with sal volatile administered by Gilbert Smith of the drawing office. The four engines which had been in the Power House were inadequate to deal with the extra work in the war largely because they could not build up enough pressure on the compressor which was used as a power source for the riveting and caulking hammers. Subsequently, the engine which had gone wrong was replaced by a 311 h.p. Allen engine.

In the fitting shop, a few new machines were installed to augment those existing. One of the additions brought in for war work was an electric pipe threader. Out in the yard, to help platers erect the large vessels required by the Admiralty, some new cranes came in, saving a great deal of heavy labour.

II. Women come in to replace men called up

As with many other workplaces during the war, the yard did not escape some of its workforce being called up to serve in the army or navy. Pollocks lost a considerable number of labourers to the services or to work on more pressing matters such as the flying boats at Short Brothers, Rochester. By 1942, it was found necessary to employ women to fill roles as labourers supervised by a

The fitting shop stores were kept neatly in boxes on shelves which ran along the side of the fitting shop.

forelady, Mrs Ruth Hudson, the wife of Pat Hudson, a turner. Several of the women were employed in the stores handing out the smaller components which went towards the building and fitting out of ships, among them being Ada Sparrow and Florence Partridge. They sometimes found that when there was not enough work, they would be asked to paint green the boxes in which the items were kept.

Two uniformed women, Rosie Hedlam and Mrs Pearson, replaced a man on the gate as timekeeper checking workers in and out, their uniforms having been made by Rosie Hedlam.

Women provided much-needed assistance to the craftsmen. Chris Sunley, a riveter, was helped successively by Ella Reynolds and Kath Christian, each of whom as rivet heaters, became effectively third men in the rivet gangs. Indeed, Kath proved so useful at the yard that she was offered a full-time job after the war, but she declined as the forelady had left. Ella Reynolds, later in the war, was to be found minding the engines in the boiler house which heated the fitting shop.

Women, including Gladys Lawrence, Joan Hart and Millie French, assisted with the wire-brushing and linseed oiling of the hulls of ships prior to painting. None of the women taken on at the yard received as much pay as the men whom they replaced. The women had all gone by 1946.

In addition to the women at the yard, a number of men came in from Whitstable and one or two from local public houses to avoid being called up. A local paint and hardware shop proprietor, Bob Cooper, fittingly came to the yard and worked in the paint gang.

III. Pollocks' vessels 1939–49

The programme of standard coasters continued, the yard giving a quote to the Admiralty in 1940 for a "Landina" type coaster similar to *Camroux I* as follows:

SN1776 26/1/1940 estimated costs of *Empire Creek*.

Material basis *Camroux I* and *Camroux II*		£6,340
less main engine	1,644	
Auxiliaries	98	
	163	
Power windlass	300	£2,205
		4,135
less hold ceiling		88
		4,047
+20%		809
		4,856
plus main engine	£3,013	
Aux	210	
	102	
Winches	500	
Steel masts and derricks	150	
Hand windlass	74	4,049
		8,905
Labour	£2,868	
less supervision	61	
	2,807	
+20%	561	
	3,368	
+ sup + H M 12%	404	
	3,772	
+84%	3,168	
+ insurance	20	
	6,960	6,960
		15,685
Profit 15%		2,380
		£18,245

Two coasters at this price were purchased for Sir Amos Ayre of the Admiralty, built under Lloyd's Register and the Board of Trade and named *Empire Creek* and *Empire Crag*. The first of these became the *Milborne* after several changes of name and was eventually sold to Greek buyers.

A small submarine tender was built for use by the Turkish Navy. Named the *Imla Layteri*, she was very luxuriously fitted out with lots of chrome in the plumbing. She was delivered via the Cape and Suez Canal.

A variety of sizes of lighters were built during the war, most being given numbers rather than names as was the wartime practice. Also, pontoons and torpedo targets were sent out to Singapore. Towards the end of the decade large lighters were constructed for use in Aden, some of these being as big as 700 tons.

Ship No. 1756 *Mexshell II*, a Widdop-engined tank launch supplied to Southampton in 1940. One of a pair designed to serve the Empire flying boats.

More obviously wartime vessels were the tank launches *Mexshell II* and *Mayshell*, delivered in 1940–2 to serve Empire Flying Boats at Southampton, the FAASP general tender *RN AIR 1A*, a Yarwood design, to ferry Seafire aircraft between depots and carriers, and a set of eight RAF refuellers, seven of which were supplied to Dumbarton and one to Tewkesbury, which were used for operations with Sunderland and Catalina flying boats in the UK and possibly Gibraltar.

The *RN Air 1A* sailed after her sea trials to the Clyde and was allocated for duties as desired by Flag Officer in Charge, Greenock. In March 1944 she transferred to Kirkwall where she stayed till July, then to Irvine for refit. In the autumn of 1944, she went to Ayr, then to Douglas, Isle of Man. During 1945 visits were made to Liverpool, Granton and Lowestoft, then to Alloa for a further refit. By July 1946, she was at Rosyth for repairs prior to being paid off in October. She was sold to Henrik Ameln of Bergen early in 1947.

Landing craft came to the yard partly built, and there were completed. Several of these were supplied including *TLC 148*. *TLC 350* of the same class was not sectional. Both of these had very powerful engines, one being petrol fuelled. To keep the larger Naval vessels well provisioned, a number of store vessels were built on the lines of the "Loreta" class of coasters. One of these, the *C 647*, was on service with SNSO Malta in 1951. She was approved for disposal in September 1968.

More unusual were the wooden pontoons built beside the old drill shop, each bearing a coil. They were used to detect mines, which would be triggered by the little craft and allow safe passage for vessels carrying the essential supplies for the war effort. To protect the coasters and other vessels, yards, including Pollocks, used the process of degaussing, that is passing a wire round the ship and creating a magnetic field, thus demagnetising the ship. Later, this operation was carried out mostly at Tilbury. Once ships had been demagnetised, compass corrector coils would be fitted so that the compass would work normally. If

Ship No. 1814 *1057*, a refueller for the Royal Air Force. The group includes Don Gibbons, Ron Smith, Hugh Chambers and Colin Coulson.

armour plating was applied to the hull, it would be of mild steel known as "Molly Mushy", while a very hard non-magnetic armour plate would be applied to wheelhouses of purpose-built and converted vessels which would not interfere with the compass. The latter substance was very difficult to drill, and drilling was usually carried out at Chatham.

Two naval ammunition vessels were supplied in 1943–4, named *Mortar* and *Howitzer*. *Mortar* transported ammunition between Upnor and warships. In 1962 she was being used as a torpedo recovery vessel. At some stage she was purchased by Peter Herbert of Bude for general trading. The *Howitzer* was launched in 1943, having cost £21,500 to build. She was believed to be the first ship to enter Cherbourg after the United States occupation. She was never registered and was used as a harbour ammunition lighter. Her accommodation was for three officers and five ratings. After the war, she served at Portsmouth till 1969, and was finally broken up in the Medway in 1984.

The largest ships to be built at the yard during the war were two Fleet Air Arm auxiliary vessels, based on a Philip's design, the first of an original order of four and built towards the end of hostilities in the expectation that the war in Japan would last a long time. Work on one of these, named *Ripon*, included one of the earlier attempts at the installation of radar. Reg Flint had to ascend the mast to drill holes for the radar platform, and had to rig up scaffolds to do so. From the top of this scaffold, he could see to Brenley Corner. 990 tons displacement and 172′ long, the vessels each had twin Crossley engines producing 960 b.h.p. and large fuel tanks.

Ripon's sea trials took place on VE Day in May 1945, and at Gravesend on the measured mile, Bill Shields said that when the announcement came over the radio of the end of the war, all the ships on the river began to sound their hooters in joyful cacophony. *Ripon* and her sister *Seafox*, were designed to carry aircraft between aircraft-carriers and shore bases, and each could carry four

SEAFOX

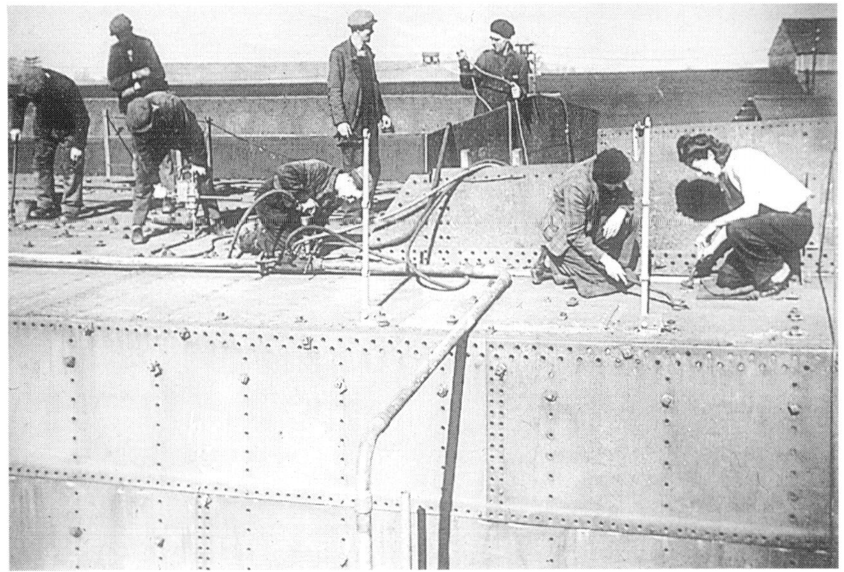

The group working on the deck of Ship No. 1839 *Seafox* includes Kath Christian, Ella Reynolds and Reg Bottle.

Seafires with folding wings in a special hold and a light bomber on the deck aft. *Seafox* had her sea trials on another momentous day — VJ Day — which signalled a complete end to the Second World War.

Ripon (RN Air 4A) went back to Douglas in September 1945, to Plymouth possibly for repairs, then back to Douglas by November 1945. In January 1946 she was at Alloa for repairs and in late May appeared at Liverpool. In 1947 she visited Portsmouth and then Cairnryan. On 9th November 1948 she was in collision with the *Seafox*. The latter vessel sustained damage to the activating gear on her starboard forward sea boat davits. In 1952 the *Ripon* was used as a storeship until alternative accommodation in the Clyde became available, which was expected to be by the end of the year. In 1956 she was placed on a list of aircraft transports for possible sale to Ecuador. This sale would not appear to have gone through, as she was eventually sold to the Crown Agent for the Colonies on behalf of Llewellyn Wall on 13th January 1959.

Seafox (RN Air 5A) was commissioned on 18th November 1946. Her operational base was Cairnryan. On 18th January 1947, she was in collision with s.s. *Dorothy Rose* and suffered a slight dent to her port breakwater. She was withdrawn from service as an aircraft transport on 23rd April 1951 and let to the Superintendent of Torpedo Experimental Development until August 1951 for use as a tender for unspecified trials to be carried out in the approaches to the Clyde. On completion of these duties she was converted to the requirements of

Opposite: Ship No. 1839 *Seafox* was one of a pair of Fleet Air Arm Auxiliary vessels designed to carry aircraft between aircraft carriers and shore bases. She is seen being towed past Standard Wharf by Knights tug *Keston*. On the blocks in the yard is Ship No. 1844 *Goldhind*.

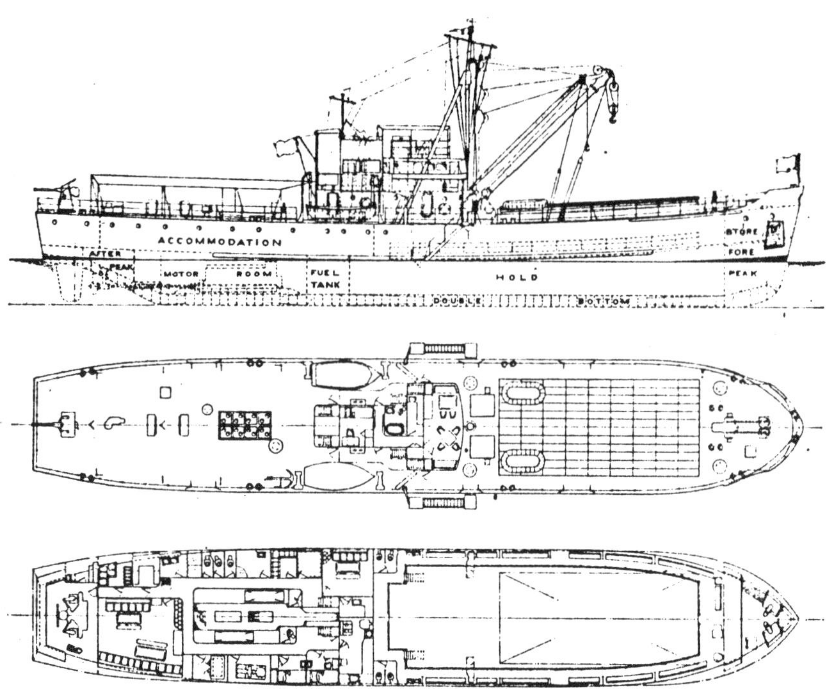

the Ministry of Transport and Lloyds Register of Shipping for operating with a Mercantile crew, with her name unchanged as a Royal Fleet Auxiliary. She was operated by the Director of Stores as a Coastal Store Carrier, principally within the area Clyde, Londonderry, Belfast and Liverpool. On 27th September 1952 she was in collision with s.s. *Harold Sleigh*, receiving minor damage. She was eventually disposed of to Lloyd's Albert Yard and Motor Packet Services Ltd., Clausentum Yard, Northam Bridge, Southampton, on 15th December 1958.

The end of the war made superfluous the other two FAA auxiliaries which had been ordered, to have been named *Sea Gladiator* and *Sea Hurricane*. They were cancelled in 1947.

Regular customers of Pollocks, Goldsmith's, stepped in and agreed to buy the two unwanted vessels for use as merchant vessels. Each was lengthened by eight feet and converted from twin to single screw. One of the spare engines was used to refit a tug, *Mercedes* ex *Silverstone*, which had been mined at Rochester and the complete stern blown out. Goldsmith's had the auxiliaries renamed *Goldhind* and *Goldlynx* to fit in with the rest of their fleet of coasters and barges. The first of this pair was launched in December 1948, the launch being described in the "Kent Messenger" for 24th December as follows:

"The good ship *Goldhind* launched at Faversham, largest merchant vessel to be built at the busy Kent yard. The sides of Faversham Creek were thickly lined with interested spectators at the launching at Messrs James Pollock, Sons & Co. Ltd.'s shipyard on Saturday, of the motor vessel *Goldhind*, the largest commercial vessel they have produced there.

Ship No. 1841 *Vic 56*, a steam-powered victualling lighter, one of a set of four similar vessels, the latter pair of which were too late for war service.

"The launching took place in brilliant sunshine, and the gaily fluttering flags and bunting lent a festive air to the scene, enlivened by broadcast music. It was indicative of the industrial activity and prosperity Faversham is now enjoying, and it reflects much credit upon the progressive firm of Messrs Pollock.

"Mrs E.J. Goldsmith, wife of the chairman of the owners, Messrs E.J. & W. Goldsmith Ltd., the well-known London shipowners, carried out the launching ceremony, after christening the ship, wishing her 'God Speed, and all who sail in her,' in the time-honoured way.

"As is usual at the shipyard owing to the limited width of the creek, the vessel was launched broadside on, entering the water at some speed and causing a wave and much spray, amidst much applause.

"Among those present were: Mr and Mrs E.J. Goldsmith, Mr Paul Goldsmith, Mr and Mrs M.B. Pollock, Mr G. Findlay (Hon. Clerk, Worshipful Company of Shipwrights) and Mrs Findlay and Mr John Weir as well as many other friends of the owners."

Goldhind changed her name several times during her merchant career, being called *Purple Emperor* in 1951 and *Towai* in 1955. Her sister ship *Goldlynx* became the *Springwood* in 1951 and *Leafoam* in 1953.

In order to fulfil all the war work and the increased amount of work which was to come to the yard in the aftermath of hostilities, the yard was extended to the north across some old allotments, the extra space thus created being used to lay out steel stock and for the construction in plates and angles of lighters for shipment abroad, especially to Africa, some being 250 feet long. Trade was indeed good after the war, with the yard building many lighters for the Thames, more tugs, including three of 54', the *Soebang, Soeanggi* and *Nigretia* for Africa, and motor barge *Sir Frederick*. Silvertown Services again called upon Pollocks to build tugs for use on the Thames, a pair being built, named *Silverdial* and

Ship No. 1868 *Soeanggi*, a motor tug with a 90 b.h.p. Widdop engine, was supplied to Batavia in 1948.

Silverbeam, each with Atlas Polar engines, to be launched after 1950. Two coasters named *Nervo* and *Knox* after two of the "Crazy Gang" were sold to London & Rochester Trading, having originally been commissioned as VICs.

Many firms had received compensation for damage to their ships which had happened during the war, and spent it on having the vessels repaired or converted. Goldsmith's, in particular, wanted many of their barges repaired, the *Saxon* and *Spartan* each coming to Pollocks for new bottoms.

The war had made it necessary for the firm to bring its drawing office to Faversham, but the one used from 1939–47 was small. In 1941, Marshall Pollock had discussed with his father the construction of a new drawing office, the old one to be kept as a surveyors' room. This was not done till 1947, using the canteen which was put up on site for the duration of the war.

The firm made a great deal of money during the war through the sale of vessels to the Admiralty and the disposal of the leftover coasters and a landing craft which went into service on the gravel pits of Johnson Bros. at Aylesford. However, it seems that relatively little of this was used to modernise the yard.

IV. Working conditions

The war itself effected significant changes in conditions at the yard. Prior to the involvement of the Admiralty, the only facilities for catering were provided in a small mess room. The war saw the erection of a canteen in 1940, the building put up being built from the structure of the cricket pavilion at the Davington Cricket Ground which the firm's Social Club had used in the 1930s. Much of the preparation of the building for use as a canteen was carried out by Mrs Flowers, Mrs Meadows and Una Carter. The canteen daily provided tea at 10 a.m. and at 3 p.m., and lunches for 30–50 workers at 12.30, records being kept of the number supplied on the sheets required by the Ministry of Food for rationing. The forms were dealt with by the office. In the canteen, there would generally be a separation of the yard men from the office staff or the women. The food would be plain but substantial, including lots of potatoes, either mashed or

Ship No. 1924 *Silverdial* was one of a pair of tugs for Silvertown Services. The group for her launch are on a dais rigged up for the occasion.

"Smashed". The canteen, as mentioned earlier, became the drawing office after the war.

Another facility created by the war, and the influx of women, was decent toilets. Hitherto, provision had been of doorless huts, but with both sexes present, clearly these were inadequate.

By the end of the decade, records showed that the maintenance costs of the yard, with all its facilities and offices were as follows:

Details of shipyard maintenance 1949			£
Maintenance labour			1,325
Gatekeeper's labour			260
Coal, gas, coke and water			590
Fav. Council Electr. ac/s			1,120
Telephone			184
Sundries			280
Tool repairs	labour	875	
	materials	1,028	1,903
Wharf & Building yard	labour	470	
	materials	465	935
Cable and hose			353
Sundry materials			210
			£7,160

V. Components

The yard continued to support other local industries and firms elsewhere throughout the war and into the peace, as the Marine Purchase Journal shows:

Marine Purchase Journal
September 1940 page 68

Date	Firm						
Sept 6	Colvilles Ltd.	3	9	170	1	4
Sept 10/21	Dorman Long & Co.	2	6	80	14	8
4/25	South Durham Steel	2	2	180	3	4
Aug 5/31	Buck & Hickman	4	0	19	0	3
Aug 12	Iwett, Frank & Son	8	2	2	0	3
—	F. & E. Pordage	9	5	98	18	8
Sept 28	Appleby Frodingham	6	9	138	18	5
Aug 23–4	Wm.Cory & Son	2	12	80	0	0
22	Denny, Mott & Dickson	6	5	64	6	4
2	A. Bax Chambers	12	6	12	12	11
17	Barclay & Mathieson	6	1	63	9	9
25/28	Brooks & Walker	13	11	39	5	3
12/13	Phil Johnson	3	5	10	16	0
30	E. Le Bas & Co.	9	4	23	4	0
9/23	Murex welding process	2	2	7	6	5
12/28	Stewarts & Lloyds	8	8	26	16	11
27	Walsall Conduits	1	0	1	1	8
31	T.A. Whittle	2	8	2	6	2
Aug 14–Sep 6	R.H.H. Stanger	14	11	7	5	0
Aug 15–Sep 11	T.W. Familoe	6	8	39	11	6
Jul 15–Sep 23	T.U. Barber & Sons	4	6	1	5	5
Sep 30	Faversham Water Co.	4	7	7	0	4
17	Fellows Bros	5	1	1	6	1
1	Finrod Paint & Varnish	3	7	20	2	6
Jun 1–Sep 30	Gilletts, Fav. Ltd.	3	1	1	8	3
Sep 4	Salter Paint & Colour Co.	1 0	0	21	9	0
Aug 10/16	Rivet, Bolt & Nut Co.	5	5	73	8	4
Apl 15	H. Widdop & Co.			7	0	1
Jun 1	H. Widdop				5	7
Aug 15	H. Widdop			346	0	0
29	Kitchen's Reversing Rudder	5	7	142	0	0
Sep 21	Anti friction Metals Co.	3	7		8	5
10/25	British Oxygen Co.	3	12	11	19	4
27	Detel Products Ltd.	6	3	8	13	7
4/26	W.B. Dick & Co.	8	10	66	12	3
4/24	Essanbee Products	6	9	3	18	9
24	W. & E. Moore Ltd.	3	8	1	12	1
30	Alfred Olby	2	3	7	7	7
13	Pegler & Landen Ltd.	7	8	3	16	6
		£11 2	4	£1,793	12	11

VI. The Home Guard and Rescue Party

Not only were the workers at the yard busy on just shipbuilding activities. Many formed the second platoon of the strong 9th Home Guard Battalion, or were in a heavy rescue squad which served to help when bombs fell. Men from the local firm of Tett's formed a light rescue squad, again inspired by Pollocks, for the boss's daughter, Dorothy was married to Marshall Pollock.

The Home Guard, like a regular army, went on training exercises at Gillingham and carried Enfield or Springfield rifles with live ammunition. Their main activity was firewatching, for which a small group would go to the yard each night, sleeping in an old shed, more being on call whenever an alarm was raised or if an appliance was needed. Also, in the winter of 1940–1 when Britain faced the possibility of an invasion, men from Pollocks Home Guard would be on duty at Ospringe Road Bridge or at the Infants' School in Orchard Place. Security was tight at the yard — men with fixed bayonets would guard the gate, and the yard was completely walled. It was almost impregnable. Relief for the men came in the form of cooked breakfasts, which would be provided by the women from the canteen. Air raid shelters were provided, and a procedure was devised whereby in an air raid, the Power House would first be shut down, then the men would go down to an allocated shelter, leaving their check on the surface so that if there was an accident, they could be identified. Percy Judges was in charge of the Home Guard despatch riders.

With their cut-down cars converted into ambulances, and trucks carrying heavy equipment, one driven by Bill Swan, the yard's well-equipped Heavy Rescue Squad proved useful in the aftermath of the bombing of Canterbury, and at Detling, an assignment which took three days, according to Una Carter, whose father, Charlie, was there. They also helped survivors when houses were bombed at the corner of Newton Road, Faversham, one of which belonged to Mr and Mrs Wood. Some of the men who were involved in these activities during the war said that frequently they put in as many as a hundred hours in a week by the time they had done forty-seven hours shipbuilding and their time on public security duties.

VII. Marshall Pollock's outside interests

The hard work which was put in at the yard by all Pollocks' employees was rewarded handsomely by the Admiralty, from whom Marshall Pollock made more money than he expected. Since the marriage to Dorothy Pye into which Marshall had entered in 1937 had produced only daughters, with some of the money, he set up a trust for the girls. Also, he chose to invest in property, and purchased the Ferry Inn at Harty, set up Abbot's Craft furniture shop and Abbot's Court Restaurant and bought John Mills' clothing shop next to Faversham's Municipal Offices, rather than invest in much-needed new machinery to replace some which was patently out of date in the yard. In this, Marshall was a victim of circumstances, but some of the employees criticise the lack of reinvestment when Marshall had the opportunity.

The accounts of the businesses which Marshall had set up involved work by Company employees. They were kept by Ron Hofer, Company Secretary, and his staff.

Pollocks continued their interest in Faversham Institute through the Social Club, which in 1948 held a large party for the children of Faversham, at which each was given a toy made by the craftsmen in the carpenters' shop. The Social Club also continued its cricket matches with other local teams, and annual outings. In 1939 Pollocks' Social Club had financed the provision of a maple dance floor, at no expense to the directors of the Lecture Hall.

A new venture was the organisation by Pollocks in the 1940s of large dances held in the Institute, at which nationally known dance bands would play, such

CIVIL DEFENCE RESCUE PARTIES.
POLLOCK'S SHIPYARD DEPOT, FAVERSHAM.

Pollocks' Social Club held a party for local children in Faversham Institute. Some of the toys which were handed out at this event were made by carpenters at the yard.

as Harry Davidson, Billy Ternent or Victor Sylvester. The money collected at the door by Tom Jordan would go to charity. One of these dances was held on 3rd January 1947. The programme of dances on this occasion was as follows:

Programme of Dances

M.C. — Mr A.J. Latimer

8.30 p.m.
"The Jive Bombers"
Modern Ballroom Dances

9.15 p.m.
Harry Davidson and Orchestra

1. Military Two-step
2. Waltz
3. Veleta
4. Schottische
5. Waltz Hesitation
6. Progressive Barn Dance
7. Ladies' excuse-me dance
8. Boston Two-step
9. Twilight waltz
10. Waltz Cotillion

11 p.m.
"The Jive Bombers"
Modern Ballroom Dances

11.45 p.m.
Harry Davidson and Orchestra

11. The Washington Post
12. Waltz
13. Lancers
14. La Rinka
15. Canadian Barn Dance
16. Two-step
17. Gentlemen's excuse-me dance
18. Marina
19. Polka
20. The Last Waltz

Request items in both halves of Harry Davidson's programme

Carriages 1.30 a.m.

The yard's Civil Defence Rescue Party used a variety of vehicles, and attended several incidents in the war including the aftermath of the bombing of Canterbury.

"THOSE WERE THE DAYS"
"THIS IS THE NIGHT!"

FRIDAY, JANUARY 3rd
THE INSTITUTE, FAVERSHAM

8.30 p.m. to 1.30 a.m. In aid of the Hospital for Sick Children, Great Ormond Street, London

JAMES POLLOCK SONS & CO. LTD. PRESENT

Britain's Foremost Dancing Combination

HARRY DAVIDSON

and His Famous Radio Dance Orchestra

In a special programme of Old-Time Dance Music Direct from the record-breaking B.B.C. Series every Saturday night--" THOSE WERE THE DAYS "

SUPPORTED BY

THE JIVE BOMBERS

Music in Modern Ballroom Tempo

M.C.: Mr. A. J. LATIMER from "Those Were The Days"

TICKETS 10/6 EACH

Non-Stop Dancing throughout the evening

LICENSED BUFFET

Tickets Obtainable from:--The Shipyard, Faversham; The Abbot's Court Restaurant, and The J.P.S. Social Club.

Conveyance supplied to Sittingbourne after the dance. All rights of admission reserved

F. AUSTIN & SONS (PRINTERS) LTD., FAVERSHAM

A new venture in the 1940s was the organisation of large dances in the Institute. The poster is for a dance held in 1947.

Marshall Pollock was also active in the Kent Ship & Boat Building Employers' Association, of which he was the Chairman from the late 1940s until his death in 1966. A major rôle of this organisation was to agree rates of pay and working conditions, through the wages sub-committee of which Marshall was a member, with the Confederation of Shipbuilding Trades Unions. After the end of the war, one of the Association's main concerns, however, was the shortage of timber. The Kent Association were leading lights in the National Federation of Ship & Boat Builders, their representatives to this body from the 1940s being Marshall Pollock and Robert Anderson of Anderson, Rigden & Perkins.

VIII. Walter Pollock's activities

Meanwhile, in London, a further enhancement of the reputation of Pollocks in shipping circles was taking place. Walter Pollock, as Master of the Worshipful Company of Shipwrights, was responsible for the organisation of a major exhibition at the Royal Horticultural Hall. This was done from the London office in Lloyds Avenue and involved a considerable amount of work by Alec King and Alec Challice. A detailed record of the preparation and content of the exhibition was drafted out in Walter's own hand in a large, thick file such as he kept copies of his daily letters to Challice, and this constituted almost a complete rough for the exhibition catalogue. Walter wrote the foreword to this catalogue, stating the significance of the display in the shipping world in the aftermath of the Second World War.

"This exhibition of the Worshipful Company of Shipwrights is intended to reflect the enormous strides made in British ship construction for the mercantile marine throughout the world in general and in this country in particular, and for the Royal Navy.

"To encourage the younger generation to enter these industries, scientifically, technically and practically, and to increase the knowledge of those engaged in shipbuilding; it is fitting that this exhibition should have been arranged by the Company of Shipwrights, since it is one of the most ancient City guilds, the freemen and livery of which represent in the twentieth century every branch of the maritime industries, the most essential to a community of islanders who are linked by many ties with the greatest Empire which has ever existed. The seas are the essential highways of the British peoples, and consequently it is vital to their social life and economic welfare that they should have at their service the best designed, best built and the best operated ships.

"The air has become a further medium of the overseas carrying trade in the present century, and the aims and interests of the Company of Shipwrights embraces all connected with the construction and operating of ships of the Air and Air Commerce.

"It is the desire of the Company of Shipwrights, which has existed since the earliest days of ocean-going ships but is still progressive in all its activities, to encourage the young men of this country to take an interest in the art of naval architecture and the craft of shipbuilding. Several thousand tickets for free admission have therefore been issued to apprentices and students. Any profit from the exhibition will go to the charitable funds of the Company.

"It is proposed that on the conclusion of the Exhibition the Company of Shipwrights shall start a collection of models and other interesting exhibits to be ultimately housed for exhibition in the Shipwrights' Company Hall, when it is possible to proceed with the plan for providing the guild with a home in the heart of the City of London, which will be worthy of its history, its traditions and its future. For this purpose many liverymen and others interested will no doubt be pleased to donate exhibits.

"It is appropriate that this exhibition should be held at the close of the Second World War which could not have been won without British designed, British built, British manned and British managed ships — upwards of 7,000 of them.

"In organising this exhibition, the first we hope of many more ambitious projects, the Worshipful Company of Shipwrights has once more justified its existence as a progressive fraternity which regards it as an honour to sponsor an exhibition which is so vitally concerned with the future of this island nation, as well as of the other nations which pay allegiance to His Majesty, our Permanent Master.'

Walter Pollock, Chairman, Exhibition Committee."

A volume of papers entitled "Shipbuilding and Ships" included papers by many notable figures in shipbuilding at the time. Walter contributed a paper entitled "Building a Ship", with illustrations of some of his yard's vessels.

The exhibition was the largest in the world, and featured Pollocks' vessels and the engines which many other firms supplied to propel them, also there were stands for many shipping firms from London and ports all over the world. In addition, Pollocks presented a cup for the most educational display by a firm.

Walter continued, with the help of Challice and the staff of the Faversham drawing office, during and after the war to write books on the vessels built by his shipyard, and the methods used to build them. With Challice, in his regular letters, Walter discussed the layout and text of two volumes, "Small Vessels" published in 1946, and "Building Small Ships" published shortly after Walter's death in 1947.

The standing of Walter Pollock in the shipping world right up to his death was remarkable. A letter to Alec King during the preparation for the exhibition also hints at the standing of Pollocks internationally. Alec was at the time posted in the Far East, the war in Japan having just finished. The writer, Alec Challice mentions that if King should visit Clyde Shipbuilders' office in Granville, New South Wales, he should say that he is an old "Pollockian". Challice also mentioned Walter Pollock's pleasure in hearing about the Port Said Engineering Co. with whom the firm must have had dealings at some time.

IX. Pollocks' offices

By 1940 the staff in the London Office was being run down, while that at Faversham was being increased, headed by Reith. The drawing office under the supervision of A.M. Smith took on more staff to cope with the increased workload put upon the firm by the Admiralty orders. Up to fifty drawings would be required for some of the larger vessels.

The main office, which did nearly all of the business of the firm, employed about fourteen people. It contained a dictaphone, but little other machinery as most of the ledgers were written by hand. An adjacent small office which employed three contained the "Cardex" system of laminated cards, which would have plastic tags put on when an item was on order, at maximum or at

The drawing office was brought down from London to Faversham during the Second World War.

minimum. The cards occupied six green cabinets each with ten drawers. The cash office, headed by Alf Stroud the Chief Cashier, had enamel bell-shaped lamps.

The office staff, unlike the yard men, had a clocking-in device to record the commencement and completion of their hours at the yard. The member of staff would write his name against the time in red which appeared and the machine would "ding". Office hours were 8 – 12 and 1 – 5.30, with the luxury of being able to toast a cheese sandwich over the fire in winter for a hot lunch. Wages in the offices were not particularly high, even a fully-fledged qualified draughtsman only receiving about £4 in the late 1940s, or £5 for work in the cash office. Unlike the yard workers, most of the office staff were not in trades unions.

For the girls in the secretarial office under Margaret Smith, the régime was not easy. In the days before easy elimination of mistakes in typescript, bad mistakes meant that the whole manuscript had to be re-typed — this despite the fact that the girls could easily be put off by the noise outside the office windows.

The London Office remained open in a limited form, run by McGill and Challice primarily as a source of contacts for the firm, and as the headquarters of the export agency run by Challice as a sideline to his work for Pollocks. The office remained the major source of orders for quite a few more years.

Sources

"Kent Messenger", 24th Dec. 1948, re-launch of *Goldhind*.

"Alec ends his age of the train". "Faversham News", 16th November 1984.

Catalogue for the Worshipful Company of Shipwrights' Exhibition, 1947.

"The first ship and the last". Karen Franek in "Faversham News", 4th June 1976.

"50 years ago". "Faversham News", Friday 24th February 1989.

Chapter 8
THE TURN OF THE TIDE. THE 1950s

The period was chiefly one of fairly good fortune at the yard. However, there were some problems both at the start and the end. There were some significant changes in personnel and further involvement by Marshall Pollock in events of wider than shipyard significance, notably the 1953 floods.

The early 1950s saw a general boom in shipbuilding in the wake of the Second World War but, gradually, there was more competition from Japanese welded ships, about which at first Pollocks did not worry. By the end of the decade, the carriage of freight was beginning a period of major change. Lorries were beginning to replace lighters in the transport of cement and grain. Therefore, the demand for both lighters and tugs fell. This would hit Pollocks hard, for these craft formed the backbone of their work.

I. Lighters and tugs

The 1950s began with problems in obtaining steel stocks due to the shortage caused by the war, a situation which repeated that at the end of the First World War. Matters became so serious that Marshall Pollock suggested to one of his wages clerks, David Daniels, that he should look for work elsewhere. Daniels subsequently went to the office at Bowaters Paper Mill, Sittingbourne. Despite this setback, the yard continued to gain many orders for lighters early in the decade, from their regular customers. Two hopper-barges were supplied to M.B. Dredging, which were named *Hamper MI* and *Howler MG*. Swim-barges named *Ironshaft* and *Ironflint* were built for the General Steam Navigation Company, for regular customers, Everard's of Greenhithe *(Cardiff* and *Caprice)* and for London & Rochester Trading Co. The last-named company bought a set of barges named after six of Snow-White's seven dwarfs. The plates required for this set were as follows:

Materials required for six 160-ton barges
4 strake plate ceilings e.g. nos. 2001-4, 2005-6 for London & Rochester Trading. Zed Bar Floors, Plate Girders, No Keelsons.

S.C.1	6 plates	12′6″ × 44″ × 5/16″
S.C.2	6 plates	17′5″ × 46″
S.C.3	6 plates	17′9″ × 48″
S.C.4	6 plates	17′9″ × 48″
S.C.5	6 plates	17′6″ × 48″
S.C.6	6 plates	12′4″ × 48″
S.C.7	6 plates	12′6″ × 48″
S.C.8	6 plates	17′5″ × 48″
S.C.9	6 plates	17′9″ × 48″
S.C.10	6 plates	17′9″ × 44″
S.C.11	6 plates	17′6″ × 47″
S.C.12	6 plates	12′4″ × 48″

Unless the yard had the required amount of steel in stock, they would have to order, sometimes from Consett as for two barges named *Fishbourne* and *Calbourne* for Braithwaite and Dean.

The only one of the many lighters to receive a full naming ceremony was the *Charles Carter*, for Clarke's, named after the foreman shipwright whose one thousandth launch it was. The local press described the occasion as follows:

"Charles Carter launches his 1000th vessel into the creek — the name *Charles Carter.*

"Charles Carter, 76-year-old foreman shipwright at the Faversham shipyard of James Pollock & Sons will never forget the launching he supervised on Wednesday.

"For it was his 1000th launching into the creek — probably a record in this country and, for that matter, one that is likely to go unchallenged anywhere in the world.

"Old Mr Carter is unlikely to forget it, too, because as the vessel, a 160-ton barge, splashed sideways into the creek, it carried on its bows the name *Charles Carter.*

"It was indeed a unique occasion, for where in the world has a vessel been launched bearing the name of the man who cut the launching cable? Distinctive in his snow-white overalls, Mr Carter trembled a little as he supervised the last-moment arrangements which were to send the barge into the creek.

"Then, as a champagne bottle crashed onto the steel hull, he steadied himself, raised his axe slightly and then lowered it sharply to cut the rope releasing the launching triggers.

"The vessel slid silently down the greased slipway and plunged into the creek as a klaxon sounded and the assembled watchers cheered. The naming ceremony was performed by Mrs Una Clarke, wife of Mr B.D. Clarke, Manager of B.I. Transport Ltd., a subsidiary of the Rank Milling organisation. It was their suggestion that the barge was named *Charles Carter* breaking a long tradition of naming their barge fleet after their own products. After the ceremony, Mr Carter, a little overcome with emotion, discarded his overalls and sat down at a table with Mr Marshall Pollock, Mrs I. McLennan and Mrs Pollock, the shipyard directors, and officials of other companies with their wives and joined in the toasts. Mr Pollock remarked that the happenings were somewhat unique in more ways than one. Mrs Clarke, who had been kind enough to come along and christen the vessel on this occasion, shared the limelight with another figure, Mr Carter, and this happened to be the 23rd vessel the yard had constructed for B.I. Transport.

"'As far as we know,' Mr Pollock went on, 'this is the first time a Thames barge has been christened at Faversham.

"'We also have Mr John White of W.F. White Ltd. who maintain these barges in London and his great grandfather ran a yard at Conyer where Mr Carter worked before he came to Faversham.'

"Of Mr Carter he said 'He is in his thirty-eighth year here. I can remember him in about 1919 or 1920 when I used to come here as a very small boy. We used to have little wooden pegs which went into concrete barges. I used to pick them up and he used to help me,' he said amid laughter.

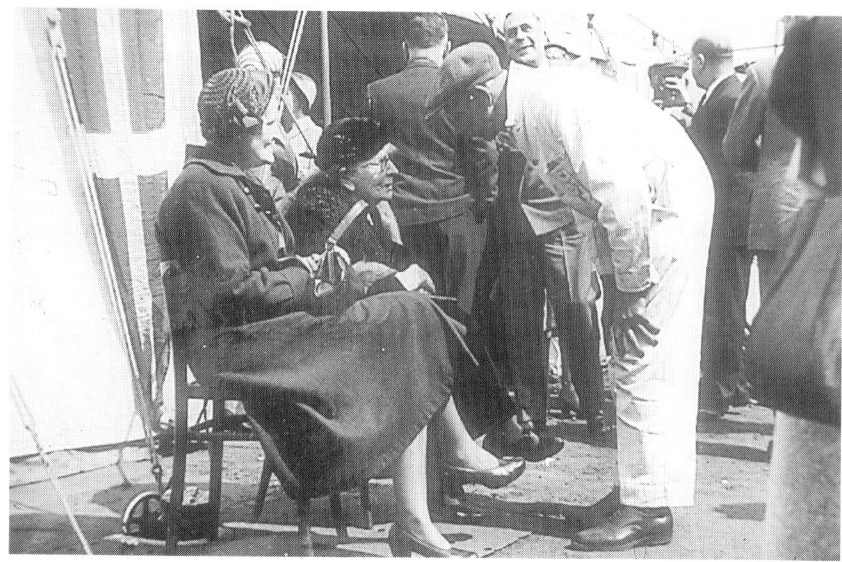

Charlie Carter talking to Lillian Pollock at the launch of the lighter *Charles Carter*, his 1,000th launch, in 1955.

"'He was only here a short time and he became foreman shipwright, and he has been that ever since. We are sure that no other foreman shipwright has ever achieved such a record of launchings. It is a magnificent achievement. We can also claim that one of the vessels he launched is one of the largest built in Kent.'

"Congratulating him on a wonderful achievement, Mr Pollock said he wished to make a presentation on behalf of the shipyard. He slipped a cover off what looked like a filing cabinet and revealed a television set.

"Mr Clarke referred to Mr Carter's 'fantastic achievement'. 'It was an extraordinarily good record in these days when craftsmanship had almost become a thing of the past. But craftsmanship had made this country and if we had more Charles Carters about we should not be in danger of slipping as we were today,' he went on. 'I wish him good health and hope he will make his two thousand,' he added, handing Mr Carter a memento which he thought would remind him that craftsmanship still amounted to something in this country — a travelling clock in a hand made leather case.

"There was one other present for the foreman shipwright — a case of pipes presented by Mr H.F. Dickins of Appleby Frodingham, of the United Steel Companies Group.

"There was a gift also for Mrs Clarke as a memento of this occasion — a beautiful silver trinket box presented to her by Mr Pollock on behalf of the shipyard.

"Also present at the ceremony were Mr Gilbert Findlay, Hon. Clerk to the Worshipful Company of Shipwrights, Mr Green of Associated London Flour Millers Ltd. and Mrs Green, Mr Crickenden of the Medway Milling Co. Maidstone, Mr and Mrs John White, Mr Haigh of the lighterage department of B.I. Transport, and Mrs Haigh and Mr W.A. Challice, London office of James Pollock & Sons, and Mrs Challice.

Ship No. 2046 *Charles Carter*. The launch was described as a unique example of a vessel being named after the man who cut the launching cable.

"Mrs Clarke was presented with a bouquet by Keith Lawrence aged fifteen, an apprentice fitter and the smallest boy at the shipyard, whose late father was a rivet-heater for the company, and whose step-father is employed as a lorry driver."

The firm continued to launch tugs for home and abroad throughout the decade. Two were for Silvertown Services, who had also purchased Pollocks' tugs in the 1930s. These 1950s tugs were named *Silverdial* and *Silverbeam*. They were delivered in 1950, having been built over the period 1947-9. Those destined for abroad included four launch tugs to be registered in Lagos, Nigeria. They were named *Panda, Panko, Panya* and *Panpo*, and were accompanied by four 60′ steel unicraft of quite shallow draft. The unicraft were built in the North Yard, then taken apart and despatched in plates and angles. Another motor tug for Africa, this time for the United Africa Co. was *Lobe*, a Widdop-powered tug built in 1951–3, at the launch of which an apprentice plater, Alan Newman, presented a bouquet to the owner's wife. *Lobe* helped to construct a wharf at Lagos, but it was not long before she sank. She had been sent to Africa with her engine packed separately in a crate.

At the end of the decade, three large tugs were constructed with British Polar engines for the Port of London Authority. These were very strong, and would be used to pull barges of rubbish down river. They were named *Lord Devonport, Lord Ritchie* and *Lord Waverley*, and some of the templates were made by the young loftsman, Geoffrey Chambers, supervised by Charlie Downs.

One of the first few Pollocks to bear flags of convenience was the 1959-built tug *Cosray 25* later renamed *Grainthorpe*. Registered in Nassau, she was bought by Costain's for work on an £8 million contract to build a six-mile mole at Burutu in the Niger delta to defeat mud blocking the harbour. *Cosray 25* had been launched by nine-year-old Susan Whittaker in February 1960, and was towed out the first few miles of her long journey to Africa.

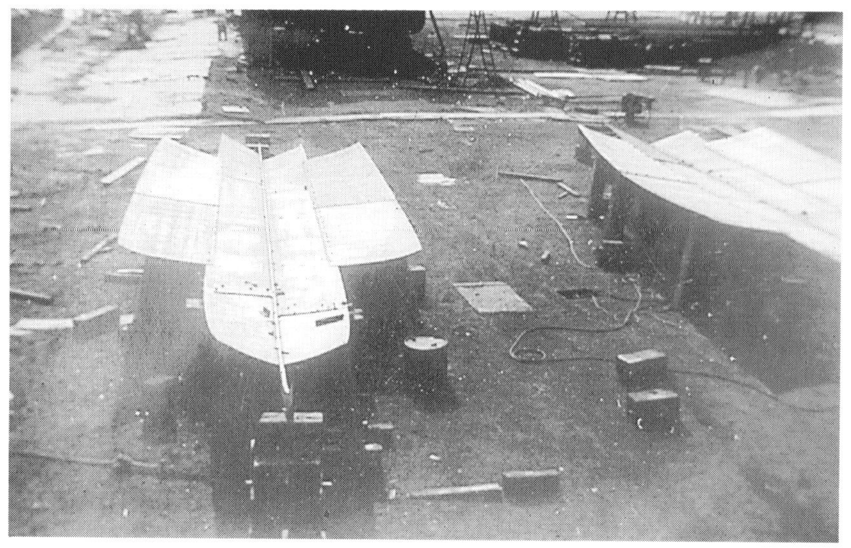

An unusual view of the keels of the tugs *Lord Ritchie* and *Lord Waverley*.

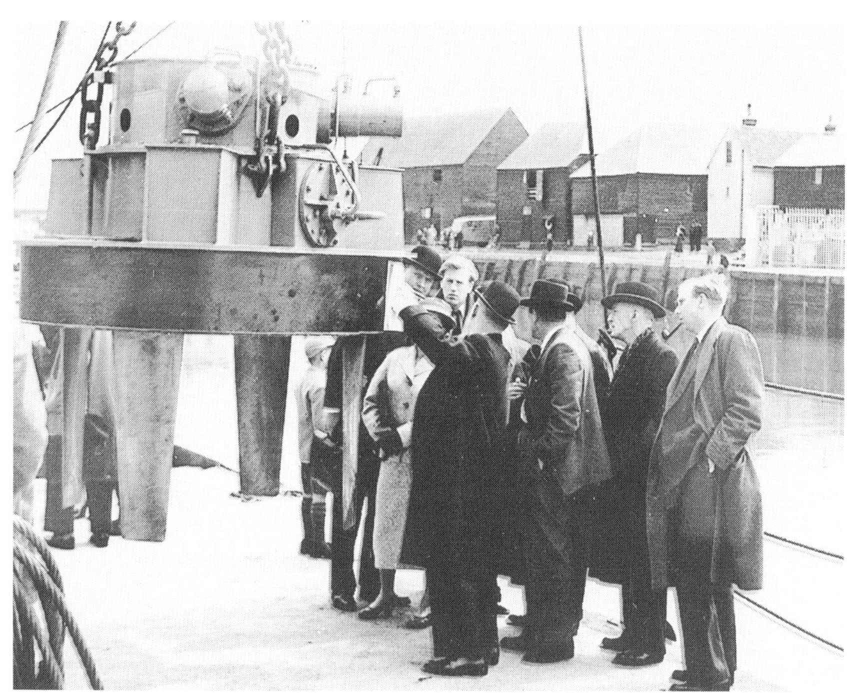

One of the largest vessels built at the yard, Ship No. 2060 *B.P. Haulier*, was fitted with a Voith-Schneider propeller and no rudder, enabling her to manoeuvre in very shallow water.

Ship Nos.2036 – 2037 *Panpo* and *Panya*, a pair of launch tugs seen on sea trials. They were supplied to Lagos, Nigeria, in plates and angles.

II. Tankers

One of the largest of all the vessels built at the yard was the river tanker *B.P. Haulier*, built in 1953 – 5 for service in the Thames estuary. She was very well-known in the area because of her six trips each week to Faversham's oil depot opposite the shipyard site, bringing 84,000 gallons per week from the Isle of Grain. *B.P. Haulier* was fitted with a Voith-Schneider propeller unit, which made it possible to dispense with a rudder. The vessel could easily move in very shallow water, and be very quickly away from her moorings. The construction of the ship was not easy, for there was a lot of confined space work on her. The launch of this important vessel was filmed for the Pollock family collection by Ron Dron. This was one of the few occasions when the men who had built the ship were photographed, standing at the stern of their masterpiece. Repairs to the *B.P. Haulier* after her launch at Faversham on 22nd April 1955 usually took place at Gravesend or at Doust's repair yard at Rochester. The *B.P. Haulier* is still afloat at the time of writing, as a water boat in Greece.

Before the *B.P. Haulier* had been launched, the yard had begun a tanker for the Union Lighterage Co. to be named *Ulco*. The estimates for the cost of steel for this 162′6″ × 33′ × 10′6″ tanker remain in the Company records at Woolwich. They read as follows:

Notes on approximate cost of stainless steel cargo tanks of *Ulco*.

A. Tank shell including bulkheads, internal bulkheads, longitudinal bulkheads, main deck in way of cargo tank.

Gross weight of plates	51.74 tons
Gross weight of sections	7.14 tons
	58.88 tons

B.P. HAULIER
FAVERSHAM

B. Trunk sides, top and trunk stiffeners, beams and brackets etc.

Gross weight of plates	13.12 tons
Gross weight of sections	4.32 tons
	17.44 tons

Total A + B = 76.32 tons

Approximate cost:

Item A	Plates	47.91 tons nett	
	less 25%	11.98	
		35.93	
	+ 8%	2.87	
		38.80 tons gross at £460.5 per ton	= £17,867.4
	Sections	6.61 tons nett	
	less 25%	1.65	
		4.96	
	+ 8%	.39	
		5.35 tons gross at £509.5 per ton	= £2,725.8
			Total £20,593.2
Item B	Plates	12.15 tons nett	
	less 25%	3.04	
		9.11	
	+ 8%	.73	
		9.84 tons gross at £460.5 per ton	= £4,531.3
	Sections	4.00 tons nett	
	less 25%	1.00	
		3.00	
	+ 8%	.24	
		3.24 tons at £509.5 per ton	= £1,650.8
			Total £6,182.1

Summary Total £26,775.3 — 57.23 tons

extra cost to owners	£26,775 stainless
	£ 3,311 less mild steel
	£23,464
+ 10%	£ 2,346
	£25,810

The engines for *Ulco* were ordered from the German firm of K.H.D., Cologne, 500 b.h.p. Deutz engine. They were imported in January 1957. After her launch, the name of *Ulco* was painted on the stern by Geoffrey Chambers.

Opposite: immediately before the launch of the *B.P. Haulier* the men who had contributed to her construction were photographed standing at her stern. l-r: J. Jordan, W. Shead, J. Weaver, A. Stroud, W. Jemmett, H. Sunley, J. Groom, E. Gripps, C. Godden, H. Packman, B. Jemmett, J. Ribbans, L. Jacobs, C. Sunley, R. Puttock, T. Jordan, G. Moon, C. Shipp, B. Jones, E. Shead. Middle Row: N. Gregory, F. Pierce, C. Boodle, A. Wise, J. Finn, R. Wade, C. Downs, N. Lloyd, J. Branson. Bottom: D. Shead, J. Gregory, R. Wise, R. Butcher, H. Terry, R. Puttock.

Ship No. 2105 *Ulco*. Geoffrey Chambers, who worked in the loft is painting the name on the stern.

Ship No. 2075 *Lastholme*, a mud hopper for Eastwoods at Conyer. She used to dredge the local creeks including Faversham.

Ship No. 2108 *S.H.B. Seahorse*, a salvage vessel and buoy lifting ship for Southampton Harbour Board.

Around the same period as the *B.P. Haulier* and *Ulco*, an unusual motor barge was being constructed at the yard for Eastwood's, the brickmakers. Frank Willmott describes the vessel as a mud hopper, and she had a Ruston-Bucyrus crane on her forecastle. She was named *Lastholme* and was one of the few Pollocks vessels to be Faversham-registered. Willmott's description continues as follows:

"*Lastholme* was powered by a 60 b.h.p. Harbormaster unit, turning a centrifugal screw. *Lastholme* could nip over to Southend on one tide for a freight of sand. As Eastwoods had to find sufficient work to keep her going, *Lastholme* was given the job of annually clearing mud berths in other creeks. Faversham creek would take six weeks. Crown Quay was cleared once a year and Otterham Quay was another job *Lastholme* did in between running over to Leigh for mud. Gradually the use of mud in brickmaking became outdated. The calcium chloride which fused the clay together and gave the bricks their nice yellow hue now came in 1-cwt bags. So, in 1966 *Lastholme* was sold away to the Sheerness Harbour Board. A sad day for Alf Harknett as this ended an era of Eastwood's water transport and Alf was their very last skipper."

III. More unusual vessels

In 1956, a vessel was begun which combined the functions of salvage vessel and buoy-lifting ship. Named *S.H.B. Seahorse*, she was destined for the Southampton Harbour Board. Her gear was complicated, and had to be fetched by lorry-driver Charlie Lennard from Southampton. It included on deck an electrically driven Clarke Chapman winch which could lift seven tons at fifty feet per minute; also two heavy-duty electric capstans, a heavy-duty mast and derrick, and at the bows, two heavy horns each with two sheaves for heavy loads and buoy handling. The engines comprised two sets of Gardner diesel engines,

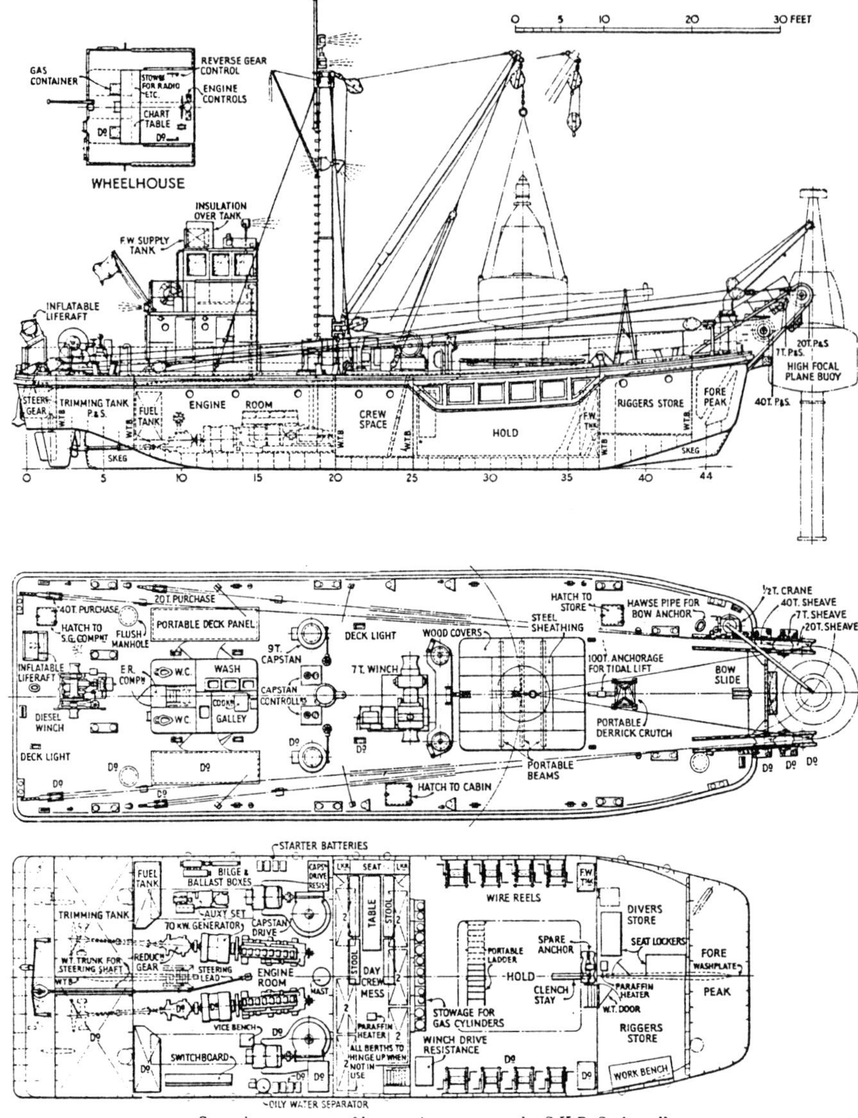

General arrangement of buoy maintenance vessel "S.H.B. Seahorse"

Ship No. 2118 *P.L.A. 18184*, a reclamation vessel for the Port of London Authority. She was designed to pump ashore spoil dredged from the London Docks.

coupled to an Allen generator to power the deck machinery, and an auxiliary set in the engine-room which had a Lister FRIMA diesel engine coupled to a Hamworthy general service pump.

After her launch and fitting out, the *S.H.B. Seahorse* went on speed and manoeuvring trials in the East Swale on 20th November 1958, and lifting trials were carried out satisfactorily in the London Docks on 24th November. The vessel left Gravesend at 1.30 a.m. on Tuesday 25th November and arrived at Southampton at 12.15 a.m. on Wednesday 26th November.

Perhaps the most unusual of the craft built at the yard was a reclamation plant for the Port of London Authority commenced in 1957. The plant was featured in an issue of the "Crossley Chronicles". The aim was to produce a pumping unit to pump ashore spoil dredged from the Authority's docks and the Thames at Purfleet. *P.L.A.18184* as the plant was called could pump out spoil from both the Authority's 1,000-ton hopper barges and its new 2,000-ton capacity Grab Hopper Dredger *Long Reach*. Pollocks also supplied 3,000 feet of 27-inch shore pipeline.

"The hull is built to heavy scantlings well protected by timber belting and capable of withstanding heavy usage from craft coming alongside. The main items of equipment are duplicated so that all machinery repairs can be carried out without taking the plant out of service, and allowing the main dredging pumps to be run singly, or in series for pumping long distances." These comprised: two main dredging pumps, two diluting pumps, two generating sets of 75 kW, two flushing pumps, one jetting pump, two compressors, pipe winches which were electrically driven. There were two electric capstans, made by Thomas Reid of Paisley. The control room and accommodation were modern and well-equipped. The plant had a capacity of 1,500 tons of dredged spoil per hour, which it could pump to a distance of 3,500 feet.

The installation, Crossley's said, proved most successful at Purfleet, and when reclamation had been completed there, it would be moved elsewhere.

Charlie Godden with goggles and a group of boilermakers and some of the 3,000 feet of pipework supplied with *P.L.A. 18184*.

Ship No. 2120 *Toledo*, a steel yacht built for Marshall Pollock's nephew, Alan McLennan, in 1959.

In total contrast to the reclamation plant, the yard was asked by Marshall Pollock's nephew to build a small private yacht. Thirty-five feet long, she was built in the drill shop and equipped with a 10 b.h.p. Albin auxiliary engine. Alan McLennan took possession of her late in 1959. She was named *Toledo*.

IV. The yard

In the yard there were some changes in equipment. Several ex-army American "Diamond T" heavy lifting vehicles were brought in. They were fetched from Sevenoaks by Stanley Flowers. Each could lift forty tons, and they would be used for lifting loads off ships, or putting engines into vessels. Winches were taken off them for use in the yard.

Some new buffing tools were tried by Horace Lennard, including one which was hydraulic, to augment the electric ones already used to smooth the edges of plates.

Wages were still relatively low at the yard, for example, the absolute maximum wage for a lorry driver in the mid-1950s was £12, for a loftsman £10 and for a labourer, about £4. These wage levels precipitated a strike in 1957 which was, in fact, part of a national shipyard strike for increased wages. A television film crew came to the yard to interview a couple of men, and also a government minister, Chris Chataway. The strike lasted three weeks. The apprentices, among them Sid Gregory, worked through it on repair work to the coaster *Ferrocrete*. The labourers were asking for an extra 7/6d, semi-skilled men for 11/- extra and the craftsmen for 15/- more in the pay tins in which they always received their money.

The workforce at the yard had stabilised at around 150, including eight in the paint gang, other labourers, welders, platers, riveters and fitting-shop men.

Marshall Pollock and Stanley Flowers in a DUKW. The amphibious vehicle was used by Pollock to visit the Ferry Inn at Harty, Sheppey, which he owned.

By the 1950s several stalwart employees of Pollocks, some of whom had been at the yard since it had first been laid out at Faversham were coming towards retirement. Among the first to go in this period was the blacksmith, Jim Fettes, in 1951, who had been at the yard about ten years; also leaving was the charge-hand of the heavy gang, Clem Ware, who had begun as a rigger on the early vessels.

A major loss to the yard was the retirement of the foreman shipwright, Charlie Carter. It came about twenty launches after the celebrations which had surrounded his 1,000th. Carter had been with the firm for thirty-eight years, and had reached the age of seventy-seven. The axe with which he had launched over 1,000 ships since the *Molliette* in 1918 would be mounted and displayed in the offices. Carter was showered with good wishes and gifts from the employees at the yard, and from the Pollock family. Most importantly, Marshall Pollock said, at the presentation ceremony to Carter, the yard was losing one of its foundations, since Carter had seen the place grow from a disused brickfield to the shipyard it had become by the 1950s. As Pollock said, Carter well-deserved his retirement.

Charlie Carter was followed out of the yard by his son, Wilf, who went to work at Doust's yard at Rochester. After the departure of the Carters, the new foreman shipwright was Charlie Dane, another old-timer, but he retired at the end of the decade.

In order to replace a number of men who had been at the yard for some considerable time, a fair number of apprentices were taken on, especially as shipwrights and carpenters. These included Colin Birch, John Drowley, Maurice Epps and Stanley Bushell. A few apprentices were taken on in the fitting shop, including Keith Lawrence, and to help Charlie Downs in the loft, Geoffrey Chambers came in to learn the loftsman's trade.

The drawing office also lost a leading figure in the 1950s. Its chief draughtsman, Alexander McTurk Smith, retired, and again a presentation was held.

Overall, the yard had been fairly busy in the 1950s with shipbuilding and with work for various local firms. A sample of the firm's customers in the period can be seen in the Pollocks' Shipyard Job Number Book:

9/7/51	PS 909	Canterbury Sheet Metal	Bend your plates to instructions
"	PS 910	Cancelled	
"	911	Eastwood's, Conyer	Supply 19 plates to template
10/7/51	912	R.E. Martin	Roll plates to ½"
10/7/51	913	T.M. Scutt, Ford Manor	Grind 20 pea cutter blades
"	914	H.S. Tett	36 pieces of ⅛" plate
12/7/51	915	T. Neame, Macknade	Shear plate into 6 pieces
13/7/51	916	R.E. Martin	Bend two angles to template
"	917	Aylward Bros, Teynham	Weld chassis to instructions AKT 912
"	918	S.N. Ltd	Caulking copper boiler
15/7/51	919	C.F. Doyle	1 off drawing y845
17/7/51	920	Cardox	Welding condenser tubes
"	921	Biggleston, Canterbury	Supply 1 flange 18′ dia ¾" + 1¾" dia
"	922	Lecture Hall	Repairs to boiler
"	923	Heaters Ltd	Welding repairs to boiler
"	924	Elgars	Fairing and rolling screen plate

V. Outside activites

As he had been during the war, Marshall Pollock proved public-spirited during the 1953 floods. At the shipyard, the West yard was completely under water and the fitting shop awash. Many blocks floated away, and not all were retrieved. Despite these problems at his own yard, Marshall was quite prepared to rescue other people from difficulties on the marshes and across the Swale, on Sheppey. The rescues accomplished by Marshall and his DUKW were reported by "Evening News Reporter", Tuesday 3rd February 1953, as follows:

"Their courage saved 24 in the flood

"Cool courage and resourcefulness are the qualities that count for most in the kind of disaster which hit the South-East coast and the Thames Estuary. You would not guess on meeting him that 49-year-old Mr Marshall Pollock, shortish, broad-shouldered, bespectacled Managing Director of a Faversham, Kent, shipyard was outstanding in these qualities.

"But on Saturday night and Sunday when the flood waters raged around Faversham and when a weasel manned by American troops became bogged, the courage and resourcefulness of Mr Pollock and his 32-year-old mechanic, Stanley Flowers, saved the lives of at least 24 people.

"In his amphibious Jeep with a 60 m.p.h. wind thrusting great waves over them, Mr Pollock and Mr Flowers made journey after journey over a period of twenty hours rescuing people from exposure and exhaustion and taking them to safety.

"At 4.30 on Sunday morning the police had raised Mr Pollock at his home at Chilham, six miles from Faversham and asked if he could help with his boats. Mr Pollock drove to his shipyard where he found Stanley Flowers already there starting the Jeep. He, like Mr Pollock, had realised that their little vehicle with its shallow draught would be of more use than any boat.

"The area police chief had sent a message that all help was wanted on the coast, but Mr Pollock had heard that an old man was stranded in a farmhouse nearby. 'We'll go there first,' he said. With the mechanic driving the Jeep and Mr Pollock following in his car, they made their way to the farmhouse. They found an old man clinging chest-high in the water to a fence and took him to safety. Next, Mr Pollock was told that a bus was stranded at Iwade. With the Jeep pitching as if in the open sea, Mr Pollock, Mr Flowers and Mr Appleby made their way to Iwade.

"They found the bus. More than twenty people were sitting on top of the seat backs of the lower deck. Others from a taxi and two motor cycles had managed to join them as their own vehicles became submerged. All had been there ten hours and a number were on the point of collapse. With Mr Pollock acting as a control centre on the nearest dry land, Stanley Flowers made five journeys backwards and forwards over the tumbling waters, bringing the small crowd to land.

"'Then we heard that some people, including two babies, had been cut off in their cottages on the Isle of Sheppey,' said Mr Pollock. 'Someone had rowed out to them but could not get back. I decided that our small craft could not possibly make it, so we sent out another rowing boat with some milk for the babies. The boatman at least would be able to get there even if he could not row back against the gale.'

"Late yesterday, hours after the main danger had passed, Mr Pollock and his mechanic were still doing their best to help the hard-hit farmers. As I talked to him, he was making plans to rescue seven horses stranded at Uplees outside Faversham. 'If we can get a halter round the neck of one, the others, if they aren't past it, will perhaps follow and wade or swim to dry land,' he said."

At the time, Marshall owned the Ferry Inn at Harty on the Isle of Sheppey and for the duration of the flood, the public house was kept supplied with provisions by recourse to the Jeep.

He also owned several properties in the town which he had purchased with his wartime profits. One was the Hole in the Wall public house, in Preston Street, Faversham, run by the son of Pollocks' chief draughtsman, Gilbert Smith. The administration of Marshall Pollock's business interests in Faversham was conducted by Mr Challice of the London Office, and by Ron Hofer, the Company Secretary, at Faversham. Correspondence between Challice and Pollock on 31st March 1953 reveals problems at the furniture shop which Pollock owned, with blocked drains. Neighbouring shops, Pollock said, should contribute to the cost of renewing those drains. At this time, Pollock still owned a restaurant, Abbot's Court, at 7A Market Place, which he had purchased from Julius Thomas Conrath of Herne Bay, on 27th December 1944.

A symptom of a growing malaise Pollock found in the 1950s was that his workers were no longer willing to give up their free time to build a carnival float for entry to the local torchlight procession. Whilst keeping a representative on the Carnival Club (Mr Hobbs, the timekeeper), Pollock chose to give a donation to the Club in place of his men's time.

Despite its excellent facilities for drinking, playing darts and table tennis, which must have made it almost unrivalled in the league, the Pollocks Social Club declined sharply in the mid-1950s. The cricket team had gone by this time.

Eventually, the club building in East Street was closed, and the shipwrights put in a new floor before it was sold to Harry Messenger. A decade later, the building, in disuse, suffered a fire, and the interior had to be completely refurbished before it could be put to a commercial office use.

Marshall Pollock continued to be closely involved in the work of the Kent Ship & Boat Builders Employers' Association, the meetings of which were held at Faversham Shipyard. Throughout the 1950s the main item of discussion at the meetings of the Association was the training of apprentices. In advance of any legislation on the matter, the Kent Association was trying to encourage apprentices to go on technical courses as part of their training. The National Federation were asked by education authorities including Kent to prepare the syllabus for a boat building course to be taught at technical colleges. At first, it was planned that most of the apprentices in the South-East would go to Southampton, but due to accommodation costs, courses for Kent apprentices were instead set up at Medway and at Canterbury where some of the staff, Stanley Flowers and Eric Curling, were ex-Pollocks fitters. A list of the number and distribution of apprentices between the various trades was drawn up to determine the viability of individual courses. Via a sub committee of the Kent Association including representatives of the Confederation of Trades Unions and the Kent Education Committee, the relevant parties were kept informed of developments towards an appropriate scheme of practical training in a yard with theory at college which the apprentice would be urged to attend. It was recognised that owing to the small number of shipyards in Kent it would be difficult to find places for large numbers of apprentices to get practical training, but still Kent had been acting well in advance of national guidelines for training in the shipbuilding industry which finally appeared after the Industrial Training Act 1963, when firms were expected to contribute to the cost of providing training.

Problems relating to steel supplies for small yards were discussed by the Association, also the pay claim which had caused the strike in the early part of 1957.

Sources

"Bricks and Brickies". F.G. Willmott, 1972.
"Travelling Shipyard Worker (80) Dies". "Faversham News", 2.11.84.
"The First Ship and the Last". Karen Franek in "Faversham News", 4.6.76.
"Their Courage Saved 24 in the Flood". "Evening News Reporter", 3.2.53.
"Charles Carter Launches His 1000th Ship". 1955.
"Charles Carter Retires with More than 1000 Launches behind Him". 1956.
"Crossley Chronicles". Publication No. 2425, Number 224.

Ship No. 2123 *Danby Cross*, a tug for the Tees Towing Company, she was fitted with a Kort-nozzle propeller.

Denton, a personnel launch completed after the closure of the yard. Reuben Lennard is standing beside the partly-built craft.

Ship No. 2138 *Sun III*. The *Sun* tugs were unusual in that the steel needed came from several different suppliers, since their frames were very complicated. Another spectacular sideways launch.

Chapter 9
THE 1960s. A DECADE OF INCREASING DIFFICULTIES

The decade was one which brought a sequence of unfortunate events to the firm of Pollocks. The fall in demand from the London lighterage trade had already begun to bite. The firm was still producing a few vessels for firms with African interests, but their total output was very small. There was so little work that even on a shorter working week of 42½ hours, later only forty hours, craftsmen and labourers had to be paid "lying-time".

After an illness which lasted for about a year, Marshall Pollock died in 1966. Not long before, the London Office, source of many orders, had been closed following the death of Alec Challice. With very little work, the yard soldiered on under Alan McLennan, letting space for yachts to winter and completing a few orders. Alan died in 1969 after three years of difficulty running the failing yard. His brother, Derek, became Chairman. Ivy McLennan resigned and a new board of directors was elected. These continued in office until they could no longer trade, then reluctantly entered into voluntary liquidation, an auction being held to dispose of the firm's remaining assets. The demise of the Faversham yard would thus bring to an end the 96-year venture in shipbuilding and engineering begun by the skilful and well-travelled James Pollock.

I. Barges and tugs

The few swim-barges which the yard built for the Thames, mostly of 265 tons, contained a far greater proportion of welding than those of the previous decade. The steel from which these were built came mostly from stock which was being used up. So short were stocks after the construction of the barge *Binsted* in 1963 that more had to be ordered which delayed the delivery of the second of this pair of barges. The last two barges built at the yard and welded by Bert Crockford were of 500 tons, named *Greybear* and *Greyfox*. The welders hoped that there would be an opportunity to develop welded barges, but this was not to be. The *Greybear* and *Greyfox* were some of the very last vessels to be completed before the yard closed in 1970.

Tugs provided the major part of Pollocks' work in this last decade of their existence. The first of these was the *Danby Cross* which was lofted out by Geoffrey Chambers, his senior in the loft, Downs, being absent through illness. A scrieve board was used to show the lines of the vessel, and buttock lines to assist matching up the plates in cross-section. The large tug, Crossley-engined, had a Kort-nozzle propeller. She was delivered to the River Tees, to be registered at Middlesboro' on 8th August 1961, for use by the Tees Towing Company. Her launch earlier in the same year was a colourful event, for the vessel was painted blue and scarlet.

Most famed of the Pollocks tugs of recent years were the three built for Alexander's for use on the River Thames. The first of these, *Sun XXIV*, was begun in 1960 and was described by Alexander as the best boat he had ever had built.

Ship No. 2127 *Sun XXIV*, a motor tug, one of the three built at the yard for use on the Thames for Alexanders.

The second, *Sun III*, with a 1340 b.h.p. Mirrless diesel engine was supplied on 22nd April 1966, and shortly afterwards had an accident with a liner and her oil-bunker was stove-in. She was towed to Pollocks for repairs and Pollocks men, among them Boodle, the plater, and Flint, a driller, were called back in from their holidays. Alexander needed her finished in ten days, and said to Bill Weaver when he came to check on progress, "Good job she was a Pollocks ship, or she would have sunk." Weaver felt quite pleased at this tribute to his and his colleagues' labour. In fact, it was unusual for the *Sun* tugs to come to Faversham for repairs, since they were normally repaired at Sheerness, by Alexander's themselves. The *Sun* tugs had very complicated frames, and as the steel for them had been bought in from a number of different suppliers, they were mostly riveted, but with welded butts.

The last *Sun* tug, *Sun XXVII* was the last vessel on the official launch list of Pollocks. She was the last Thames-styled tug to be built for ship-towing. Also a fire-fighter, she was skippered by Pridmore. *Sun XXVII* was the last vessel to be worked on by Jim Weaver, who had joined the firm as an apprentice on their second Faversham vessel, the *Violette*, in 1918.

Sea trials for *Sun XXVII* were conducted over the measured mile at Gravesend, and among those on board were Charlie Lennard and Albert Stroud. These two men had to be hurriedly put ashore when the tug was called upon to go out on a salvage job.

After the launch of *Sun XXVII*, Alexander's ordered a personnel launch to ferry skippers from Gravesend to the tugs moored in the river. This, named *Denton*, was not completed till just before the closure of the yard, much of the fitting out being done by Ron Smith.

Ship No. 2144 *Sun XXVII*. The order for the tug came on the day the yard had been destined to close. She was launched in 1968, the last of the official launch list.

Had it not been for the order of *Sun XXVII*, the yard's history might have ended in 1966. Many of the men had already been laid off and some had found other jobs. The order came on the day before the yard was going to close and some of the men lost the chance of redundancy pay through being kept on, as very few got it in 1970. Since 1965, the riveters, Jim Weaver and George Moon, had been making brackets as the amount of riveting had declined sharply. For the burner, Ernie Cripps, employment was insecure, and in 1967 he was given at short notice the following discharge note:

Faversham Shipyard.
To check no. 186   28 JUL 1967
Please note that your services will not be required after 4.30 p.m. Friday (Date) 25 AUG 1967.
If we require your services we will duly notify you.
JAS. POLLOCK, SONS & CO. LTD.
PER A. Stroud
Note. ALL TOOLS MUST BE RETURNED TO STORE SO THAT CLEARANCE NOTE MAY BE GIVEN TO PAY OFFICE BEFORE WAGES ARE PAID.

II. Launches

A few service and medical launches were constructed for at home and abroad. The *Curlew*, for Freetown, Sierra Leone, to be used by Palm Line (Agencies) Ltd., was 40′ long, and unusually had a Caterpillar D333T marine engine. Her purpose was to escort ships entering the port of Freetown. The engines as Caterpillar advertised had the following qualities:

"1. Low power-weight ratio. Advanced metallurgy combined with a turbo-charger and aftercooler gives more power per stroke.

Ship No. 2132 *Curlew*, a caterpillar-engined harbour launch for use in Freetown, Sierra Leone.

Ship No. 2139 *Kurra Falls*, a passenger launch built in 1966 for use in Lagos, Nigeria.

Ship No. 2124 *Humphrey Morris*, a medical launch for the Port of London Authority, on sea trials off the Isle of Sheppey.

2. Reliability. Years of Caterpillar research and experience produce designs based on rugged simplicity for trouble-free days at sea.
3. Economy. Cat four cycle Diesel Engines — at low initial cost — provide smokeless economical power for long range cruising."

Two medical launches were built before 1965. The larger of these, *Humphrey Morris* of 97'4" had a Ruston diesel engine. She was built for the Corporation of London, and was followed to the same destination by the smaller *Victor Allcard*, one of the few vessels to be launched end-on from the slipway instead of sideways. This latter was named after Sir Victor Allcard, a City Alderman. Whilst Keith Lawrence worked the winch at this launch, the stirring tune "Rule Britannia" was played, as was usual at the sideways launches. In 1964 Pollocks were able to advertise that all three of the medical fleet of the Corporation of London had been built by them, the third being the late 1930s *Alfred Robertson*. Pollocks claimed in the same advertisement to be "Builders of the better craft on the Thames".

The *Humphrey Morris* was designed to serve as a floating ambulance-cum-hospital, with a doctors' consulting room and a small hospital to take two stretcher cases and three sitting cases. Her duties included boarding inward-bound ships in the London River to check against infectious diseases and bring ashore any sufferers. All her accommodation was very modern, with settees, fans to blow hot or cold air as required, and telephones. A special stretcher cradle was used to tranship patients on stretchers, devised by Pollocks with a footrest to enable the doctor to accompany the patient. The vessel was based at Gravesend. Although successful later, the *Humphrey Morris* on her sea trials had been plagued by engine vibration caused by the 5-cylinder Ruston diesel, which had to be remedied with the use of a barred section on the tachometer and a five-bladed propeller.

III. Coasters and salvage vessels

Two coasters were built for Everard's, for their China Clay work, in 1960–63. Named *Capacity* and *The Duchess*, they were built alongside each other. After *The Duchess* was launched, *Capacity* was moved across the yard on slipways laid flat, a laborious job which took many hours, to the launching position.

A smaller motor barge for the coasting trade, a 111'9" vessel named after the owner, James Prior, the *James P* was launched in 1963, and was fitted with a 150 b.h.p. Skandia engine. She was used in the sand and gravel trade on the Colne.

A pair of all-welded salvage vessels was built, the *Broadness* and the *Stoneness*, part of a series of modern lifting and salvage craft built to assist the PLA's main salvage vessel, the *Yantlet*. Some of the welding on the two Pollocks salvage ships was done by Colin Frake, one of the welders taken on in the late 1950s. He used some new CO2 equipment brought in for the purpose, but although quite new, it kept breaking down, and the welder had trouble meeting Lloyd's insurance requirements. Both vessels had a very complicated control room. The steel for these two came from a number of different suppliers, including Appleby and Frodingham, Parker's and Consett Steel. Whilst one of the salvage vessels was on sea trials, Marshall Pollock who happened to be aboard, was taken ill. This proved to be a sign of worse illness to come.

Ship No. 2131 *James P* named after her owner, James Prior, and designed for the sand and gravel trade.

The yard continued to receive enquiries about whether they could supply vessels for regular customers, Everard's and Cory's until 1969, and could have had plenty of work had their tenders been accepted. As late as 2nd February 1970, just three weeks before the yard closed, John Tyrell, an Irishman, enquired of Pollocks whether they could build for him a mussel dredger.

IV. The yard and repairs

As the decade progressed, the amount of steady work at the yard declined. Only about eighty men were still working at the yard. The North Yard had already been let to Parker's for steel storage, and the store used by Percy Judges for storing fittings was full of furniture early in the decade from a relative of Marshall's house. The remaining men would spend a great deal of time in the "bug-hutch" smoking, or eating Mars bars bought from a window manned by Dot Smith. There, they would wait for something to do. When Alan McLennan was in charge of the yard, he would sometimes come in and ask the men to go and help pick apples for his neighbour whilst being paid their normal wages.

Riveting having been almost completely supplanted, the old system of piece-work went too, and men would be paid at day-rate, of if there was no work for them, be paid lying-time. The practice began in 1960, and some weeks several of the skilled craftsmen would have to be paid for doing nothing, as shown by the examples below:

11/3/64

Richards	wages	3	18	11	fitter
Feaver	"	2	13	7	welder
Boorman	"	6	7	8	welder
Frake	"	5	7	0	welder
Tappenden	"	2	13	7	welder
Downs	"	3	7	3	loftsman
		£24	8	0	

Ship No. 2128 *The Duchess*, a clay carrier for Everards, one of a pair built in 1963.

16/8/64					
Salmon	holiday pay 1963–4 £10	2	7	fitting shop-winches	
29/10/67					
Raines	wages	7 17	3	turner	
Godden	"	12 12	0	burner	
		£20 9	3		

Unlike his uncle, Alan expected the craftsmen to be able to turn their hands to most of the different crafts, and not to wait for a specific man as they had in the past for the burner, Harry Packman, who was still, in the late 1960s the Secretary of the Boilermakers' Union. Riveters would often turn their hand to buffing.

Alan McLennan had replaced Marshall Pollock on the Kent Ship & Boat Building Employers' Association after Marshall's death on 24th May 1966. Much of the time at the Association was spent discussing pay and conditions. The Kent Wages and Productivity Agreement between the Confederation of Shipbuilding Trades Unions and the Association was revised particularly with regard to time-keeping, tea breaks and overtime. The result of the 1967 alterations was the agreement quoted below:

"Wage/Productivity Agreement between the Kent Ship & Boat Building Employers' Association and the No. 7 District Committee of the Confederation of Shipbuilding & Engineering Unions dated 8th December 1967, and to come into force from Monday 11th December 1967.

"The bonus will be paid provided the four clauses mentioned below are observed, failure to do so with any one of the clauses means the loss of the whole of the bonus for that particular pay week.

Ship No. 2133 *Broadness* on sea trials. The vessel is still afloat, and was recently employed at the salvage of the Thames pleasure cruiser, *Marchioness*.

"**Clause 1. Timekeeping**

Prompt starting and finishing not only at the beginning and end of the working periods of the day but before and after tea breaks. Time-keeping is meant to read that official times of the establishment shall be maintained and habitual bad time-keeping eliminated unless the Employee has asked and been granted prior leave of absence or he proves to the satisfaction of the firm that his absence was due to sickness or other causes beyond his control.

"**Clause 2**

Unnecessary waste of time after completing any particular job, reporting to foreman or chargehands their availability for further work, eliminating where men are working together in groups for only the necessary person to draw stores etc. the remainder to continue with their work.

"**Clause 3. Tea Breaks**

The morning tea break must be limited to ten minutes from stop to start and no more. The afternoon tea break to be eliminated entirely unless working after 4.30 p.m. in which case the tea break will be allowed at 4.30 p.m. provided an employee is working a minimum of two hours overtime.

"**Clause 4. Overtime**

Ready co-operation to work overtime as required: It is by general agreement and having regard to the Agreements that both sides agree that systematic overtime shall not be allowed unless agreed to by both bodies. It is further agreed that ship repairing being of an emergency nature, overtime cannot be avoided.

"The Kent Ship & Boat Building Employers' Association undertake to see that as far as possible an equitable distribution of overtime is made amongst the operatives concerned.

"That should the Confederation consider that there is ground for complaint in the matter of overtime, they should make representation to the Kent Association when the matter will be investigated. All matters arising re overtime must be dealt with by the Joint Bodies and Signatories to this Agreement."

Ship No. 2133 *Broadness*, one of a pair of modern salvage vessels. The control room included much complicated equipment.

One of the repair jobs done at the yard in the 1960s was the lengthening of the gravel barge *Bert Prior*. An extra 7'6" was inserted at either end of the hold.

A bonus of 10d per hour was to be paid by the firms which signed the Agreement, although Alan McLennan was reluctant to apply this on a uniform basis to all his workers. Shortly afterwards the Association agreed that any redundancies would be notified to the Shop Stewards at least two weeks in advance.

In his own yard, the Agreement was reinforced by a later document on the future of Faversham Shipyard, informing workers that the yard would not close down despite their increasing difficulties, but that all work should be completed as quickly and cheaply as possible. Most of the yard's recent contracts, it went on, had shown heavy losses, and in view of the latest pay increase, productivity should be competitive, but the high standard of workmanship for which Pollocks had become famous should be maintained. Time-keeping and the tea breaks were again discussed, and employees were urged to be as economical as possible with the use of materials and tools, and also to do a "good day's work". They should not attempt to hang out the job in order to keep jobs. This, in fact, had the reverse effect, the yard would be less competitive and more likely to close. Still, as Frake pointed out, there was very little overtime in the 1960s and delays occurred which need not have happened.

The work on which the men were expected to improve their productivity by now included a greater proportion of ship repairs. One was to the wooden motor coaster, *Queen Philippa*, skippered by Charlie Read who had worked in the 1930s at the yard as a labourer. The vessel required major repairs to her engine, and Read knew that Shields could do the work to his satisfaction better than anyone in London, where the owners wished to send her. The *Queen Philippa* was one of three 100' motor coasters built at Whitstable in 1921, the others being the *Harparees* and *Heather Pet*.

Another repair, that of J. Prior's gravel barge, *Bert Prior*, a motor barge, involved cutting the whole vessel open and removing several hundreds of rivets. This was done by the burner, Charlie Godden, and the vessel was pulled apart on the slipway and 7'6" inserted either end of the hold in order that the vessel could load full freights. The operation, which took place in 1964, was documented by Stanley Bushell.

The vessel had been built in Holland only three years previously. Later in the decade a large German vessel was towed up the creek by the tug *Calliope* whose normal duties were mostly concerned with the movement of lighters. The German ship *Birgit Muller* had a very thin bottom, which was often holed. Left to his own devices, Jim Gregory repaired the plating on the vessel, which was one of the largest to visit the creek. She was later sold by Pollocks for £7,000. During the 1960s several former "X" class lighters were modified from spoon bow to vertical bow and other alterations to meet new Board of Trade requirements following the loss of the barge *Delce* on 14th February 1962. The former "X" lighters included J. Prior's barges *Betty Hudson, Fence* and *James M.*, which were renamed *Leah P, Peter P* and *Leonard P* and were employed in the Colne sand and gravel trade.

V. Removal of records, the London Office closes

Aware of the importance of the firm of Pollocks' contribution to the technical development of shipping, Lt. Cdr. Waite from the National Maritime Museum, Greenwich, came to the yard on 23rd August 1965. He took back copies of Walter Pollock's books on shipbuilding, "Building Small Ships", "The Bolinder Book", "The Pollocks as Engineers" and "Amazon Vessels of Various Types", and also a brochure on the demonstration Bolinder trawler, *Lilias*. For the museum's records, he took plans of ship numbers 141 *(Rennie)*, 182 *(Sara Thompson)*, 212 *(The Collector)*, 238 *(Arica)*, 272 *(Guanabacoa)*, 292 *(Priestman)*, 341 *(Lassance Cunha)*, 432 *(America)* and 448 *(Caxias)*, among others. The material acquired for the museum also included general arrangement plans of *Senador Flexa, Antonio Lemos, Darent, Ravensbourne* and photographs of *Caxias* and *Sao Pedro*. Waite intended to take some later general arrangement plans for 1920s vessels. It is not clear if he ever got these, but he took company black books, which it was unusual for a museum collection to hold.

The London Office, since the 1950s, had been housed in small accommodation at 4 Lloyd's Avenue in premises leased from Lloyds of London. This had long been the source of most of Pollocks' orders, and a place to advertise the firm's products, and was now in decline. The manager, Alec Challice, in addition to his direct Pollocks work, ran an agency called "Timsales", of which he was still trustee in October 1964. His expenses for the previous twelve months as trustee, according to records held at Woolwich, were £26 10s nett, and the agency's postal address was given as P.O. Box 18080 Nairobi, Kenya. Challice ran from the office a company named James Pollock (London) Ltd. which, in the early 1960s supplied all the wire rope for the Snowy Mountain hydro-electric scheme in Australia for Perrys Engineering. James Pollock (London) Ltd. also acted as buying agents for Clyde Engineering.

Shortly afterwards, Challice, who had been running the office on a minimal staff and had maintained Pollocks' contact with the City, died and the office closed. This was a major blow to the company, although many of the London

Office's functions had already been removed to Faversham, including the drawing office run by A.M. Smith and then Phil Ellis. The export department was transferred to Faversham and run by Percy Judges. General administration had been put in the hands of Margaret Smith, who was Marshall Pollock's secretary, and her two typists, June Chapman and Sheila Mahon, and of Ron Hofer, Company Secretary and his staff. Margaret Smith's staff were also responsible for manning a switchboard which could connect incoming calls to the First Aid Room, the Foreman Plater's office, or to either of two extensions in the fitting shop.

VI. Arrangements for the future of the business

Even before Walter Pollock had been told by his doctor in 1943 to ease up on the amount of work he was doing, he had discussed with Marshall what should be done if anything happened to Marshall and there was no obvious heir. In a letter dated 23rd September 1940 Walter had suggested the appointment of other directors, including his wife, Lillian, and Marshall's wife, Dorothy. The ladies should then appoint a committee of managers from the staff, possibly including the following members: Donald McGill, Head of the London Office, Ron Hofer, Works Commercial Manager, A.M. Smith, Works Technical Manager, Alec Challice, Assistant Head of London Office, and William Reith, Company Secretary.

He further suggested that should Marshall Pollock not be able to carry on running the business, it might be disposed of. The disposal should, if possible be to the senior members of the firm, or to a new company, which would keep on the foremen and senior members of staff, at 75% of the purchase price. Staff should be encouraged to buy shares. If the ladies were to continue to control the firm, they should draw directors' fees. All those on the management committee should have an understudy to ensure continuity.

In order to encourage staff to buy shares in the firm, £10 shares should be sold to them at a discounted price of £7 10s, but the family should retain a 55% interest. In 1940, Walter estimated the value of the firm as follows, but the war would have increased its value.

Value of business	yard	£11,000
	machinery	9,500
	vessels, deferred terms	32,000
	stock & office furniture	7,500
		£60,000

When Marshall Pollock died in 1966 after a period of illness, most of those whom he and Walter had discussed putting in charge of the firm had either died or retired.

VII. After Marshall Pollock's death

Alan McLennan, son of Marshall's sister, Ivy, came in as managing director, and received considerable financial support from his mother, who mortgaged property to help keep the business going in a period when shipping was in decline.

Alan, lacking the business acumen of his uncle, was not successful in his running of the yard. There was little work, and he was a lax manager. The men

Bill Shields, who had come to the yard to work on the concrete ships in 1918 was the first man to serve for 50 years at the yard. He was presented with a certificate to commemorate the anniversary.

apparently had little respect for one of the foremen he appointed. A keen yachtsman, Alan, who had his own yacht, *Toledo,* built at the yard in 1959, let space at the yard for the wintering of yachts, the space not being needed for what little shipbuilding was going on.

One of the men whose experience could have helped Alan McLennan greatly retired late in the decade after fifty-one years of service. Bill Shields who had been with the firm since it came to Faversham, and who became its Chief Engineer and Marine Superintendent began a well-deserved retirement. Only a year earlier, he had become the first shipyarder to achieve fifty years of service, this distinction being marked by the presentation of a special certificate. Shields was replaced by John Richardson, who had been London Manager of Mirrless Diesel. It was said that he was extravagant. Another man, who had been at the yard thirty-four years, Albert Lines, the foreman plater, had retired in 1964.

On 23rd August 1969 Alan McLennan died at the young age of thirty-eight while sailing. He was out with his brother, Derek, and had a heart attack on board the craft. There had been a history of heart disease in the family, but it was a shock to everyone that Alan should die so young. Ivy decided to do as her father had suggested in 1940, and appoint a managing director from within the firm. Philip Ellis, who had considerable experience in the drawing office, was appointed, aided by Company Secretary, Ron Hofer, the last survivor of Walter Pollock's suggested team. They valiantly tried to revive the yard, but decline, it appeared, was inevitable after the name of Pollock had gone. Work consisted of a few repairs, including that of the *Birgit Muller*, the completion of the two welded barges and the *Denton* on which Tom and Ron Smith worked.

Negotiations continued on possible orders including two tugs for Maracaibo and a large venture involving GKN first mentioned to Pollocks in 1969, to open

A small presentation was made to Albert Lines on the event of his retirement on 28th January 1964. Albert, like his father, was a plater.

up a port and railway link to Zambia for the better exploitation of the country's resources, especially copper. Pollocks might have gained much business building harbour service vessels and tugs. This never came off although the estimates and drawings had been well-received. These possible orders had been discussed at a board meeting chaired by Derek McLennan on 29th January 1970, when the GKN contract still seemed as if it might come to Pollocks. The financial position of the company was bad. It was stated that the West yard was being sold and suggested that the business should be reduced to that of a general engineer's, selling off the wharf, increasing the drawing office and fitting shop, and changing the use of the platers' shop. The woodworkers would be laid off, but about sixty people kept on. The Medway Ports Authority still seemed willing to give the contract to repair the creek bridge to Pollocks. At this time, 50% of the *Denton* had been erected. In February, it was reported that the firm had tendered for a cargo and passenger pontoon for Nigeria, a 1,000-ton motor barge for Blue Circle and a tanker for Shoosmith, Howe and Partners. These could have given the yard continuity of work.

On 24th February 1970 Lloyd's List contained the following report:

"Faversham Yard to close down.

"One of the best known shipbuilding yards, James Pollock, Sons & Co. Ltd., Faversham, is to go out of business. This is because of continuing increases in materials and labour costs which make it more and more difficult to predict future prices. In particular the recent price increase in steel has played a big part.

"Messrs James Pollock, who have built over 2,000 ships varying in size from barges up to coasters of 1,100 tons d.w. said yesterday that because of the lack of shipbuilding orders it was not possible to continue the business of the company and the directors have had no alternative but to put the company into liquidation. They have asked the National Westminster Bank to appoint a receiver.

"The firm itself has been in existence for ninety-six years, but for the first part of its life it was engaged as consultants. In 1916 it opened an emergency Admiralty Shipbuilding Establishment at Faversham to build concrete coasters, and in fact built two before the end of hostilities. Since then the yard has specialised in small craft. An achievement of which the company is particularly proud is that the Faversham yard built for the PLA the largest reclamation plant ever constructed in the United Kingdom.

"A director of the firm told me yesterday that the firm had been on the threshold of some big orders but they had offered a fixed price. Then followed the sharp increase in steel prices and an additional labour cost which made the contract impracticable.

"Shipbuilders throughout the country are finding it extremely difficult to budget for the future. There seems little point in tendering for contracts without some form of materials and labour clause. This is to their advantage in the current sellers' market but if and when the boom is over stability of costs must be controlled to enable shipbuilders to have a fair crack of the whip.

"The Faversham yard has an employment force of about eighty and unless something golden turns up in the near future, they will have to be declared redundant."

On the day after this appeared, a number of cars came into the yard, and the men knew instantly that something was wrong. Notices went up to the effect that the firm was going into liquidation, and it closed at the end of the week on Friday 27th February. For most of the men, there was no holiday or redundancy pay, just pay for the previous week's work. This was small reward for many who had given Pollocks dedicated service for many years. Percy Judges assisted the receiver in winding up the export department.

After the closure, the local trades union branches met with Faversham's Member of Parliament, Terry Boston, who negotiated with the receivers about redundancy pay. He wrote to Eric Varley, Minister of State for Industry, who suggested that money might be forthcoming to help any firm taking over the yard and accepted that the Faversham area was one where Industrial Development Certificate applications might be treated sympathetically, implying that it had relatively high unemployment. Boston had also contacted Tony Benn at the Ministry of Technology and Power, and Barbara Castle at the Ministry of Employment. As it turned out, Charlie Downs mentioned a sum of about £500 which he received as redundancy after forty years of work for the firm in the loft. Very few men got any at all. There was insufficient cash available to give any fitting rewards for the long service which some of the employees had given.

The yard, together with all the machinery and steel stock was put up for sale at auction. All the carefully made tools for each specific job, shaped by blacksmith, Fred Liddle, which hung around the walls of the forge were left hanging there. The clocks which had been carefully tended by Charlie Godden and told the time for generations of staff were sold off.

Sources

"Faversham Yard to Close Down". Peter Fisher in "Lloyd's List", 24.2.1970.
"Down Gravesend Reach". Longshoreman in "Coast & Country", Vol. 7, No. 2.
"Longshoreman" in "Coast & Country", Vol. 6, No. 6.

Chapter 10
CONCLUSION

After the yard closed, the receiver, Mr Shedel, dealt with a sequence of enquiries from clients wishing to purchase and re-open the yard. All of these proved unsatisfactory, and two months after closure, his clearing up was finally complete. The site became vacant until 1972, when it was leased by Southern Shipbuilders Ltd., who would use the site to build river cruisers and trawlers. They struggled on for four years before closing because of crippling costs. Late in the 1970s and early in the 1980s two more river cruisers were built on the site for use on the Thames. The West yard remained disused and the old North yard given over to small units for developing industries. Only part of the original main yard is used for ship repairs. Many of the shipyard workers have moved away or found other local jobs, the older ones remaining in Faversham, annual reunions rekindling memories of the many high-quality vessels on which they worked at Pollocks' yard, and of the reputation which their employers had for nearly a century in the shipping world.

I. Enquiries immediately following closure

Shortly after the yard had closed, Philip Ellis, who stayed on for two months to aid the receiver, Mr Shedel, received an enquiry from Commander Poland, who had been injured in the Second World War and who had a family business dealing in paper-making machinery. He looked at the yard, bought a house in Faversham, presumably with the intention of living close to the business, but the receiver, having investigated Cdr. Poland's financial background declared that he could not afford to buy and service the company. Cdr. Poland withdrew.

Another interested party, Mr Graham, came in a battered old Austin car and, looking rather strange in a tweed suit and heavy boots, failed to impress the receiver. He paid two visits to the yard to see Philip Ellis and during one of these, telephoned Mr Robb at Leith, one of the famous firm of Robb Caledon, whom he knew well. He had a considerable amount of money to invest in the business which he wanted to see re-opened and expanded. The receiver again dismissed the offer. Subsequently, Graham suggested commencing shipbuilding at Stangate Creek, but Medway Ports Authority dismissed this idea out of hand.

Two Greek brothers named Frangos were the next to approach Ellis. Having visited the yard in March 1970, they wrote to Ellis on 6th April stating that they intended to build barges of 250′ × 50′ × 13′. The main problem which was causing delay was the attitude of the Medway Ports Authority, who had recently taken over from the Faversham Navigation Commission the dredging of the creek. The MPA would neither guarantee keeping the creek dredged to 1968 standards nor contemplate any extra deepening of the waterway. They argued that the suggested craft would be too large to negotiate the bends in Faversham Creek. Pat O'Driscoll was told by W.H. Williamson of Southern Shipbuilders that the largest vessel which could navigate the creek would be one of 175′ length. Yet

Father Thames, a river cruiser built by the subsequent owners of the yard, Southern Shipbuilders, in 1972. At the time of writing, the hull of the vessel lies alongside the yard and is in use as a dry dock.

Frangos brothers could have brought considerable employment to the town had they turned the shipyard into a more modern, covered operation. They were willing to consider keeping some of the senior Pollocks personnel employed. In addition, they hoped to create a centre of gas cutting, welding and pre-assembly of vessels in the perimeter workshops. Even Ellis doubted the possibility of launching vessels of 50′ breadth and 600 tons into the creek without damage to Standard Quay, or the ability of local labour to absorb the radical changes in working practices which Frangos proposed. Ellis continued to receive enquiries whether the Frangos proposal was going to materialise. Instead, the Frangos brothers, prevented by the conservatism of the Medway Ports Authority and the sinuosity of the creek from developing the Faversham site, withdrew their offer and became interested in Mr Graham's idea for developing Stangate Creek, proposing an elaborate scheme involving a railway dry dock and covered shipbuilding berths. They offered Ellis a job supervising new construction, but he declined.

II. The subsequent history of the site

By the summer of 1972, the shipyard had been re-opened by Southern Shipbuilders (London) Ltd. — Mr William Williamson, a naval architect, and Lt. Cdr. Edward Kennett, Royal Naval Reserve. Having removed the old plating machinery and erected a shed in which to construct ships, first launchings included a 50′ luxury yacht and a 155′ river boat, *Father Thames*, to be used as a cruising restaurant for Rexenter Ltd. This served on the Thames for several years, but eventually after being burnt, came back to Faversham, and at the time of writing is moored at the shipyard, her deck used for the winter storage of

Opposite: part of the shipyard site in 1989. The shipyard cottage is in the background. The vessels include the ketch *Goede Verwachting*. The yard run as Brents Boatyard only occupies the front part of the original yard.

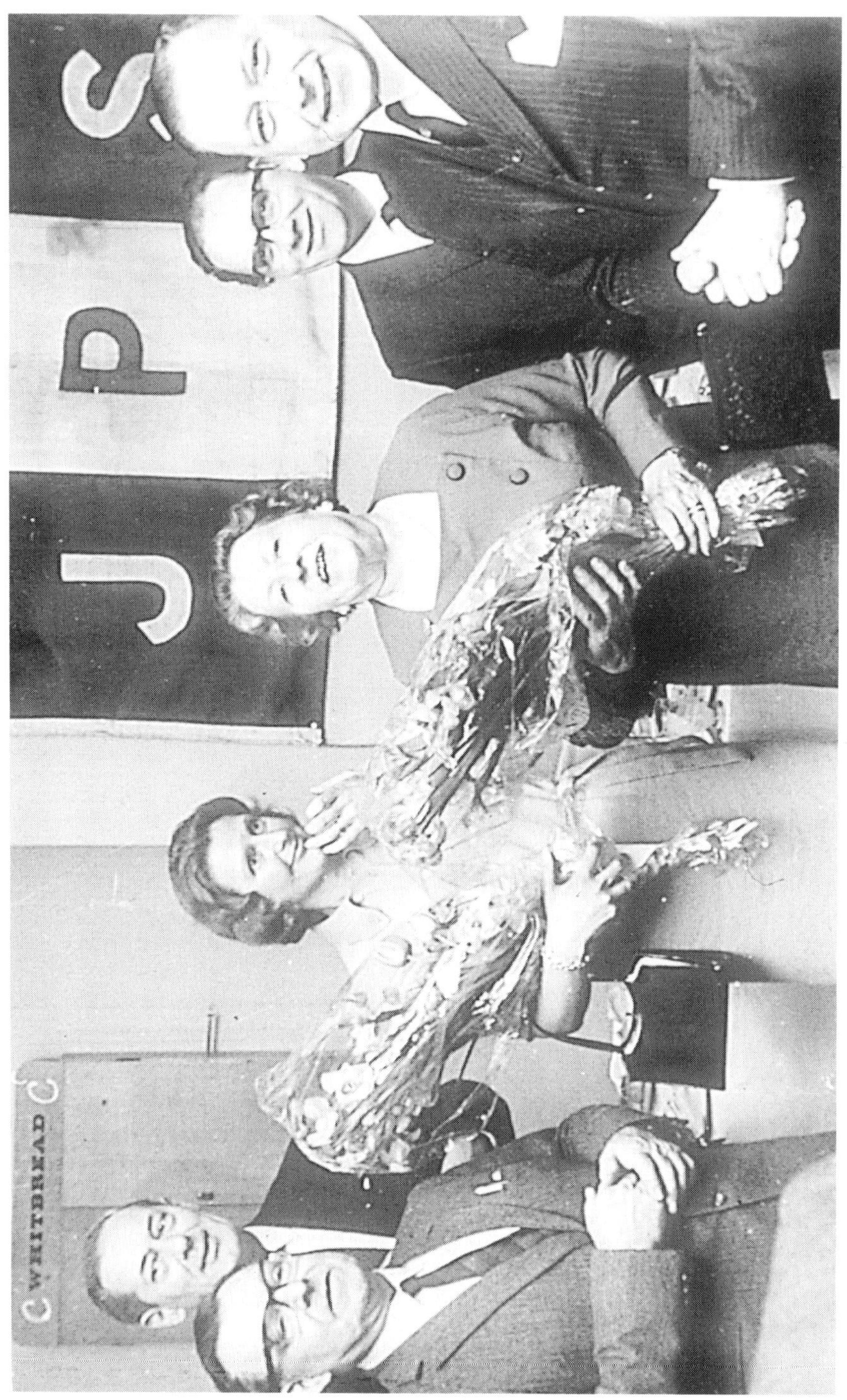
WHITBREAD

Sir Thomas More, one of a pair of Thames cruise boats built on the site in 1980–81, the most recent vessels to be launched in the traditional manner from the yard.

yachts. Southern Shipbuilders were also building trawlers. The firm faced four years of crippling costs. Their final vessel was named the *Silver Barracuda*, again for use on the Thames as a pleasure craft. The launch of this ship in April 1976 was a spectacular but sad occasion as there was no guarantee that shipbuilding would ever return to the site.

The yard lay dormant for several years until in 1979, the keels of two sightseeing boats for the Thames were laid down. The first of these, *Sir Thomas More*, was launched in the spring of 1981, the second, *Sir Richard Grenville*, later in the summer.

The West yard was completely unused, and the North yard was filled up with small units for developing industries in the early 1980s. Since the river boats have been finished, a variety of small industrialists have moved into parts of the shipyard. Only a small section of the yard is now being used for storage of yachts and small boat repairs. This is being run as Brents Boatyard Ltd. The West yard is being developed for housing and the former barge slipways have gone, replaced by a new dock. Still a few of the buildings on the site are recognisably from the Pollock era, concealed by larger modern buildings. The creek, into which such a great variety of ships had been launched this century and before, has become deeply silted due to lack of the regular use it received before the demise of shipbuilding activities and closure of the oil depot opposite the shipyard. Recently, part of the quayside along the shipyard has been built up with piling. Even the railway which came down to the bank of the creek at Standard Quay has been taken up and part of its route built over with sheltered accommodation for the elderly.

III. The men

Some of the former employees of the shipyard went to work for other large employers in Faversham and Sittingbourne, including Shepherd Neame's and

Opposite: the first of a series of annual reunions of shipyard workers was held on 20th March 1971 at the Brents Tavern on the Upper Brents, Faversham.

Whitbread's breweries, and Bowater's Paper Mill. Others moved away and found work in other towns. More who were nearing retirement age did not work again. Prompted by an idea of Albert Stroud's, from 1971 onwards every March or April a reunion was held, hosted by Ivy McLennan and held at the Brents Tavern, to which many of the workers would be invited. There, they would watch films made by Ron Dron and kept in the Pollock family collection of the construction and launch of various vessels from the 1930s onwards. The invitation card to the first reunion was worded simply, as follows:

A
REUNION
at
THE BRENTS TAVERN
on
SATURDAY 20th MARCH 1971 at 7.30 p.m.
DO PLEASE COME ALONG.

In 1980 the tenth of the reunions was held, on a Saturday in late March. The "Faversham News" covered the event:

"Workers gather for a reunion.

"It is ten years since the Faversham shipyard of James Pollock closed but every year former employees of the firm gather at the Brents Tavern, the shipbuilders' local.

"On Saturday evening fifty-eight ex-employees held their tenth annual reunion in the pub and one of the highlights of the occasion was the showing of a colour film recording one of the last big launchings at Pollocks — a splendid *Sun* class tug.

"Among those present were several former apprentices — one of whom is now a Chief Engineer on a passenger liner — who have all done well.

"Company Secretary, Mr Ronald Hofer, and Chief Engineer, Mr Bill Shields, were also at the buffet evening. The reunion is arranged each year by Mrs Ivy McLennan, sister of the late Mr Marshall Pollock, with help from Mrs Dorothy Smith whose husband Ronald was a marine engineer with the firm.

"The film, which was a nostalgic experience for all those present, was screened by Mr Ron Dron.

"A bouquet was presented to Mrs Ivy McLennan."

The venue changed in 1983 to the Brents Schoolroom, and due to illness Mrs Ivy McLennan by then aged 81 could not attend. The last of the series of reunions was held in March 1984, just before Ivy McLennan's death. Films were shown of the launch of the 1949 motor coaster, *Goldhind*, that of the *Cosray 25* in 1960 and again the film of the "Sun" tug. Forty-two people attended the reunion opened by Chief Engineer, Bill Shields, longest serving of the surviving employees.

Deaths and illness had gradually reduced the number of people able to attend the reunions at which memories of the yard and its ships had been shared. The following report appeared in the Amalgamated Society of Boilermakers, Shipwrights, Blacksmiths and Structural Engineers' Journal in July 1975:

"Faversham—It is with the deepest regret we report the death of the late Secretary, Bro. Harry Packman. Our members will recall our President, Bro. McGarvey made reference some two or three months ago to the splendid job of work Bro. Packman had undertaken on behalf of the branch and our Society. Harry during his lifetime had served on the Kent District Committee, and in fact he was the power behind our Faversham branch. The service took place at the Faversham Parish Church and was attended by many members, branch officials, District Committee members and the District Delegates, and to his widow, Doris, two daughters and family we tender our deepest sympathy."

In the last few years several more of the shipyard men have died, and many of the others are in their seventies or eighties. In a few years' time, there will be few who remember how the ships were built there.

IV. Pollocks' investments

Of the two shops which Marshall Pollock put money into, both have closed. One, Abbot's Court Restaurant, became a carpet shop, the other, Abbot's Craft, lasted till the late 1970s. Then it was split into two to become a travel agency and a bookshop. The public houses he owned are all still open, having had a sequence of landlords since the 1960s.

The Institute, into which Pollocks' men and Marshall in particular put both money and attention, has gone, much to the regret of ex-employees of the shipyard and other townsfolk, but the carnival continues to raise hundreds of pounds each year for charity. It is still the major event of the year in Faversham.

V. Summary

Since its closure, the town has sorely missed the firm of James Pollock, Sons & Co. Ltd. for its engineering skills, the employment of many men and a few women, the hope of a job with a future for the school leavers and the contribution which its Social Club and Chairman made to the social life of the town. Most of those who heard of the firm's closure had never known the town without the noise and bustle which Pollocks' yard brought to it.

Philip Ellis, ex-Managing Director, remarked to the author recently the following:

"Looking back over the years it seems to me that we had this long-established family firm, who had a first class team of skilled craftsmen, built some remarkable vessels of unquestionable quality, who could still perform technically as well as any, but who had run out of money. There were people in the industry who were showing interest and concern, but somehow official help was not forthcoming. Perhaps it became a victim of the times."

Sources

"Faversham News". 28.3.1980.

"The First Ship and the Last". Karen Franek in "Faversham News", 4.6.76.

"Digest" by Eastcoastman in "East Coast Digest", Vol. 1 No. 2.

"Faversham News", 8.4.83.

"Faversham News", 6.4.84.

"Amalgamated Society of Boilermakers, Shipwrights, Blacksmiths and Structural Engineers' Journal", July 1975.

Appendix I
DISTRIBUTION OF POLLOCKS' PERSONNEL

Managing Directors
James Pollock 1875 –
Walter Pollock 1905 –
J.M. Scott 1920s
Marshall Pollock 1935 – 66
Alan McLennan 1966 – 69
Philip Ellis 1969 – 70

Family Directors
James Pollock jnr. 1904 – 17
George Pollock till 1923, exports
Arthur Pollock 1910 – 33, Company Secretary
Lillian Pollock
Dorothy Pollock
Ivy McLennan till just before close
Derek McLennan, Chairman at close

Other Directors
J. Mackley 1920s to Bolinders of London

General and Secretary's Offices
Pat Bell pre Second World War
June Chapman 1950s – 60s
Ron Dron 1934 – 70
Kay Ellender 1940s
Ann Field 1960s Sec. Office
Ena Foreman, junior girl 1940s
Betty Gentry, under Margaret Smith 1940s
Ron Hofer, Company Secretary 1952 – 70
Harold Jacobs, office boy 1920s
Sheila King, under Margaret Smith 1942
Bessie Luckhurst 1920s – 30s
Sheila Mahon 1950s – 60s
Margaret Smith, Marshall Pollock's Sec.
Muriel Smith with Ron Dron
Jill Tutton Accounts 1940s – 50s

Stock Records
Alec King 1940s ex London
Ron Spratling 1940s

Wages/Cashiers Office
David Daniels 1940s
Harold Hutchinson 1932 – 70
Kathy Larson 1960s
Flora Parfect post war-end
Alf Stroud, Chief Cashier 1927 – 70
Dorothy Taylor
William Taylor 1927 – war

Buyers etc.
Bill Swan, Steel stockist/ stock management 1928 –
Warren Topping, Chief Buyer 1934 – 70

Management
Mr Colinese early – 1923
C. Hadlow, Under Manager 1920s. To Canal Co.
Alf Hitchon, Assistant Manager 1925. To Vancouver
George Johnson 1920s – 35

Lighter Owner Apprentices
Michael Braithwaite 1940s
Henry Higgs
Tony Knight
Humphrey McCann
Charles Hadfield
Mr Wragg c.1918

London Office
W. Alec Challice 1930s – 60s
Mr Faint, King's successor
Miss Edith Holmes 1940s
Alec King 1935 – war
Henry Lamputt, London Drawing Office till 1939
Donald McGill 1933 –
William Reith, later Company Secretary till 1952
E. Wilson
Fred Mumby

Drawing Office
Eric Bliss 1920s
Geoffrey Chambers 1956 – 7
A.S. Cork
Dave Ellis 1950s to New Zealand
Philip Ellis 1940s – 60s
Stan H. Ellisdon, London
Alec Francis 1950s – 60s
Richard Griggs 1950 – end
Nigel Hills 1947 –
Don Morley 1950s
Derek Palmer 1950s
A. Savege to Hessle
Alexander McTurk Smith, Chief 1939 – 60
Gilbert Smith, on and off in 1940s – 60s
Katherine Smith, Tracer in war
F.W. Talbot 1920s to Lloyds
Harold Taylor
James Wells 1930 – 70 for engineers
John Smith 1943 – 48

Platers
Frank Akhurst, platers' help
Bob Allen
Sam Archer 1920s
Mr Barton 1920s
Tommy Blenkinsop 1920s

Charlie Boodle 1920 –
Jack Branson 1920s – 60s except 1938 – 43
Joe Brewer 1930s from Dartmouth
Keith Calton
Jack Chandler 1920s – 30s
Henry Cribben 1930s
Sid Goldfinch 1940s
Jim Gregory 1950s – 60s
Sid Gregory 1955 – 61
Joe Groom
Bill Hawkett
Les Jacobs 1920s, charity apprentice
Reg Jacobs 1920s –
Ben Jones, foreman, marker off 1926 –
Sid Lennard, to Erith
Dave Liddle 1950s
Albert Lines, snr and jnr
Charlie Mann, liner boy 1920s
Sid Martin, liner boy 1920s left 1938
Alan Newman 1950s – 60s
Harry Owen 1926 –
Sid Pinnington
Johnny Popple 1920s
George Porter 1930s from Dartmouth
Mr Potts 1920s to Mersey
Fred Ribbans, later foreman 1934 – 70
Jack Ribbans
Don Shead
Ernie Shead 1920s
Dick Simons, also on furnace
Jack Snowball, foreman plater 1925
Mr Spencer 1920s
Harry Stockwell 1920s
Albert Stroud, later foreman 1934 – 70
Hamilton Terry
Mr Timmins 1920s
Ernie Thompson, foreman after Snowball
Vic Trosh, late 1930s
John Wade
Brian Weaver 1950s
Derek Weaver, into Navy
Arthur Wise 1920s – 70
Roger Wise 1950s
Aubrey Taverner, platers help
Stephen Woolf 1960s

On the Gate
Tom Boodle pre-war
Rosie Hedlam during war
Bill Hobbs post war-end
Mrs Hudson during war
Jack Jordan in war
Mrs Pearson during war
Mr Wraight 1920s

Caretakers
Mr Gates very early
Mr & Mrs Holmes early on
Mr & Mrs Cyril Meadows 1940s
Mr & Mrs Ron Smith till end

Loft
Bill Adams late 1920s to Bideford
Geoffrey Chambers 1950 – 65
Charlie Downs 1930 – 70
Sid Gregory briefly in 1950s
Jack Housley 1920s
Tom Nell 1930, also drawing office
Frank Pepper 1930
Reg Stevens briefly in 1920s

Drillers
Mr Allen early
"Slim" Bailey, radial driller
Edie Beane in war
Ernie Curling 1923 – , hand drill
Harry Dungey on boats 1940s
Reg Flint war – 1970 on boats
Hubert Gorham, radial drill 1940s
Mary Jemmett, radial drill during war
Charlie Lennard, loading up
George Moore, radial drill
Eddie Norris, radial drill
Bob Punyer, driller in fitting shop
Dick Relf
Fred Shepherd 1930s – war
Bill Stone
Chris Tyler, loading up

Shipwrights & Carpenters
Tommy Beer 1920s, ex of Cremer's
Colin Birch, shipwright
Mr Bristow, shipwright 1920s
Stanley Bushell, shipwright 1952 – 70
Jim Butler, carpenter
Charles Carter from start, foreman
Wilf Carter, son of Charlie 1929 – 57
Reg Cheney, carpenter. To Australia
Bill Clarke
Harry Collins till 1937
Percy Dadson, shipwright
Charlie Dane, foreman after Carter
Roger Dane 1960s, carpenter
Ian Dennett 1950s
Bert Diamond 1920s
John Drowley 1950s – 60s
Chris Ellingworth, shipwright
Harvey Elliss
Alf Epps
Maurice Epps, shipwright 1950s
Alan Foreman, shipwright
"Chick" Clarence Fowle 1923 –
Mr Jeffery, on concrete ships
Pete Liddle, carpenter
Ralph Marsh, shipwright
Arthur Marshall, during war
Joe Moat, carpenter, later foreman
Florrie Partridge, with Wilf Carter during war
Percy Read 1932 – 50s

Terry Richards, carpenter 1950s
George Rigden 1920s
John Scott, shipwright 1950s
Ronnie Skipper 1960s
Nelson Trigg, carpenter 1920s
Len Walker, during war
Charles Sinden 1920s

Riveters and Rivet Gangs (Boilermakers)
Bobby Allen, liner boy, later plating
"Podge" Bill Betty, holder up 1930s
Mick Bloom, holder-up
Reg Bottle, hand
Jack Burford, rivet heater
Peter Butcher, holder-up
Alf Claringbold, rivet heater 1927–39
Bill Cork, holder-up 1930s
Ernie Cripps 1920s hand
Goff Dane, rivet heater
Arthur Dunn, riveter pre-war
Len Emptage, holder-up
Fred Fox 1920–3
Jack Fletcher, hand
Charlie Frost 1920s–30s
Fred Gerard, rivet heater 1920s–30s
Charlie Godden, hand & machine 1918–
George Gulliford, rivet heater 1922–24
Hatch brothers, hand
Harry Hall, from Dartmouth
"Cherry" Hills 1930s–
Percy Hoad, rivet boy
Mr Hutton, rivet boy
Bill Jemmett 1941–67
Tom Jordan from 1926
Mr Millard 1920s
Wilfred Moon, riveter from 1930s
Harry Packman, also burning
Frank Pearce, holder-up
"Rasher" Phipps, rivet heater 1940s
Mr Puddock, riveter
Ella Reynolds, rivet heater in war
Fred Saunders, rivet boy
Wally Service, hand
Charlie Shipp, riveter 1920–50
Sid Smith, later to Dartmouth
Chris (Joe) Sunley, holder-up 1920s–
Harry Sunley 1930s–
Tom Tanton, rivet boy 1920s
Charlie Taylor, Chairman of Boilermakers
Harry Thomas, holder-up
Bill Tucker, holder-up
Sid Uden
Fred Weaver, gone by 1934
Jim Weaver, from start
John Weaver, rivet boy 1920s
Charlie Weedon, from Dartmouth
"Ginger" Woodward hand

Power House
Bill Cornelius 1940–
Bill Holmes
Cyril Meadows
Tom Smith briefly

Canteen
Vi Birch
Eva Blackman
Una Carter 1940–4
Daisy Ely
Mrs Flowers, washing up
Mrs Meadows, cook WWII
Dot Smith

Fitting shop (some in AUEW)
Geoff Athawes
Alf Baker
Nelson & Ernie Beer
Mr Bellinger, foreman in 1918
Bill Bishop 1920s
Alf Bodicker, charge hand 1920s
Jim Burnett, from Dartmouth 1930s
John Care
Hugh Chambers, plumber
Bert Collins, to Northfleet 1918–27
Geoff Cookson
Brian Couchman 1960s
Alan Coulson
Colin Coulson
Ian Coulson
Eric Curling, to Canterbury Tech.
Arthur Cutler, during war
Bill Davy 1920s
George Ferguson
Stanley Flowers 1932–54
Lionel George 1930s
Don Gibbons
Fred Green
Mr Harvey 1940s
Alf Hitchon, early Chief Engineer
Pat Hudson 1923, turner
Barry Jordan late 1950s
Dave Jordan 1940s–50s
George Juniper, pipe-fitter
Brian Kennett 1950s
Alec King (also office staff)
Jacob Korenbrander
Jock Law
Keith Lawrence
Norman Martin, pipe-fitter
Fred Meopham 1940s
Dominic Nacci, under Hudson
Archie Osborne, under Ron Smith
Stan Owen 1920s
George Partis, sureal winches
Don Pinnington 1940s, to J.W. Cook
Don Pullen post war
Bob Punyer
Sid Raines 1930s–60s, turner
John Richardson, Eng. Director 1967–70
Cyril Salmon, sureal winches

Don Saunders 1940s
Bill Shields 1918 – , Chief Engineer
Charlie Shrubsole
Harry Smith 1920s
Ron Smith till end
Arthur Sparrow
Frank Sparrow 1931 – 48
Ken Starling
Henry Sutton before war
Bert Taylor, esp. BOT items
Charlie Thunstrom
John Wass 1918 –
Percy Wass began 1918, Bolinders
Ron Waters 1940s
Bert "Bud" Wensley in war, sureal winches
Bill and Fred Flory 1920s on *Lee-Lee* and *Linton*
Jack Wheeler, apprentice fitter 1920s
Jim Waters 1920s
Robert Wraight 1963 – 68

Lorry/Crane Drivers (some TGWU)
"Slim" Bailey, crane driver
Tom Boodle (also on gate)
Ted French
Cecil Gardner
Charlie Hadlow, tractor driver 1950s
Jim Harvey, also a labourer
Charlie Lennard
Harry Smith, lorry driver
Chris Tyler 1924 – 68

Blacksmith's Forge
Ernie Bottle, striker 1940s
Jim Fettes, gone by 1951
Bill Hudson 1930s
Fred Liddle, early
Tom Mann 1920s
Alf Partridge 1930s
Harold Summers 1950s
"Peggy" Wildish

Concrete Ships 1917 – 20
Charlie Carter
Austin Cornelius
Mrs Epps
Mr Farmer, supervisor
Charlie Godden
Mrs Heyland
George Ledner
May Post
W.F. Shields
Mrs Skipper
Ida Wade
Edie Wade
Captain Smith
Joe Wade, engineer foreman

Stores
Albert Boorman during war, chief storekeeper
Nellie Bowden during war
Margaret Bulley during war
Alec Featherstone early on, checker
Sam Graham, preceded Featherstone
Joan Hudson (Marr Tindall)
Mrs Hudson, in charge of yard women
Percy Judges, Bolinders, then supplies and navigation equipment
Ernie Leakey 1940s
Spencer Marshman
Cecil Pile 1932 – 70 except war
Ada Sparrow during war, ex of Short's

Electrical work
Edgar Bulley up to 1950s
Jimmy Eames 1940s
Margery Head during war
Mr Hicks dismissed
Chas Marshall, Chief Electrician
Robert Tumber, after Bulley 1964 – 70

Welders
Brian Boorman 1950s
Bob Britton 1960s
Bert Crockford, snr & jnr
Alf Farndale
Colin Frake 1950s – 60s
Bert Jemmett 1940s
Freddy Liddle
Peter Maxey 1960s
Dennis Morgan
Andy Mullins 1960s
Mick Pearce 1950s
Roger Relf 1950s
Peter Revell 1950s
Ron Wade

Caulkers
Freddy Bolt early
George Hunter 1920s
Sam Joliffe 1920s
Jimmy Jordan 1920 – , hand then machine
Steve Millen, under Sam Joliffe
George Moon, utility man
Edward Porter, ex of Dartmouth
Bill Shead 1920s – war
Reg Shead before and after war
Jim Snowball 1920s
Charlie Taylor

Coppersmiths
Ralph Coker 1932 – , under Shields

Furnace
Micky Baldock 1920s –

Frank (Cockle) Cox 1940s
Joe Dane
Jack Finn 1936–, also plating
Clarence Hills
Mr Hodges early 1920s
Bob Johnson 1930s–, in charge
Mr MacNally briefly
Arthur Pordage
Robin Ramsden 1920s
Albert Simons 1920s
Dick Simons 1920s
Harry Tannyan
Frank Ward 1935–70
Bill Weaver snr early till 1940s
Charlie Woodward

Burners
Ernie Cripps, taught by Godden
Charlie Godden from 1920s, ex a riveter
Harry Packman (Boilermakers' Sec.) later in plating shop

Ambulance Man
Harry Ing from start

Wartime Women
Mrs Boodle, cleaner in carpenters shop
Ivy Brice
Elsie Claringbold
Joyce Dunk, wire-brushing
Millie French
Joan Hart, wire-brushing
Babs Holbrook
Peggy Liddle
Lucy Relf
Dot Smith, also canteen

Hydraulic "Windy" men
Harold Cremer 1920s
Bill Lennard
Horace Lennard 1940s–58
Stuart Swaffer

Stagers
Harry Coleman 1940s
Harry Downie 1940s
Frank Sagrott 1943–
Bill Seymour 1940s–50s

Paint Gangs
Bert Beeton 1950s
Bert Booty 1930s, also heavy gang
James Buffee 1950s
Bob Cooper during war
Jim Ellis 1930s
Jim Glass
Charlie Hill 1930s
Bill Jacobs till 1960s, also launch gang
Tommy Mallion
George Stevens 1920s
Bill Towells, paint sprayer 1920s–
Tim Tyler, paint sprayer 1920s–

Labourers
Harold Amos, steel gang in war
Albert "Rowdy" Ashby
Bill Bartlett 1950s
Charlie Beer, on shears
Albert Bones, platers' help
Charles Browning
Kath Christian, platers' mate in war
Donald Clancy
Tom Cummins 1937–9
Harry Fairbrace, snr & jnr
Charles Frake 1950s, ex bargemaster
Geoffrey French 1960s
Sam Galligan 1920s
Alec Gamble, platers' help & bolts
Frank Gregory, heavy gang
Stan Gregory
Toby Gurr, platers' mate 1950s
Jim Hams, sweeping up
Charlie Hart 1950s–60s
Sid Henderson, platers' help 1932–5
Lil Homewood, made brackets in war
Wally Hulks 1930s briefly
Ted Hunt, launch gang
George Hunter, launch gang, ex hand caulker
Tom Jacob
Ben & Ernie Jemmett 1920s
Bert Jemmett
Fred King, helped burners
Jack Last, launch gang 1950s–60s
Gladys Lawrence, wire-brushing
Albert Lennard, in loft
Reuben Lennard 1933–
Geoff Lightfoot post war
Ivo Lloyd, launch gang
Sam Matthews, launch gang and service bolts
Peter Moon, countersinker
Alf Patridge, laid out rivets
Bill Poole 1930s
Charlie Read 1930s
Darkie Rhodes, on service bolts
Mr Riley, countersinker
Arthur Salmon c.1920
George Smith, for fitting shop. AUEW chair
Sid Sparks 1940s
Jim Speed 1920s
Tommy Spinks, for fitting shop
Alf Stedman 1920s
George Stedman 1920s–
Jim Tanner during war
Herbie Taylor, in fitting shop
Chris Tyler
Clem Ware, rigger, charge hand of heavy gang
Bill Weaver, service bolts 1934–
Alf Willis, countersinker 1922–39
Fred Wise 1950s, furnace and shears
Mr Rooke, labourers foremen 1918

Appendix II
SHIPYARD PERSONNEL AS AT 25.2.70

This list does not account for broken service by journeymen, some of whom went to Bristol to work in the 1930s.

No.	Name	Occupation	Date started
11	Tumber, R.	Electrician	31.3.64
14	Shortland, D.	Electrician	4.3.68
33	Marshall, C.G.	Electrician	16.3.34
1	Lawrence, K.B.G.	Engineer	8.10.62
2	Jordan, B.F.	Engineer	2.6.69
15	Punyer, R.C.	Engineer	16.5.40
32	Rymer, F.	Engineer	18.8.69
38	Juniper, G.H.	Engineer	14.8.50
39	Wass, P.S.A.	Engineer	23.11.31
101	George, J.L.	Engineer	8.7.41
153	Ferguson, G.H.W.	Engineer	18.1.37
3	Clarridge, P.H.	Engineer App.	8.9.69
4	Jemmett, B.	Engineer App.	8.9.69
5	Muddiman, S.D.	Engineer App.	8.9.69
12	Williamson, J.R.	Engineer Lab.	23.6.64
16	Taylor, H.T.	Engineer Lab.	28.1.57
37	Pile, C.R.	Storekeeper	29.7.46
184	Fairbrace, H.I.	Labourer	4.3.46
22	Harvey, J.H.	Transport	7.3.61
43	Hadlow, C.P.	Transport	9.10.56
81	Lennard, C.A.J.	Transport	23.5.35
24	Saunders, P.R.	Shipwright App.	8.9.69
90	Downs, C.	Loft	29.4.30
40	Crockford, B.H.	Welder	7.12.60
42	Feaver, R.J.	Welder	26.8.63
61	Tappenden, P.M.	Welder	19.8.63
62	Downs, B.	Welder	27.8.62
84	Mullins, A.	Welder	17.2.69
20	Ellingworth, J.	Pl/Welder App.	15.8.66
21	Kay, T.	Pl/Welder App.	16.4.68
41	Wade, J.R.	Pl/Welder App.	20.4.65
52	Belsom, A.C.	Pl/Welder App.	18.8.69
56	Wise, F.	Pl. labourer	14.9.53
57	Gurr, A.	Pl. labourer	31.10.50
91	Lennard, R.	Pl. labourer	9.10.50
147	Bone, A.	Pl. labourer	26.3.41
96	Lennard, A.A.	Pl. labourer	20.4.53
149	Sagrott, F.G.	Pl. labourer Furnaceman	10.12.45
155	Ward, F.A.	Pl. labourer	28.10.35
75	Catt, D.A.	Gen. labourer	29.4.68
76	Tyler, W.J.	Gen. labourer	22.9.39
87	Gardner, R.E.H.	Gen. labourer	2.10.62
113	Hobbs, W.	Gatekeeper	14.1.46
127	Weaver, J.	Riveter	19.2.35
178	Jordan, T.H.	Riveter	27.5.40
139	Moon, G.A.	Riveter	8.11.48
74	Jemmett, W.J.	Riveter	10.7.39
116	Sunley, C.G.	Riveter	25.11.40
186	Cripps, E.A.	Burner	19.4.49

59	Shead, R.A.	Caulker	1.4.68
105	Jordan, J.O.	Caulker	17.9.40
44	Epps, B.F.	Driller	27.3.62
53	Flint, R.G.	Driller	1.12.41
112	Curling, E.F.	Driller	15.3.33
51	Wise, R.	Plater	29.12.52
58	Patching, M.	Plater	20.8.62
60	Gregory, F.E.	Plater	19.2.68
72	Jacobs, L.C.	Plater	6.8.41
107	Finn, J.	Plater	17.2.36
135	Wise, A.B.	Plater	5.3.40
158	Boodle, C.E.	Plater	2.2.40
23	Bushell, S.F.	Shipwright	18.8.52
70	Fowle, C.	Shipwright	28.4.41
89	Ellingworth, C.A.	Shipwright	19.8.63
25	Dennett, I.B.	Joiner	31.8.64
35	Richards, T.R.	Joiner	24.4.63
	Dron, R.	Staff	26.6.34
	Hutchinson, H.	Staff	14.11.32
	Smith, Miss M.	Staff	28.2.40
	Parfect, Miss F.M.	Staff	20.8.40
	Griggs, R.D.	Staff	8.8.49
	Stroud, A.E.	Staff	29.1.34
	Smith, R.	Staff	16.3.64
	Judges, P.B.	Staff	29.9.28
	Swan, S.W.J.	Staff	15.5.30
	Field, Miss A.G.	Staff	16.2.70
	Moat, E.	Staff	16.12.37
	Smith, Mrs D.L.	Canteen/caretaker	16.3.64
	Ellis, P.	Staff	31.12.62
	Hofer, R.	Staff	9.7.34
	Stroud, A.J.	Staff	11.1.27
	Wells, J.	Staff	30.7.34
	Topping, W.	Staff	22.1.34
	Richardson, J.R.	Staff	3.1.69
	Overs, J.	Staff	5.1.70

Year	Ship No.	Name	Destination/Owner	Dimensions L	B	D	Engines HP	MP	LP	ST	Boiler DIA	LEN	LBS	Type	Builder
1872	1.	*Emma Ludhorf*	R. Amur	145′0″	25′0″	4′6″	16″		19″	48″	4′9″	13′4″	75	Iron S Wheel	Godfroy, Hamburg
	2.	*Molodietz*	R. Amur	45′0″	8′9″	4′0″	6″			6″				Launch	
1875	3.	*Isabel*	Montevideo	100′0″	14′0″	8′0″	12″			16″	7′0″	10′0″		Cargo	
1877	4.	*Palm Flower*	Hereford	115′0″	17′0″	10′9″	17″		32″	20″	10′0″	8′4″		Yacht	Hamilton, Pt Glasgow
1879	5.	*Gleam*	Calcutta	49′3″	7′2″	3′6″	6″		6″	8″	2′6″	7′3″	120	Fast Launch	
1881	6.		London	65′0″	22′0″	6′0″								3 Hopper Barges	
	7.	*Progresso*	Para	55′5″	17′0″	10′9″	10″			10″				Amazon Launch	E. Hayes, Stony Stratfd
1882	8.	*Mauritius*	Mauritius	50′0″	11′0″	5′5″	9″		17″	14″	6′0″	8′0″	180	Launch	
1883	9.	*Colonel Smith*		135′0″	22′0″	11′3½″	23″		44″	28″			100	Trawler	T. Green, Blackwall
1884	10.	*Tilbury*	LTSR	140′0″	22′0″	9′0″	34″		34″	36″	11′6″	6′6″	30	Ferry	J&K Smit, Kinderdyk
	11.	*Otter*	Brisbane	128′0″	21′0″	11′0″	15½″		30″	20″	12′6″	10′6″	100	Sea Tug	Ramage & Ferguson, Leith
	12.	*Victoria*	Weymouth	165′0″	19′2″	8′9″	16″		28″	20″	9′6″	8′6″	80	Paddle	J&K Smit
	13.	*Ville Du Havre*	Havre	160′0″	20′0″	10′0″	25″		44″	36″	13′0″	10′0″	100	Paddle	
	14.	*Eagle*	London	82′4″	17′5″	9′7″	19″		35″	22″	10′6″	10′0″	90	River Tug	
	15.	*Awarua*	Bluff Harbour	110′0″	20′0″	10′0″	28″		28″	48″	8′6″	10′3″	40	Sea Tug	T. Green
	16.	*Mona*	Queenstown	97′0″	19′0″	11′0″	20″		40″	24″			90	Sea Tug	Smit & Zoon, Kinderdyk
	17.	*Falcon*	London	96′9″	19′3″	11′3″	20½″		40″	24″	12′0″	10′6″	100	Sea Tug	Morton, Leith
	18.	*Condor*	London	90′7″	19′3″	11′10″	20½″		40″	24″	11′8″	10′0″	100	Sea Tug	Morton, Leith
	19.	*Hawk*	London	96′9″	19′3″	11′3″	20½″		40″	24″	11′8″	10′0″	100	Sea Tug	
1885	20.	*Eagle*	Melbourne	125′0″	22′0″	15′3″	19″		35″	22″	14′0″	10′6″	100	Sea Tug	Pearce, Dundee
	21.	*Fairy*	Bristol	47′0″	10′0″	6′6″	7½″		14″	19″	5′3″	6′6″	100	River Tug	Newall, Bristol
	22.	*Fay*	Bristol	47′0″	10′0″	6′6″	7½″		14″	9″	5′3″	6′6″	100	River Tug	Newall, Bristol
	23.	*Dragon*	London	66′6″	13′6″	7′0″	12″		26″	18″	8′8″	9′6″	100	River Tug	Newall, Bristol
	24.	*Scorpion*	London	66′6″	13′6″	7′0″	12″		26″	18″	8′8″	9′6″	100	River Tug	Newall, Bristol
	25.	*Illaroq*	Sydney	165′0″	26′0″	14′5″	23″		44″	33″	14′0″	10′6″		Steel Collier	Wigham Richardson
	26.	*Cygnet*	Tasmania	120′0″	17′3″	9′0″	16″		32″	18″	10′6″	9′6″	100	Passenger	Davis & Clow, Abingdon
	27.	*Progresso*	Lake Managua	128′0″	24′0″	7′9″	11″		11″	12″	7′3″	5′0″	90	Passenger	
1886	28.	*Power*	Plymouth	110′0″	19′6″	11′10″	15″	23″	40″	27″	12′0″	10′3″	150	Sea Tug	Uskside, Newport
	29.	*Racer*	Queenstown	120′0″	20′0″	13′1″	15″	23″	40″	27″	12′6″	10′6″	150	Sea Tug	Boolds, Sharer Sunderld
	30.		Turkey	66′6″	13′3″	7′5″	11″		22″	16″	8′6″	7′0″	100	River Tug	
	31.		Turkey	66′6″	13′3″	7′5″	11″		22″	16″	8′6″	7′0″	100	River Tug	
	32.	*Rainham*	London	80′0″	17′0″	7′2″	11″		22″	16″	8′6″	7′0″	100	Steam Barge	Surridge, Millwall
	33.	*Beaver*	Brisbane	135′0″	21′6″	11′6″	17″		34″	18″	13′0″	10′6″	100	Sea Tug	Ramage & Ferguson
1887	34.	*Electra*	Sydney	160′0″	27′0″	11′6″	23″		42″	30″	15′6″	11′1″	80	Cargo	Russell, Pt Glasgow
	35.	*Python*	London	56′6″	13′3″	7′4″	11″		22″	15″	7′6″	7′0″	100	Barge Tug	E. Wales, Hull
	36.	*Wasp*	London	59′6″	14′0″	8′0″	11″		22″	18″	8′0″	8′6″	100	Barge Tug	E. Wales, Hull
	37.	*Adjundante*	Amazon	130′1″	24′10″	8′3″	16″		32″	20″	10′3″	9′6″		Cargo & Passenger	
1888	38.	*Advance*	Archangel	100′0″	21′0″	11′0″	13″	19″	33″	24″	11′6″	10′0″	160	Sea Tug	Harvey, Hayle
	39.	*Rio Branco*	Amazon	208′0″	31′0″	10′1″	13″	20″	32″	27″	15′6″	12′0″	160	Cargo & Passenger	Russell, Pt Glasgow
	40.	*Joao Alfredo*	Amazon	208′0″	31′0″	10′1″	13″	20″	32″	27″	15′6″	12′0″	160	Cargo & Passenger	Russell
	41.	*Marquesa de Saturnance*	Spain	290′0″	40′2″	21′4″	22″	35″	58″	42″	13′10″	10′6″	160	Cargo	
	42.	*Duquesa de Vista Hermosa*	Spain	290′0″	40′2″	21′4″	22″	35″	58″	42″	13′10″	10′6″	160	Cargo	
	43.	*Samson*	London	69′0″	16′0″	9′0″	15″		30″	20″	10′0″	9′0″	100	Barge Tug	Union Lighterage
1889	44.	*Alexandra*	Rio de Janeiro	163′6″	28′0″	12′2″	13″	20″	32″	24″	12′0″	10′0″	160	Cargo & Passenger	Seath, Rutherglen
	45.	*Colchester*	Colchester	85′0″	18′0″	7′0″	12½″		24″	16″	8′0″	8′0″	100	Cargo	Mackenzie, Blackwall
1890	46.	*Adder*	Calcutta	46′0″	9′0″	4′6″	6½″		13″	8″	5′6″	7′3″	120	Launch	
	47.	*Tabatinga*	Amazon	160′0″	26′0″	7′9″	9″	14″	22″	18″	10′6″	11′6″	150	Cargo & Passenger	Scott, Greenock
	48.	*Guanary*	Amazon	160′0″	26′0″	7′9″	9″	14″	22″	18″	10′6″	11′6″	150	Cargo & Passenger	Scott, Greenock

	Ship No.	Name	Destination/Owner	Dimensions L	B	D	Engines HP	MP	LP	ST	Boiler DIA	LEN	LBS	Type	Builder
	49.	*Madeira*	Amazon	170'0"	28'0"	8'6"	9"	14"	22"	18"	9'9"	12'0"	160	Cargo & Passenger	Russell
	50.	*Javary*	Amazon	170'0"	28'0"	8'6"	9"	14"	22"	18"	9'9"	12'0"	160	Cargo & Passenger	Russell
	51.	*Champion*	London	73'0"	16'0"	9'0"	15"		13"	20"	10'0"	9'0"	100	Barge Tug	Union Lighterage
	52.	*Oberon*	C. Howard & Sons	310'0"	41'0"	19'0"	23½"	38"	62"	42"	15'0"	10'6"	160	Cargo	Bartram, Sunderld
	53.	*Flamingo*	Amazon	160'0"	24'1"	8'3"	10"	16"	26"	18"			160	Passenger	
1891	54.	*Belem*	Amazon	170'0"	31'0"	8'9"	9"	14"	22"	18"	9'9"	12'0"		Amazon	Russell
	55.	*Labrea*	Amazon	170'0"	31'0"	8'9"	9"	14"	22"	18"	9'9"	12'0"		Amazon	Russell
	56.	*Penedo*	Brazil	200'0"	30'0"	13'0"	17"	27"	44"	30"	12'8"	13'6"	160	Cargo & Passenger	Grangemouth D'yd
	57.	*City of London*	London	135'0"	23'6"	12'3"	12½"	20"	33"	24"	10'9"	10'0"	160	Cargo	Schlesinger Davis
1892	58.	*Alert*	Cape Town	115'0"	21'0"	12'0"	19"		38"	24"	12'0"	9'9"	100	Seagoing Tug	Eltringham
	59.	*Onca*	Amazon	75'0"	19'0"	6'1"								Lighter	
	60.	*Surubirn*	Amazon	75'0"	19'0"	6'1"								Lighter	
	61.	*Jacaré*	Amazon	75'0"	19'0"	6'1"								Lighter	
	62.	*Capivera*	Amazon	75'0"	19'0"	6'1"								Lighter	
	63.	*Union*	London	64'0"	15'0"	8'0"	13"		26"	20"	9'6"	9'0"	120	Barge Tug	Union Lighterage
1894	64.	*Puri*	Calcutta	260'0"	33'10"	15'11"	21"	33"	52"	30"	18'0"	13'8"	160	Passenger	Gourlay, Dundee
1895	65.	*Leao*	Amazon	53'0"	10'0"	5'6"	8½"		14"	9"	6'0"	6'6"	100	Launch	
	66.	*Prudente de M*	Amazon	178'0"	29'0"	8'9"	10"	16"	26"	21"	10'3"	13'0"	160	Amazon	Russell
	67.	*Laura Sodre*	Amazon	178'0"	29'0"	8'9"	10"	16"	26"	21"	10'3"	13'0"	160	Cargo & Passenger	Russell
	68.	*Paes de Carvalho*	Amazon	178'0"	29'0"	8'9"	10"	16"	26"	21"	10'3"	13'0"	160	Cargo & Passenger	Gourlay
	69.	*Antonio Olyntho*	Amazon	178'0"	29'0"	8'9"	10"	16"	26"	21"	10'3"	13'0"	160	Cargo & Passenger	Gourlay
	70.	*Gaivota*	Amazon	123'0"	22"6"	8'6"	8"	13"	20"	18"	11'6"	9'9"	160	Amazon	Rodger, Pt Glasgow
	71.	*Titania*	C. Howard & Sons	350'0"	45'0"	24'4"	24"	39½"	65"	42"	12'9"	11'4"	160	Cargo	Bartram
	72.	*Beta*	Amazon	70'0"	14'0"	5'8"								Lighter	
1896	73.	*Flash*	Calcutta	90'0"	12'0"	6'2"	7½"	10½"	16½"	10"	W. Tube B.		225	Launch	
	74.	*Cassipore*	Amazon	153'0"	25'0"	10'6"	13"	20"	32"	24"	10'0"	12'0"	160	Cargo & Passenger	Russell
	75.	*Sapucaia*	Amazon	174'4"	28'0"	10'6"	9"	14"	22"	18"	10'0"	12'0"	160	Cargo & Passenger	Rodger
	76.	*Barcellos*	Amazon	174'4"	28'0"	10'6"	9"	14"	22"	18"	10'0"	12'0"	160	Cargo & Passenger	Rodger
	77.	*B. Constant*	Amazon	80'0"	12'6"	6'3"	8"		14"	10"	6'3"	7'6"	130	Amazon	
	78.	*Perseverance*	Preston	120'8"	22'7"	11'0"	17"		34"	24"	H.S. 1792		100	Sea Tug	Allsop, Preston
	79.	*Alagoas*	Amazon	82'0"	22'6"	7'6"								Lighter	
	80.	*Bahia*	Amazon	82'0"	22'6"	7'6"								Lighter	
	81.	*Cera*	Amazon	60'0"	17'3"	6'0"								Lighter	
	82.	*Pernambuca*	Amazon	60'0"	17'3"	6'0"								Lighter	
	83.	*Resolute*	Bristol	71'0"	15'9"	9'0"	14"		28"	22"	9'3"	10'3"	120	Tug	Stothert, Bristol
	84.	*Reliance*	Bristol	71'0"	15'9"	9'0"	14"		28"	22"	9'3"	10'3"	120	Tug	Stothert
	85.	*Margaret*	London	71'0"	15'9"	9'0"	14"		28"	22"	9'3"	10'3"	120	Tug	Rennie, Greenwich
	86.	*Sutton*	London	314'0"	44'0"	23'3"	22½"	37"	61"	42"				Cargo	Rodger
	87.	*Ulverston*	London	314'0"	44'0"	23'3"	22½"	37"	61"	42"				Cargo	Rodger
1898	88.	*Wallsend*	Sydney	165'0"	27'0"	13'6"	21"		45"	33"	13'6"	10'6"	120	Cargo	Murdoch & Murray
	89.	*Beatrice*	London	350'0"	45'0"	26'9"	24"	39½"	65"	42"	13'9"	11'4"	160	Cargo	
	90.	*Hero*	London	75'0"	18'6"	11'6"	16"		35"	24"	12'0"	10'0"	130	River Tug	Union Lighterage
1899	91.	*Campos Selles*	Amazon	238'0"	35'6"	11'9"	15"	23"	38"	24"	11'0"	18'0"	175	Cargo & Passenger	
	92.	*Justo Chermont*	Amazon	238'0"	35'6"	11'9"	15"	23"	38"	24"	11'0"	18'0"	175	Cargo & Passenger	
	93.	*Augusto Montgo*	Amazon	145'6"	29'0"	9'0"	12½"	20"	32"	24"	13'0"	10'0"	175	Cargo & Passenger	Rodger
	94.	*Quaty*	Amazon	88'6"	16'0"	5'6"								Lighter	
	95.	*Peruguica*	Amazon	88'6"	16'0"	5'8"								Lighter	
	96.			86'0"	20'0"	12'0"								Caisson	
1900	97.	[illegible]	King's Lynn	65'0"	15'6"	8'0"	12"		24"	16"	8'3"	8'6"	135	Tug	

	98.	*Maud*	London	70'0"	17'0"	9'6"	15"		32"	20"	11'0"	9'6"	120	Tug	Rennie
	99.	*Antonio Lemos*	Amazon	150'0"	30'0"	7'0"	21"		42"	54"	6'2"	11'9"	130	Sternwheeler	Lobnitz, Renfrew
	100.	*Cymbeline*	C. Howard & Sons	350'0"	45'0"	26'9"	24"	39½"	66"	42"	13'9"	11'4"	160	Cargo	Bartram
1901	101.	*Imogen*	C. Howard & Sons	360'0"	46'0"	28'6"	24½"	40"	66"	45"	14'3"	11'6"	180	Cargo	Bartram
	102.	*Conservator*	King's Lynn	96'0"	19'6"	11'0"	17"		35"	24"	12'0"	10'6"	130	Sea Tug	Allsop
	103.	*Battersea*	C. Howard & Sons	224'0"	32'0"	16'3"	16½"	27"	44"	30"	13'9"	10'6"	160	Cargo (Coal)	Dobson
	104.	*Juno*	London	70'0"	17'0"	9'0"	14"		30"	22"	10'6"	9'6"	120	River Tug	Lobnitz
	105.	*Dido*	Union Ltge	70'0"	17'0"	9'0"	14"		30"	22"	10'6"	9'6"	120	River Tug	Lobnitz
	106.	*Constance*	Thames S.T. Co.	51'6"	13'0"	6'4"	10"		17"	12"	6'0"	8'6"	100	River Tug	Otto & Zonern
	107.	*Victor*	Bristol	61'6"	15'0"	7'6"	11"		22"	15"	7'6"	8'6"	120	River Tug	Stothert
	108.	*Alert*	Spain	50'3"	11'0"	5'9"	9"		18"	10"	6'0"	6'0"	120	River Tug	
	109.	*Inca*	Amazon	150'0"	31'0"	6'0"	15"		27"	54"	6'6"	13'6"	140	Sternwheeler	Yarrow, Poplar
	110.	*Colibri*	Amazon	39'11"	8'9"	3'10"	5½"		5½"	7"	4'6"	5'6"	100	Launch	Yarrow, Poplar
	111.	*Sydney*	(C.S.R.Co.) Sydney	62'0"	11'3"	4'4"	7"		14"	9"	6'0"	7'6"	120	Launch	
1905	112.	*Desterro*	Manaos	45'0"	9'0"	4'6"	6"	11'	8"		5'0"	5'6"	120	Launch Tug	Rowhedge I W
	113.	*Prompt*	Colchester	100'0"	19'6"	8'6"	13"		26"	18"	9'6"	9'0"	130	Cargo	Hepple, S. Shields
	114.	*India do Brazil*	Amazon	150'0"	33'0"	10'0"	10"	16½"	26"	21"	13'6"	10'0"	180	Amazon T S	Murdoch & Murray
	115.	*Oyapock*	Amazon	150'0"	26'0"	10'6"	12½"	20"	32"	24"	13'0"	10'6"	175	Amazon	Rodger
	116.	*Rio Mar*	Amazon	204'0"	35'6"	10'9"	14"	21½"	35"	24"	13'9"	16'0"	175	Amazon T S	Gourlay
	117.	*Enfield*	Thames S.T. Co.	76'9"	13'3"	4'9"								Canal Barge	F. Braby & Co.
	118.	*Waltham*		76'9"	13'3"	4'9"								Canal Barge	
	119.	*Cheshunt*		76'9"	13'3"	4'9"								Canal Barge	
	120.	*Elliott*	London Bunker Co.	46'0"	15'0"	5'9"					6'0"	5'6"	100	Whipping Barge	De Ritter
	121.	*T.C. Lighter No.11*		80'0"	25'0"	9'6"	8½"		8½"	12"	7'0"	8'6"	120	Lifting Lighter	Rennie
	122.	*T.C. Lighter No.12*		80'0"	25'0"	9'6"	8½"		8½"	12"	7'0"	8'6"	120	Lifting Lighter	Rennie
	123.		Bangkok	105'0"	23'0"	9'0"								Towing Lighter	Otto & Zonern
	124.		Bangkok	105'0"	23'0"	9'0"								Towing Lighter	Otto & Zonern
	125.		Bangkok	105'0"	23'0"	9'0"								Towing Lighter	Otto & Zonern
	126.	*Ban Hong Liong*	Bangkok	227'9"	35'0"	16'10"	16"	26"	43"	30"	12'9"	11'4"	175	Cargo Steamer	Montrose
	127.		Bangkok	43'0"	8'6"	4'6"								Launch Frames	Otto & Zonern
	128.		Bangkok	36'6"	6'6"	4'6"								Launch Frames	Otto & Zonern
	129.		Bangkok	62'6"	16'0"	6'0"								T.S. Launch	A.W. Robertson
	130.		Bangkok	40'0"	10'0"	4'0"								Swim Lighter	Otto & Zonern
	131.		Bangkok	86'0"	16'0"	9'4"								Launch Frames	Otto & Zonern
	132.	*Redcap*	Thames S.T. Co.	80'6"	21'0"	7'1"								Swim Barge	
	133.	*Redcar*		80'6"	21'0"	7'1"								Swim Barge	
	134.	*Redbreast*		80'6"	21'0"	7'1"								Swim Barge	
	135.	*Redwing*		80'6"	21'0"	7'1"								Swim Barge	
	136.	*Redcoat*		80'6"	21'0"	7'1"								Swim Barge	
	137.	*Redstart*		80'6"	21'0"	7'1"								Swim Barge	
	138.	*Broxburn*	Thames S.T. Co.	76'9"	13'3"	4'9"								Canal Barge	F. Braby
	139.	*Ware*		76'9"	13'3"	4'9"								Canal Barge	
	140.	*Hertford*		76'9"	13'3"	4'9"								Canal Barge	
1906	141.	*Rennie (ex Rene)*	London	32'0"	7'0"	3'6"	5"		9"	6"	3'10"	4'9"	120	Launch	Napier, So'ton
	142.	*Prompt*	Colchester	110'0"	21'0"	9'0"	14"		28"	20"	10'6"	9'3"	130	Coasting Steamer	Hepple, S. Shields
	143.		Bangkok	105'0"	23'0"	9'0"								Towing Lighter	Otto & Zonern
	144.		Bangkok	105'0"	23'0"	9'0"								Towing Lighter	Otto & Zonern
	145.		Bangkok	105'0"	23'0"	9'0"								Towing Lighter	Otto & Zonern
	146.	*Agnes*	Thames S.T. Co.	71'0"	18'0"	9'10½"	14"		30"	22"	11'3"	9'6"	130	Barge Tug	Koopman, Dordrecht
	147.	*Laju*	Bangkok	20'0"	5'0"	3'0"	10 B.H.P. Motor							Motor Launch	
	148.	*Brani*	Bangkok	30'0"	5'9"	3'8"	15 B.H.P. Motor							Motor Launch	
	149.		Bangkok	40'0"	10'0"	4'0"								Swim Lighter	Otto & Zonern

	Ship No.	Name	Destination/Owner	Dimensions L	B	D	Engines HP	MP	LP	ST	Boiler DIA	LEN	LBS	Type	Builder
	150.		Bangkok	40′0″	10′0″	4′0″								Swim Lighter	Otto & Zonern
	151.		Bangkok	40′0″	10′0″	4′0″								Swim Lighter	Otto & Zonern
	152.		Howarth Erskine, Bangkok	45′0″	8′6″	4′0″								Launch Frames	Otto & Zonern
	153.	*Imperatrize Theresa*	Amazon								9′0″	5′0″	180	Donkey Boiler	
	154.	*Perseverance*	Amazon								9′0″	5′0″	180	Donkey Boiler	
	155.	*Esperance*	Amazon								9′0″	5′0″	180	Donkey Boiler	
	156.	*Betty*	Hay's Wharf	82′0″	21′6″	10′6″	14″	21½″	35″	24″	13′6″	10′0″	175	Barge Tug	Cran, Leith
	157.	*Tupy*	Amazon	150′0″	33′0″	10′0″	10″	16½″	26½″	21″	13′9″	10′6″	175	Amazon T.S.	Murdoch & M.
	158.	*Aymore*	Amazon	150′0″	33′0″	10′0″	10″	16½″	26½″	21″	13′9″	10′6″	175	Amazon T S	Murdock & M
	159.	*Andira*		130′5″	28′0″	9′0″	12½″	20″	32″	24″	13′9″	10′6″	175	Amazon	Rodger
	160.	*Teffe*		130′5″	28′0″	9′0″	12½″	20″	32″	24″	13′9″	10′6″	175	Amazon	Rodger
	161.		Bangkok	43′0″	8′6″	4′6″								Towing Lighter	Otto & Zonern
	162.		Bangkok	36′6″	6′6″	4′0″								Launch Frames	Rowhedge I W
	163.	*Melba*	S. Williams, London	78′0″	19′9″	7′3″								Swim Barge	Thames I W
	164.	*Medea*		78′0″	19′9″	7′3″								Swim Barge	
	165.	*Melita*		78′0″	19′9″	7′3″								Swim Barge	
	166.	*Mantua*		78′0″	19′9″	7′3″								Swim Barge	
	167.	*Mecca*		78′0″	19′9″	7′3″								Swim Barge	
	168.	*Mersea*		78′0″	19′9″	7′3″								Swim Barge	
	169.	*Medina*		78′0″	19′9″	7′3″								Swim Barge	
	170.	*Medusa*		78′0″	19′9″	7′3″								Swim Barge	
	171.	*Majorca*		78′0″	19′9″	7′3″								Swim Barge	
	172.	*Minorca*		78′0″	19′9″	7′3″								Swim Barge	
	173.	*Monica*		78′0″	19′9″	7′3″								Swim Barge	
	174.	*Madeira*		78′0″	19′9″	7′3″								Swim Barge	
	175.	*Oriente*	Manaos	40′0″	8′0″	4′3″	5″		10″	6″	4′9″	5′6″	120	Launch Tug	
	176.	*Macadam*	Gt Yarmouth	97′0″	22′6″	8′4″								Coasting Steamer	Union Lighterage
	177.	*Toro*	London	71′0″	17′6″	10′0″	14″		30″	22″	10′6″	9′6″	130	Barge Tug	
	178.	*Rani*	Fiji	108′0″	24′0″	9′0″	11½″	18″	29½″	18″				Engines	
	179.	*Natal*	Manaos	45′0″	11′0″	4′3″								Towing Lighter	Rowhedge I W
	180.		Amazon	20′0″	5′0″	2′5″	5½ B.H.P. Motor							Motor Launch	
	181.	*Petrel*	Kedah	28′0″	6′0″	3′0″	15 B.H.P. Motor							Motor Launch	
	182.	*Sara Thompson*		40′0″	8′8″	3′10″	5″		10″	6″	4′6″	5′6″	130	Launch Tug	Rowhedge I W
1907	183.	*Darent*	R. Thames	96′0″	23′0″	12′9″	14″	21½″	35″	24″	13′6″	10′6″	180	Dredging Tender	Ferguson
	184.	*Ravensbourne*	Thames Conservancy	77′0″	17′0″	9′0″	14″		30″	22″	11′3″	9′6″	140	Survey Launch	Cox, Falmouth
	185.	*Senador Flexa*	Manaos	50′0″	10′9″	4′9″	7″		14″	9″	5′6″	6′0″	130	Launch Tug	Rowhedge I W
	186.	*Vikay*	Bangkok	70′0″	16′6″	5′9″	9½″		18″	12″	6′6″	7′0″		Steam Lighter	Otto & Zonern
	187.	*Arturo Holland*	Uruguay	36′0″	9′9″	4′0″	6″		11″	8″	4′9″	5′3″	120	Ferry Launch	Rowhedge I W
	188.	*Silverio Nery*	Manaos	45′0″	9′3″	4′6″	6″		12″	10″	5′3″	5′9″	130	Launch Tug	Napier, So'ton
	189.		Howarth Erskine, Bangkok	36′0″	7′6″	3′9″								Launch Frames	Rowhedge I W
	190.	*Ember*	London	45′0″	11′3″	5′10″	8″		16″	10″	6′0″	7′0″	120	Launch Tug	Forrest, Wyvenhoe
	191.		for 'Darent'	16′6″	5′0″	2′3″	8 B.H.P. Motor							Motor Launch	Rowhedge I W
	192.	*Halo*	Hay's Wharf	81′10″	21′5″	7′6″								Swim Barge	Rennie
	193.	*Keppel*		81′10″	21′5″	7′6″								Swim Barge	
	194.	*Nesbitt*		81′10″	21′5″	7′6″								Swim Barge	
	195.	*Hood*		81′10″	21′5″	7′6″								Swim Barge	
	196.	*Zuyder Zee*		81′10″	21′5″	7′6″								Swim Barge	Pot Bros, Holland

	197.	*Van Tromp*		81'10"	21'5"	7'6"								Swim Barge	
	198.	*De Hoek*		81'10"	21'5"	7'6"								Swim Barge	
	'99.	*Van Dyck*		81'10"	21'5"	7'6"								Swim Barge	
	200.	*De Ruyter*		81'10"	21'5"	7'6"								Swim Barge	
	201.	*Van Loon*		81'10"	21'5"	7'6"								Swim Barge	
	202.	*Oetzes*		81'10"	21'5"	7'6"								Swim Barge	
	203.	*De Wit*		81'10"	21'5"	7'6"								Swim Barge	
	204.	*Enriqueta*	Rio								9'6"	9'6"	200	Marine Boiler	
	205.	*Villa Riobranco*	Para	30'0"	7'9"	3'9"	5"		10"	6"	4'0"	5'0"	100	Launch	Rowhedge I W
	206.	*Marreca*	Amazon	100'0"	20'0"	7'0"								Lighter	Finch, Chepstow
	207.	*Mutum*		100'0"	20'0"	7'0"								Lighter	
	208.	*Papagaio*		80'0"	17'0"	6'0"								Lighter	
	209.	*Periquito*		80'0"	17'0"	6'0"								Lighter	
	210.		Bangkok	40'0"	10'0"	4'0"								Swim Lighter	Otto & Zonern
	211.	*Adur*	Cowes	39'3"	9'6"	5'0"	6"		12"	8"	5'0"	5'6"	135	Seagoing Tug	Forrest
	212.	*The Collector*	Karachi	90'0"	20'0"	8'11"	12"		24"	18"	12'0"	10'6"	130	Twin Screw Tug	Eltringham
	213.	*Felisimo Soares*	Rio	72'10"	16'3"	7'6"	11"		22"	14"	8'9"	8'9"		1903 and	
	214.	*Andorinha*	Rio	68'0"	12'3"	6'0"	11"		22"	14"				1904	
	215.	*Active*	Bristol	61'6"	15'0"	7'6"	11"		22"	15"	7'6"	8'6"	120	River Tug	Stothert
	216.	*Ada*	Monaco	50'0"	9'8"	4'6"	6"		12"	8"	5'3"	5'9"	130	Launch Tug	Collis, So'ton
	217.	*Guida*		50'0"	10'9"	4'9"	7"		11"	9"	5'6"	6'0"	130	Launch Tug	Rowhedge I W
	218.	*Gaivota*	Amazon								11'6"	9'9"	160	Marine Boiler	Gourlay
	219.	*Cassipore*	Amazon								12'0"	10'0"	160	Marine Boiler	
	220.	*Miramar*	Manaos	60'0"	11'9"	5'10"	8"		16"	10"	6'6"	7'0"	130	Launch Tug	Rowhedge I W
1908	221.		Bangkok	70'0"	16'6"	7'6"								Towing Lighter	Rennie
	222.		Bangkok	70'0"	16'6"	7'6"								Towing Lighter	
	223.	*F.M.S. No.1*	Malay States	70'0"	16'6"	7'6"								Towing Lighter	Hepple, S. Shields
	224.	*F.M.S. No.2*		70'0"	16'6"	7'6"								Towing Lighter	
	225.	*F.M.S. No.3*		70'0"	16'6"	7'6"								Towing Lighter	
	226.	*F.M.S. No.4*		70'0"	16'6"	7'6"								Towing Lighter	
	227.	*Titania*									8'6"	8'0"	80	Donkey Boiler	
	228.	*Lobato de Miranda*	Para	50'0"	12'0"	5'2"	9"		18"	12"	6'6"	7'0"	120	Wooden Launch	
	229.	Para C.C.1	Para	18'0"	5'9"	2'3"								Steel Ship's Boat	Mechan
	230.	*Para C.C.2*		18'0"	5'9"	2'3"								Steel Ship's Boat	
	231.	*Para C.C.3*		18'0"	5'9"	2'3"								Steel Ship's Boat	
	232.	*Thuns I*	Rio	105'0"	24'0"	9'0"								Towing Lighter	Tranmere Bay D Co.
	233.	*Thuns II*		105'0"	24'0"	9'0"								Towing Lighter	
	234.	*Thuns III*		105'0"	24'0"	9'0"								Towing Lighter	
	235.	*Thuns IV*		105'0"	24'0"	9'0"								Towing Lighter	
	236.	*Dagmar*	Rio				11"		22"	14"	8'3"	8'6"	120	Engines	
	237.		New Zealand				8"	13"	21"	16"				Engines	
	238.	*Arica*	Chile	32'0"	8'0"	3'10"	5"		10"	6"	3'9"	4'9"	140	Ferry Launch	Rowhedge I W
	239.		Rio	71'0"	22'0"	9'0"								Towing Lighter	Hepple
	240.		Rio	71'0"	22'0"	9'0"								Towing Lighter	
	241.	*Espadarte*	Para	65'6"	15'3"	7'9"	13"		26"	18"	9'0"	9'0"	130	Seagoing Tug	Hepple
	242.	*Princeza*	Para	24'0"	5'9"	3'0"	4"		8"	5"	2'9"	4'0"	120	Launch Tug	
	243.	*Brimsdown*	Thames S.T. Co.	77'1"	13'3"	4'9"								Canal Barge	Pot Bros
	244.	*Bow*		77'1"	13'3"	4'9"								Canal Barge	
	245.	*Bromley*		77'1"	13'3"	4'9"								Canal Barge	
	246.	*Stratford*		77'1"	13'3"	4'9"								Canal Barge	
	247.	*Tottenham*		77'1"	13'3"	4'9"								Canal Barge	
	248.	*Old Ford*		77'1"	13'3"	4'9"								Canal Barge	

	Ship No.	Name	Destination/Owner	Dimensions L	B	D	Engines HP	MP	LP	ST	Boiler DIA	LEN	LBS	Type	Builder
	249.	*San Pedro*	Valparaiso	84′5″	20′0″	10′8″	11″		22″	16″	7′6″	8′0″	130	Machinery	
	250.	*Esperanto*	Lisbon	115′0″	22′0″	9′10½″	14″		28″	20″	10′6″	9′3″	130	Coasting Steamer	Cochrane, Selby
	251.	*Plover*	Thames S.T. Co.	57′0″	16′6″	5′3″								Swim Punt	Pot Bros
	252.	*Pelican*		57′0″	16′6″	5′3″								Swim Punt	
	253.	*Palm*		57′0″	16′6″	5′3″								Swim Punt	
	254.	*Peggy*		57′0″	16′6″	5′3″								Swim Punt	
	255.	*Pigeon*		57′0″	16′6″	5′3″								Swim Punt	
	256.	*Penguin*		57′0″	16′6″	5′3″								Swim Punt	
	257.	*Python*		57′0″	16′6″	5′3″								Swim Punt	
	258.	*Peace*		57′0″	16′6″	5′3″								Swim Punt	
	259.	*Phyllis*		57′0″	16′6″	5′3″								Swim Punt	
	260.	*Pixie*		57′0″	16′6″	5′3″								Swim Punt	
	261.	*Panther*		57′0″	16′6″	5′3″								Swim Punt	
	262.	*Piper*		57′0″	16′6″	5′3″								Swim Punt	
1909	263.	*Mary Blake*	Thames S.T. Co.	71′0″	19′0″	9′10½″	14″		30″	22″	11′3″	9′6″	130	Barge Tug	Hepple
	264.	*Adur II*		70′0″	15′9″	7′9″	13″		26″	18″	9′6″	9′0″	130	Seagoing Tug	Hepple
	265.	*Romano*		80′0″	17′9″	9′10″	15″		32″	22″	11′0″	9′9″	130	Seagoing Tug	Hepple
	266.	*Para C.C.IV*		16′0″	4′9″	2′0″								Steel Ship's Boat	
	267.	*Para C.C.V*		16′0″	4′9″	2′0″								Steel Ship's Boat	
	268.	*Para C.C.VI*		16′0″	4′9″	2′0″								Steel Ship's Boat	
	269.	*Lady Alice*		53′0″	13′0″	5′3″	6½″		13″	8″	5′6″	5′6″	110	Water Boat	
	270.	*Fortaleza*		35′0″	8′6″	4′4″	5″		10″	6″	4′6″	4′9″	120	Launch Tug	Rowhedge I W
	271.	*Guiomar*		30′0″	7′9″	3′11″	5″		10″	6″	4′0″	5′0″	130	Launch	Rennie
	272.	*Guanabacao*	Cuba	140′0″	55′0″	14′2½″	19″		42″	27″	Bablock & Wilcox			Ferry Steamer	Laird, Birkenhd
	273.	*Pioneer*													
	274.	*Resource*	Cochin	56′0″	12′9″	6′6″	10″		20″	14″	7′9″	7′9″	130	Tug	Rennie
	275.	*Ibeno*	African Assoc. Co.	16′0″	5′3″	2′0″								Ship's Boat	Ditton
	276.	*Guanabacoa I*	Cuba	20′0″	6′0″	2′9″								Ship's Boat	Rowhedge I W
	277.	*Guanabacoa II*		20′0″	6′0″	2′9″								Ship's Boat	Rowhedge I W
	278.	*Knot*	Nile	14′0″	5′9″	2′0″								Sailing Boat	Rowhedge I W
	279.	*Sujcop*	Cuba	30′0″	7′9″	3′3″	23 B.H.P. Motor							Motor Launch	J. Bacon
	280.		China	40′0″	11′6″	4′0″	10 B.H.P. Motor							Bucket Dredger	Hepple
	281.	*Aspeab*	Bombay	101′0″	25′0″	7′6″								Towing Lighter	Hepple
	282.	*Luxmi*		101′0″	25′0″	7′6″								Towing Lighter	
	283.	*Mehi Daria*		101′0″	25′0″	7′6″								Towing Lighter	
	284.	*Shamrock*					11″		24″	18″	7′6″	8′9″	160	Machinery	
	285.	*Thistle*					11″		24″	18″	7′6″	8′9″	160	Machinery	
	286.	*Sabia*									5′6″	12′3½″	120	Loco Boiler	For Laird
	287.	*Bheestie*	Felixstowe Dock & Rly Co.	67′0″	15′6″	8′0″	12″		24″	18″	8′6″	8′0″	130	Water Boat & Tug	Hepple
	288.	*Puss*		57′0″	16′6″	5′3″								Swim Punt	
	289.	*Pern*		57′0″	16′6″	5′3″								Swim Punt	
	290.	*Parrot*		57′0″	16′6″	5′3″								Swim Punt	
	291.	*Pearl*		57′0″	16′6″	5′3″								Swim Punt	
	292.	*Priestman*	London	122′0″	26′6″	5′3″	16″		34″	23″	12′0″	10′0″	135	Grab Hopper Bge	Smith's Dock
	293.	*Voevoda*	Vladivostock	75′0″	16′6″	8′6″	14″		30″	21″	10′6″	9′9″	130	Icebreaking Tug	Hepple
	294.		Para	16′0″	4′9″	2′0″								Ship's Boat	Mechan
	295.		Para	12′0″	4′6″	2′0″								Ship's Boat	Mechan
	296.	*Catita*	Manaos	30′0″	7′9″	3′11″	5″		10″	6″	4′0″	5′0″	130	Launch Tug	Rowhedge I W

	297.	*Rachel*	Manaos	30′0″	7′9″	3′11″	5″		10″	6″	4′0″	5′0″	130	Launch Tug	Rowhedge I W
	298.		Thames S.T. Co.	77′9″	14′6″	3′6″								Canal Barge	Piper, Greenwich
	299.			77′9″	14′6″	3′6″								Canal Barge	
	300.			77′9″	14′6″	3′6″								Canal Barge	
	301.			77′9″	14′6″	3′6″								Canal Barge	
	302.			77′9″	14′6″	3′6″								Canal Barge	
	303.			77′9″	14′6″	3′6″								Canal Barge	
	304.			16′0″	5′0″	2′0″								Steel Ship's Boa	
	305.			16′0″	5′0″	2′0″								Steel Ship's Boa	
	306.			16′0″	5′0″	2′0″								Steel Ship's Boa	
	307.	*Fleche*		30′0″	7′0″	3′3″	16 B.H.P. Motor							Motor Launch	J. Bacon
	308.		Cochin	50′0″	15′0″	5′6″								Towing Lighter	Tranmere Bay D Co.
	309.		Cochin	50′0″	15′0″	5′6″								Towing Lighter	
	310.		Cochin	50′0″	15′0″	5′6″								Towing Lighter	
	311.		Cochin	50′0″	15′0″	5′6″								Towing Lighter	
1910	312.	*Travers*	Trinidad	70′0″	16′0″	7′0″	50 B.H.P. Bolinder							Motor Barge	Rennie
	313.		Smith's Dock	60′0″	16′0″	7′0″								Towing Lighter	
	314.		Smith's Dock	60′0″	16′0″	7′0″								Towing Lighter	
	315.		Smith's Dock	45′0″	14′6″	5′6″								Towing Lighter	
	316.		Smith's Dock	45′0″	14′6″	5′6″								Towing Lighter	
	317.		Smith's Dock	80′0″	20′6″	8′0″								Towing Lighter	
	318.		Smith's Dock	80′0″	20′6″	8′0″								Towing Lighter	
	319.	*Shamrock*		70′0″	15′9″	7′9″	11″		24″	18″	7′6″	8′9″	160	Tug Hull	Smith's Dock
	320.	*Thistle*		70′0″	15′9″	7′9″	11″		24″	18″	7′6″	8′9″	160	Tug Hull	Smith's Dock
	321.	*Beluga*		56′0″	12′9″	6′6″	10″		20″	14″	7′9″	7′9″	130	Tug	Smith's Dock
	322.	*Helvetia*		56′0″	12′9″	6′6″	10″		20″	14″	7′9″	7′9″	130	Tug	Smith's Dock
	323.		Cochin	45′0″	14′6″	5′6″								Towing Lighter	Smith's Dock
	324.		Cochin	45′0″	14′6″	5′6″								Towing Lighter	
	325.		Cochin	45′0″	14′6″	5′6″								Towing Lighter	
	326.		Cochin	45′0″	14′6″	5′6″								Towing Lighter	
	327.	*Retiro*		23′0″	5′9″	2′10″	2½″		5″	4″	3′0″	2′8″	140	Launch	
	328.	*Crestuma*		50′0″	10′9″	4′9″	7″		14″	9″	5′6″	6′0″	130	Launch Tug	Rowhedge I W
	329.														
	330.	*Cabral*	Amazon	174′6″	35′0″	9′3″	14″	22¼″	37″	24″	15′6″	10′6″	180	Steamship	Napier & Miller, Glasgow
	331.	*Barao de Cameta*		160′0″	33′0″	7′0″	13″		26″	20″	12′6″	10′6″	130	Amazon T S	Smith's Dock
	332.	*Charioteer*		85′6″	17′0″	9′6″	16″		32″	21″	11′0″	10′0″		Tug	Hepple
	333.	*Rio Jamary*	Amazon	145′0″	30′0″	8′6″	12¼″	20″	34″	22″	13′0″	10′0″	130	Passenger	
	334.										8′0″	9′0″	120	Marine Boiler	
	335.	*Sao Pedro*	Para	185′0″	25′0″	7′0″	15″		30″	22″	11′6″	10′6″	130	Amazon	Napier & Miller
	336.			26′6″	5′6″	2′10″	4″		8″	9″	2′6″	3′9″	120	Wood Launch (Machinery only)	
	337.	*Olga*	Theiner & Janowitzer	93′0″	24′0″	2′6″								Pontoon Lighter	Orr, Watt & Co.
	338.	*Carmen*		93′0″	24′0″	2′6″								Pontoon Lighter	
	339.	*Corola*		93′0″	24′0″	2′6″								Pontoon Lighter	
	340.	*Codo*		93′0″	24′0″	2′6″								Pontoon Lighter	
	341.	*Lassance Cunha*	Iborocahy & Co.	100′0″	20′0″	4′0″	10″		17½″	36″	4′0″	13′8″	160	Sternwheeler	Rowhedge
	342.	*Bodmin*		64′0″	17′9″	6′0″								Swim Barge	
	343.	*Boscastle*		64′0″	17′9″	6′0″								Swim Barge	
	344.	*Bude*		64′0″	17′9″	6′0″								Swim Barge	
	345.	*Cambourne*		64′0″	17′9″	6′0″								Swim Barge	
	346.	*Lelant*		64′0″	17′9″	6′0″								Swim Barge	
	347.	*Malpes*		64′0″	17′9″	6′0″								Swim Barge	

Ship No.	Name	Destination/Owner	Dimensions L	B	D	Engines HP	MP	LP	ST	Boiler DIA	LEN	LBS	Type	Builder
348.	*Smith's Dock No.2*		45′0″	9′0″	4′6″	40 B.H.P. Bolinder							Teak Motor Launch	Ditton
349.	*Curanja*	Manaos	120′0″	24′0″	7′0″	15″		30″	22″	11′6″	10′0″	130	Amazon	Napier & Miller
350.	*Maracaru*	Viama Silva	40′0″	8′8″	3′10″	5″		10″	6″	4′6″	5′6″	130	Launch Tug	Rowhedge I W
351.		Smith's Dock	20′0″	6′0″	2′5″								Life Boat	Seamless Steel Boat Co.
352.		Smith's Dock	20′0″	6′0″	2′5″								Life Boat	
353.		Smith's Dock	20′0″	6′0″	2′5″								Life Boat	
354.		Smith's Dock	20′0″	6′0″	2′5″								Life Boat	
355.	*Maravilha*		23′0″	5′9″	3′0″	2½″		5″	3½″	3′0″	2′8″	140	Launch	
356.	*Sentinella*		23′0″	5′9″	3′0″	2½″		5″	3½″	3′0″	2′8″	140	Launch	
357.	*Sylvia*		23′0″	5′9″	3′0″	2½″		5″	3½″	3′0″	2′8″	140	Launch	
358.	*Acuria*	Para	46′6″	11′6″	5′0″								House Lighter	Rennie
359.	*Magnus*	Thames S.T. Co.	77′3″	20′3″	7′0″								Swim Barge	Pot Bros
360.	*Magog*		77′3″	20′3″	7′0″								Swim Barge	
361.	*Main*		77′3″	20′3″	7′0″								Swim Barge	
362.	*Maplin*		77′3″	20′3″	7′0″								Swim Barge	
363.	*Maria*		77′3″	20′3″	7′0″								Swim Barge	
364.	*Mascot*		77′3″	20′3″	7′0″								Swim Barge	
365.	*Mastiff*		77′3″	20′3″	7′0″								Swim Barge	
366.	*Medina*		77′3″	20′3″	7′0″								Swim Barge	
367.	*Midge*		77′3″	20′3″	7′0″								Swim Barge	
368.	*Milly*		77′3″	20′3″	7′0″								Swim Barge	
369.	*Mouse*		77′3″	20′3″	7′0″								Swim Barge	
370.	*Myrtle*		77′3″	20′3″	7′0″								Swim Barge	
371.	*Candido Rondon*	Goodwin & Ferreira	40′0″	8′3″	4′2″	5″		10″	7″	4′3″	5′3″	140	Launch	Rowhedge
372.	*Curanjita*		23′0″	5′9″	3′0″								Launch	
373.	*Barcellos*		45′10″	10′6″	4′9″								House Lighter	Orr, Watt & Co.
374.			20′0″	6′0″	2′6″								Ship's Boat	J.Mc Gill
375.	*Acacias*		45′10″	10′6″	4′9″								House Lighter	Orr, Watt & Co.
376.			45′0″	10′6″	4′9″								House Lighter	
377.	*Lydia*		95′0″	21′0″	12′6″	14″	22″	36″	24″	14′0″	10′0″	180	Tug	Hepple
378.	*Bolinders I*	Singapore	50′0″	11′6″	5′9″	80 B.H.P. Bolinder							Motor Launch	
379.			23′0″	5′9″	3′0″	2½″		5″	3½″	3′10″	2′8″	140	Launch	Orr, Watt & Co.
380.			23′0″	5′9″	3′0″	2½″		5″	3½″	3′10″	2′8″	140	Launch	
381.		GCC				15 B.H.P. Bolinder							Motor Barge	
382.		GCC				15 B.H.P. Bolinder							Motor Barge	
383.		GCC				15 B.H.P. 1 cyl. Bolinder							Motor Barge	
384.		GCC				15 B.H.P. 1 cyl. Bolinder							Motor Barge	
385.	*Bournville I*		70′0″	7′0″	5′10″	15 B.H.P. 1 cyl. Bolinder							Motor Canal NBT	Orr, Watt & Co.
386.	*Bournville II*		70′0″	7′0″	5′10″	15 B.H.P. 1 cyl. Bolinder							Motor Canal NBT	Orr, Watt & Co.
1911 387.	*Atbara*					2 – 7x10 Winches							Coal Whipping Barge	
388.	*Europe*					2 – 7x10 Winches							Coal Whipping Barge	
389.		H.J. Stockton	30′0″	8′0″	5′3″	30 B.H.P. 2 cyl. Bolinder							Motor Tug	
390.	*Lola*	Chile	59′0″	13′2″	6′10″	10″		22″	15″	8′3″	8′0″	130	Tug	Hepple
391.	*Tamate*	New Guinea	45′0″	10′0″	6′0″ Draft	50 B.H.P. 2 cyl. Bolinder							Motor MissyBt	Vosper
392.	*Baroemoen*	Singapore				25 B.H.P. 1 cyl. Bolinder								
393.	*Father Mark*	Singapore	55′0″	15′6″	8′0″	24 B.H.P. 2 cyl. Bolinder							Fishing Boat	
394.	*Hidden Treasure*	Singapore	55′0″	15′6″	8′0″	24 B.H.P. 2 cyl. Bolinder							Fishing Boat	
395.	*Glacier*	Port Said	42′0″	11′10″	4′6″ Hold	20 B.H.P. 2 cyl. Bolinder								

399.	*May Baby*		74′0″	18′8″		120 B.H.P. 2 cyl. Bolinder						Motor Drifter	J. Weatherhead
400.	*Banba IV*	J. McMahon	34′0″	12′0″		16 B.H.P. 2 cyl. Bolinder						Aux Yacht	
401.	*Inhambane*		51′6″	12′0″	6′0″	8″		16″	12″	7′0″	6′9″	120	Steel Tug	Pimblott
402.	*Auxiliar*		51′6″	12′0″	6′0″	8″		16″	12″	7′0″	6′9″	120	Steel Tug	Pimblott
403.	*Etive*	Nelson	42′0″	9′0″	6′0″	40 B.H.P. 2 cyl. Bolinder						Motor Launch	A. Mylne, Glasgow
404.	*Acima*	S. Gomez	61′6″	12′9″	6′2″	9″		18″	12″	7′7″	7′6″	130	Launch Tug	Hepple
405.	*Macaury*	Peru	46′6″	11′6″	5′1″								House Lighter	Otto
406.	*Cheerful*	Canadian Western	76′0″	18′0″	8′9″	13″		26″	18″	10′0″	9′6″	130	Wooden Tug	Fraser Mills
407.	*Fearful*		76′0″	18′0″	8′9″	13″		26″	18″	10′0″	9′6″	130	Wooden Tug	
408.		Campbell	148′0″	33′6″	12′0″								Hopper Barge	
409.		Campbell	148′0″	33′6″	12′0″								Hopper Barge	
410.	*Ogarita*	Hawarden	88′0″	19′0″	7′6″	120 B.H.P. 2 cyl. Bolinder							Motor Barge	Hepple
411.	*29 B*	Murphy, Ireland				15 B.H.P. 1 cyl. Bolinder							Tug	
412.	*Antrim*	H. Grey	75′6″	19′0″	7′6″								Swim Barge	Pot Bros
413.	*Bantry*		75′6″	19′0″	7′6″								Swim Barge	
414.	*Clonmel*		75′6″	19′0″	7′6″								Swim Barge	
415.	*Connaught*		75′6″	19′0″	7′6″								Swim Barge	
416.	*Durboyne*		75′6″	19′0″	7′6″								Swim Barge	
417.	*Galway*		75′6″	19′0″	7′6″								Swim Barge	
418.	*Leitrim*		75′6″	19′0″	7′6″								Swim Barge	
419.	*Monaghan*		75′6″	19′0″	7′6″								Swim Barge	
420.	*Queenstown*		75′6″	19′0″	7′6″								Swim Barge	
421.	*Sligo*		75′6″	19′0″	7′6″								Swim Barge	
422.	*Tyrone*		75′6″	19′0″	7′6″								Swim Barge	
423.	*Wicklow*		75′6″	19′0″	7′6″								Swim Barge	
424.		G.C.C. Ireland				15 B.H.P. 1 cyl. Bolinder							Motor Barge	
425.	*9 M*		60′0″	12′6″	5′6″	15 B.H.P. 1 cyl. Bolinder							Motor Canal Barge	Finch
426.	*Athy*		60′0″	12′6″	5′6″	15 B.H.P. 1 cyl. Bolinder							Motor Canal Barge	
427.	*Lidador*		40′0″	8′0″	3′′10″	5″		10″	6″	4′6″	5′6″	130	Launch Tug	
428.	*Rose Macrone*	Waterford	60′0″	12′6″	5′6″	15 B.H.P. 1 cyl. Bolinder							Motor Canal Barge	
429.	*Remo*	Para	40′0″	9′0″	4′3″	6″		12″	8″	5′0″	5′6″	130	Launch	Hepple
430.	*Mapuare*		50′0″	12′6″	4′6″								House Lighter	Otto
431.	*Lingueta*	Pernambuco	61′0″	15′6″	6′6″	30 B.H.P. 2 cyl. Bolinder							Wood Motor Barge	Immisch
432.	*America*	Parnahyoa	70′0″	15′6″	5′6″	8″		14″	27″	7′3″	7′6″	150	Side Wheel Tug	Rowhedge I W
433.	*Columbia*	Parnahyoa	72′0″	18′6″	5′0″								Towing Lighter	Hepple
434.	*Venezuela*		72′0″	18′6″	5′0″								Towing Lighter	
435.	*Tury*	Maranhao	38′6″	8′9″	4′3″	5″		10″	6″	4′0″	4′2″	140	Launch	Rowhedge
436.	*Dreadful*	Vancouver	118′0″	25′0″	15′6″	15″	23½″	38″	30″	15′0″	12′0″	180	Tug	Hepple
437.	*Transport*		52′6″	11′6″	5′0″	24 B.H.P. 2 cyl. Bolinder							Demonstration	
438.	*Fitzroy*	Sydney	170′0″	30′0″	11′3″	14″	23″	38″	24″	15′6″	10′6″	180	Pass & Cargo	Napier & Miller
439.	*Nitrogen*		79′0″	17′0″	7′0″	80 B.H.P. 2 cyl. Bolinder							Tar Barge	Hepple
440.	*Papakura*	Dumbarton	60′0″	11′6″	6′0″	80 B.H.P. 4 cyl. Bolinder							Motor Yacht	McLaren Bros
441.		J.B. Hearne, New Ross				20 B.H.P. 1 cyl. Bolinder								
442.	*34 B*	New Ross				10 B.H.P. 1 cyl. Bolinder								
443.	*S.H.T. No.6*	Swansea	110′0″	29′0″	10′6″								Hopper Barge	Beorgenhout
444.	*S.H.T. No.7*		110′0″	29′0″	10′6″								Hopper Barge	N.V. Scheepswerf
445.	*S.H.T. No.8*		110′0″	29′0″	10′6″								Hopper Barge	De Jong
						2 sets								
446.	*Tury Assu*	Maranhao	200′0″	32′0″	12′0″	14″		30″	18″	15′6″	10′6″	150	Pass & Cargo T S	Napier & Miller
						2 sets								
447.	*Curupuru*	Maranhao	200′0″	32′0″	12′0″	14″		30″	18″	15′6″	10′6″	150	Pass & Cargo T S	
						2 sets								

	Ship No.	Name	Destination/Owner	Dimensions L	B	D	Engines HP	MP	LP	ST	Boiler DIA	LEN	LBS	Type	Builder
	448.	*Caxias*	Maranhao	104′6″	24′0″	6′0″	14″		22″	28″	9′6″	9′6″	150	Paddle	Hepple
	449.	*Isleford*	Glasgow	142′0″	25′6″	11′6″	320 B.H.P. 4 cyl. Bolinder							Motor Coaster	Ardrossan
	450.	*Enid*		50′0″	10′9″	4′6″	7″		14″	9″	5′6″	6′0″	130	Launch Tug	Rowhedge I W
	451.	*Motor Barge M6*					15 B.H.P. 1 cyl. Bolinder								
	452.	*Nawab*	Cambay	52′0″	12′0″	6′0″	9″		18″	12″	7′0″	7′6″	130	Tug	Hepple
	453.	*Flores*	Maranhao	82′0″	23′0″	4′0″								Lighter in Sections	Mechan
	454.	*Boa-Vista*		82′0″	23′0″	4′0″								Lighter in Sections	
	455.	*18 B*	Portadown				15 B.H.P. 1 cyl. Bolinder								
	456.	*Linda*	F.M. & C.	70′6″	7′0″	4′2″	15 B.H.P. 1 cyl. Bolinder							Motor Canal NBT	
	457.	*Anapuru*	Nunas	40′0″	9′0″	4′0″	5″		10″	6″	4′0″	4′9″	150	Launch	Rowhedge
	458.	*Fortaleza*	Goodwin & Ferreira	30′0″	8′6″	4′0″	5″		10″	6″	4′0″	5′0″	140	Launch	Simpson Strickland
	459.	*Pioneer*	France	63′0″	14′8″	6′0″	20 B.H.P. 1 cyl. Bolinder							Tug	.
	460.	*Innisagra*		67′0″	18′3″	9′0″	80 B.H.P. 2 cyl. Bolinder							Cargo Vessel	McGregor
	461.	*Inniscroon*		67′0″	18′3″	9′0″	80 B.H.P. 2 cyl. Bolinder							Cargo Vessel	
	462.	*Innisdhu*		67′0″	18′3″	9′0″	80 B.H.P. 2 cyl. Bolinder							Cargo Vessel	
	463.	*Esperanza*	Montevideo	60′0″	13′0″	6′8″	120 B.H.P. 2 cyl. Bolinder							Tug	
	464.	*Shamrock*	Portadown				20 B.H.P. 1 cyl. Bolinder								
	465.	*4 B*	Portadown				15 B.H.P. 1 cyl. Bolinder								
	466.	*31 B*	Portadown				15 B.H.P. 1 cyl. Bolinder								
	467.	*Bann Queen*	Robb, Ireland				15 B.H.P. 1 cyl. Bolinder								
							2 sets								
	468.	*Trusty*	Swansea	85′0″	24′0″	13′0″	15″		32″	24″	15′6″	10′6″	140	T S Tug	
	469.	*Thelma*	Whitehill				30 B.H.P. 1 cyl. Bolinder							Yacht	J. & G. Forbes
	470.	*Inniskea*	Glasgow	93′0″	18′9″	9′6″	120 B.H.P. 2 cyl. Bolinder							Cargo Vessel	Leith
	471.	*8 M*	G.C.C. Ireland				15 B.H.P. 1 cyl. Bolinder								
	472.	*13 M*	G.C.C.				15 B.H.P. 1 cyl. Bolinder								
	473.	*1 M*	G.C.C.	50′0″	12′6″	5′6″	15 B.H.P. 1 cyl. Bolinder							Canal Barge	
	474.	*7 M*	G.C.C.	60′0″	12′6″	5′6″	15 B.H.P. 1 cyl. Bolinder							Canal Barge	
	475.	*11 M*	G.C.C.	60′0″	12′6″	5′6″	15 B.H.P. 1 cyl. Bolinder							Canal Barge	
	476.	*12 M*	G.C.C.	60′0″	12′6″	5′6″	15 B.H.P. 1 cyl. Bolinder							Canal Barge	
1912	477.	*11 B*	G.C.C.	60′0″	12′6″	5′6″	15 B.H.P. 1 cyl. Bolinder							Canal Barge	
	478.	*Osric*	Severn & Canal Co.	80′0″	17′6″	8′0″	80 B.H.P. 2 cyl. Bolinder							Canal Barge	Simpson Strickld
	479.	*Shamrock*		55′0″	15′0″	8′0″	25 B.H.P. 1 cyl. Bolinder							Yacht	Scott, Falmouth
	480.	*Georgia*	Manaos	46′6″	10′0″	5′0″								Launch Tug	Simpson Strickld
	481.	*Brooke*	Manaos	44′0″	12′0″		15 B.H.P. 1 cyl. Bolinder								
	482.	*Earlshall*	Liverpool				120 B.H.P. 2 cyl. Bolinder							Barque	Thompson, Dundee
	483.	*St Columbia*	Killybegs	60′0″	17′0″	8′9″	50 B.H.P. 2 cyl. Bolinder								
	484.	*Itu*	Elder Dempster	55′0″	13′0″	5′3″	2 – 25 B.H.P. 1 cyl. Bolinder							T S Motor Lighter	Pimblott
	485.	*Clovis*	Parnahyoa	46′6″	10′0″	4′0″	7″		14″	9″	5′6″	6′0″	130	Launch Tug	Rowhedge
	486.		Admiralty				80 B.H.P. 2 cyl. Bolinder								
	487.	*Kamuri*	Dunedin	42′0″	9′8″		24 B.H.P. 2 cyl. Bolinder							Yacht	New Zealand
	488.	*Volage*	Vosper				15 B.H.P. 1 cyl. Bolinder								
	489.	*M 1*	Elder Dempster	29′4″	8′9″	4′3″	20 B.H.P. 1 cyl. Bolinder							S S Launch	Pimblott
	490.	*Mario*	Pernambuco	40′0″	9′0″	4′3″	40 B.H.P. 2 cyl. Bolinder							Motor Launch	Rose St, Inverness
							2 sets								
	491.	*Ronietta*	Elder Dempster	74′0″	17′6″	7′6″	9″		18″	10″	11′0″	9′6″	130	Cargo Steamer	Pimblott
	492.	*Caupolican*		30′0″	7′0″	3′6″	15 B.H.P. 1 cyl. Bolinder							Wood Launch	Simpson Strickland
	493.	*34 B*					15 B.H.P. 1 cyl. Bolinder								
	494.	*42 B*					15 B.H.P. 1 cyl. Bolinder								

497.	*Fantasy*					15 B.H.P. 1 cyl. Bolinder					
498.	*Dowley*		70′6″	16′0″	4′9″ Draft	40 B.H.P. 2 cyl. Bolinder					
499.	*Lady Sybil*	Hay's Wharf	76′0″	20′6″	11′10″	16″ 34″ 24″	13′0″	10′0″	140	Barge Tug	Hepple
500.		Wayte				15 B.H.P. 1 cyl. Bolinder					
501.	*Eva*		63′0″	14′8″	6′6″	20 B.H.P. 1 cyl. Bolinder				Barge	
502.	*Nimble*		45′0″	10′6″	5′0″	10 B.H.P. 1 cyl. Bolinder				Motor Barge	Simpson Strickland
503.	*Serlo*	Severn & Canal Co.	80′0″	17′6″	8′0″	80 B.H.P. 2 cyl. Bolinder				Canal Barge	Simpson Strickland
504.	*Wave*		90′0″	16′9″	6′3″	2 – 20 B.H.P. 1 cyl. Bolinder				T S Barge	
505.		Vosper	40′0″	9′0″		40 B.H.P. 2 cyl. Bolinder				Police Launch	
506.		Vosper	40′0″	9′0″		40 B.H.P. 2 cyl. Bolinder				Police Launch	
507.		Grand Canal C. Co.	60′0″	16′0″	6′3″	15 B.H.P. 1 cyl. Bolinder				Canal Barge	
508.		Grand Canal C. Co.	60′0″	16′0″	6′3″	15 B.H.P. 1 cyl. Bolinder				Canal Barge	
509.		Grand Canal C. Co.	60′0″	16′0″	6′3″	15 B.H.P. 1 cyl. Bolinder				Narrow Boat	
510.		Grand Canal C. Co.	60′0″	16′0″	6′3″	15 B.H.P. 1 cyl. Bolinder				Narrow Boat	
511.		Grand Canal C. Co.	60′0″	16′0″	6′3″	15 B.H.P. 1 cyl. Bolinder				Narrow Boat	
512.		Grand Canal C. Co.	60′0″	16′0″	6′3″	15 B.H.P. 1 cyl. Bolinder				Narrow Boat	
513.		Grand Canal C. Co.	60′0″	16′0″	6′3″	15 B.H.P. 1 cyl. Bolinder				Narrow Boat	
514.		Grand Canal C. Co.	60′0″	16′0″	6′3″	15 B.H.P. 1 cyl. Bolinder				Narrow Boat	
515.		Grand Canal C. Co.	60′0″	16′0″	6′3″	15 B.H.P. 1 cyl. Bolinder				Narrow Boat	
516.		Grand Canal C. Co.	60′0″	16′0″	6′3″	15 B.H.P. 1 cyl. Bolinder				Narrow Boat	
517.		Grand Canal C. Co.	60′0″	16′0″	6′3″	15 B.H.P. 1 cyl. Bolinder				Narrow Boat	
518.		Grand Canal C. Co.	60′0″	16′0″	6′3″	15 B.H.P. 1 cyl. Bolinder				Narrow Boat	
519.	*Mamfe*		70′0″	15′0″	4′0″					Sternwheeler	Pimblott
520.	*Hawarden Castle*		45′9″	10′7″		30 B.H.P. 2 cyl. Bolinder				Cruising Yacht	
521.	*Leopard*		70′0″	7′0″	4′6″	15 B.H.P. 1 cyl. Bolinder				Narrow Boat	Fellows M & C
522.	*Lynx*		70′0″	7′0″	4′6″	15 B.H.P. 1 cyl. Bolinder				Narrow Boat	Fellows M & C
523.	*Speedy*		71′6″	7′1″	4′3″	20 B.H.P. 1 cyl. Bolinder					
524.		Vosper	40′0″	9′0″		40 B.H.P. 2 cyl. Bolinder				Police Launch	
525.	*Lotus*		70′6″	7′0″	4′2″	10 B.H.P. 1 cyl. Bolinder				Canal Barge	F M & C
526.		Vosper	40′0″	9′0″		40 B.H.P. 2 cyl. Bolinder				Police Launch	
527.	*Ben Johnson*		111′0″	22′0″	9′3″	120 B.H.P. 2 cyl. Bolinder				Tank Barge	Vlaardigen
528.	*Barao de Irirocahy*		90′0″	19′0″	4′6″	10″ 17½″ 36″			160	Paddle Tug	
529.	*Lion*		70′6″	7′0″	4′2″	15 B.H.P. 1 cyl. Bolinder				Narrow Boat	F M & C
530.	*Lapwing*		70′6″	7′0″	4′2″	15 B.H.P. 1 cyl. Bolinder				Narrow Boat	
531.	*Lark*	Fellows M & C	70′6″	7′0″	4′2″	15 B.H.P. 1 cyl. Bolinder				Narrow Boat	
532.	*Quail*		70′6″	7′0″	4′2″	15 B.H.P. 1 cyl. Bolinder				Narrow Boat	F M & C Uxbridge
533.	*Lupin*		70′6″	7′0″	4′2″	15 B.H.P. 1 cyl. Bolinder				Narrow Boat	F M & C Saltby
534.	*Peacock*	Fellows M & C	70′6″	7′0″	4′2″	15 B.H.P. 1 cyl. Bolinder				Narrow Boat	
535.		Assam D Co	60′0″	10′0″	3′6″	50 B.H.P. 2 cyl. Bolinder				Sidewheeler	
536.	*Fulgens*	R. Thames	305′0″	42′0″	21′6″	22″ 36″ 60″ 42″	2x 15′6″	10′6″	180	Collier	Wood Skinner
537.		G. De Veer	36′3″	7′3″	3′4″	20 B.H.P. 2 cyl. Bolinder				Launch	
538.	*Father Mark II*		55′0″	15′6″	7′6″	40 B.H.P. 2 cyl. Bolinder				Fishing Boat	
539.	*Cassyana*		30′0″	7′9″	3′11″	5″ 10″ 6″	4′0″	5′0″	130	Launch Tug	Rowhedge
540.	*Jacy*		30′0″	7′9″	3′11″	5″ 10″ 6″	4′0″	5′0″	130	Launch Tug	Rowhedge
541.		Aberdeen	33′0″	9′2″	3′2″	12 B.H.P. 1 cyl. Bolinder				Ferry Boat	
542.	*Filo*		30′0″	8′0″	3′0″					Towing Lighter	Simpson Str
543.	*Porvenir*		59′0″	13′2″	6′10″	10″ 22″ 15″	8′3″	8′0″	130	Tug	Simpson Str
544.	*Lindola*		70′0″	7′0″	4′2″	10 B.H.P. 1 cyl. Bolinder				Narrow Boat	F M & C Saltby
545.	*Laurel*		70′0″	7′0″	4′2″	15 B.H.P. 1 cyl. Bolinder				Narrow Boat	F M & C

	Ship No.	Name	Destination/Owner	Dimensions L	B	D	Engines HP	MP	LP	ST	Boiler DIA	LEN	LBS	Type	Builder
	546.	*Lily*		70′0″	7′0″	4′2″	15 B.H.P. 1 cyl. Bolinder							Narrow Boat	F M & C
	547.	*Hidden Treasure II*		52′6″	15′9″	8′3″	40 B.H.P. 2 cyl. Bolinder							Fishing Boat	
	548.	*Juggler*		71′6″	18′9″	6′6″								Swim Barge	
	549.	*Jubilee*		71′6″	18′9″	6′6″								Swim Barge	
	550.	*Judge*		71′6″	18′9″	6′6″								Swim Barge	
	551.	*Julia*		71′6″	18′9″	6′6″								Swim Barge	
	552.	*Jumbo*		71′6″	18′9″	6′6″								Swim Barge	
	553.	*Jupiter*		71′6″	18′9″	6′6″								Swim Barge	
	554.	*Juno*		71′6″	18′9″	6′6″								Swim Barge	
	555.	*July*		71′6″	18′9″	6′6″								Swim Barge	
	556.	*Jumna*		71′6″	18′9″	6′6″								Swim Barge	
	557.	*Jungle*		71′6″	18′9″	6′6″								Swim Barge	
	558.	*Petrel*	Fellows M & C	70′0″	7′0″	4′2″	15 B.H.P. 1 cyl. Bolinder							Narrow Boat	
	559.	*Ilo No II*		60′0″	12′6″	5′6″	25 B.H.P. 1 cyl. Bolinder							Canal Barge	
	560.	*Primeira*		100′0″	23′6″	2′6″								Pontoon Lighter	
	561.	*Secunda*		100′0″	23′6″	2′6″								Pontoon Lighter	
	562.	*Terceira*		100′0″	23′6″	2″6″								Pontoon Lighter	
	563.	*Quarta*		100′0″	23′6″	2′6″								Pontoon Lighter	
	564.	*Antonio Condeiro*		35′0″	8′0″	2′0″	10 B.H.P. 2 cyl. Bolinder							Launch	
	565.	*S.H.T.6*		110′0″	29′0″	10′6″	Replaces Ship No. 443							Hopper Barge	
	566.	*Bunga*	Sarawak	91′0″	17′6″	8′6″	2 – 80 B.H.P. 2 cyl. Bolinders							T S Motor Tug	
	567.	*Colon*		59′0″	13′2″	6′10″	10″		22″	15″	8′3″	8′0″	130	Barge Tug	Ardrossan
	568.	*Panama*		82′0″	21′8″	8′6″								Swim Barge	
	569.	*Chicago*		82′0″	21′8″	8′6″								Swim Barge	
	570.	*Flacon*		80′0″	17′6″	7′9″	60 B.H.P. 2 cyl. Bolinder							Motor Barge	Leiderdorp
	571.	*America*		59′0″	13′2″	6′10″	10″		22″	15″	8′3″	8′0″	130	Barge Tug	Ardrossan
	572.	*Lettie*		81′6″	20′6″	10′10½″	15″		34″	24″	12′6″	10′0″	140	Tug	Bergenhout
	573.	*Bruno*		81′6″	20′6″	11′6″	17″		36″	24″	13′0″	10′0″	140	Tug	Bergenhout
1913	574.	*Linares*		82′0″	17′6″	8′0″	80 B.H.P. 2 cyl. Bolinder							Coaster	
	575.	*D'Emilia*		34′0″	8′9″	3′11″	5″		10″	6″	4′3″	5′3″	130	Launch Tug	Rowhedge
	576.	*The Miller*	London	81″0″	17′9″	8′3″	80 B.H.P. 2 cyl. Bolinder							Motor Barge	Leiderdorp
	577.	*Lindores*	Pernambuco	82′0″	17′6″	8′0″	80 B.H.P. 2 cyl. Bolinder							Coaster	
	578.		Goodwin & Ferreira	31′0″	6′0¾″	2′5½″								Whale Boat	
	579.	*Penguin*		52′6″	10′6″		40 B.H.P. 2 cyl. Bolinder								
	580.	*Brighstone*	Thames	75′0″	17′6″	7′9″	60 B.H.P. 2 cyl. Bolinder							Coaster	
	581.		Pacific Phosphate	28′0″	8′0″	3′10″	15 B.H.P. 1 cyl. Bolinder							Launch	
	582.	*Ilesha*		94′0″	17′0″	8′0″	2 – 50 B.H.P. 2 cyl. Bolinders							River Barge	Abdela & Mitchell
	583.	*Carita*		101′0″	21′6″	8′3″	120 B.H.P. Bolinder							Motor Barge	Abdela & Mitchell
	584.	*Fleurita*		108′6″	22′0″	9′0″	160 B.H.P. 2 cyl. Bolinder							Motor Barge (Coaster)	Abdela & Mitchell/ Rock Ferry
	585.	*Atair*	Buenos Aires	117′0″	16′6″	9′1½″	2 – 120 B.H.P. 2 cyl. Bolinders							Aux Yacht	Camper & Nicholson
	586.	*Lewes Castle*		102′6″	18′11″	8′6″	120 B.H.P. 2 cyl. Bolinder							Motor Barge	Leiderdorp
	587.		UE Singapore				20 B.H.P. 2 cyl. Bolinder								
	588.	*M 2*		32′0″	8′9″	4′3″	20 B.H.P. 1 cyl. Bolinder							Launch Tug	
	589.	*Ibusa*		59′0″	14′0″	8′6″	80 B.H.P. 2 cyl. Bolinder							Motor Barge	
	590.	*Duenna*		62′3″	10′0″	6′6″	2 – 20 B.H.P. 2 cyl. Bolinders							Yacht	
	591.	*Dolly*		24′0″	7′3″	4′6″	10 B.H.P. 1 cyl. Bolinder							Lugger	
	592.	*Launch III*		32′0″	8′9″	4′3″	20 B.H.P. 2 cyl. Bolinder							Launch Tug	

[illegible]		Elder Dempster	[illegible]	[illegible]	[illegible]	[illegible]				Launch Tug	
595.	*Fort Churchill*	Hudson Bay	80′9″	21′9″	9′1″	80 B.H.P. 2 cyl. Bolinder				Motor Lighter	
596.	*Ila*	W. Africa	140′6″	25′0″	10′0″	2 – 120 B.H.P. 2 cyl. Bolinders				Coaster	Hawthorn, Leith
597.	*Ife*	W. Africa	140′6″	25′0″	10′0″	2 – 120 B.H.P. 2 cyl. Bolinders				Coaster	Hawthorn
598.	*Panama*		60′0″	8′0″	5′0″	40 B.H.P. 2 cyl. Bolinder				Canal Tug	
599.	*Haycrone*		40′0″	7′0″	3′6″	20 B.H.P. 2 cyl. Bolinder				Launch	
600.		Foley Bros				30 B.H.P. 2 cyl. Bolinder					
601.	*Weda*		30′0″	8′0″	3′6″	10 B.H.P. 1 cyl. Bolinder				Launch	
602.	*Odlum*	Wayte				15 B.H.P. 1 cyl. Bolinder				Narrow Boat	
603.	*Muriel*		59′0″	13′2″	6′10″	10″ 22″ 15″	8′3″	8′0″	130	Steam Tug	Ardrossan
604.	*Sapho II*					20 B.H.P. 2 cyl. Bolinder				Yacht	
605.	*Quoin Island*		60′0″	14′0″	7′0″	60 B.H.P. 2 cyl. Bolinder				Launch Tug	
606.		NZSS	25′0″	6′0″	3′6″	5 B.H.P. 1 cyl. Bolinder				Launch	
607.		Pacific Phosphate	28′0″	8′0″	3′10″	20 B.H.P. 2 cyl. Bolinder				Launch	
608.		Pacific Phosphate	28′0″	8′0″	3′10″	20 B.H.P. 2 cyl. Bolinder				Launch	
609.	*Transport II*		85′0″	18′6″	9′0″	80 B.H.P. 2 cyl. Bolinder				Coaster	
610.	*Present Help*		28′4″	10′4″		8 B.H.P. 1 cyl. Bolinder				Fishing Boat	
611.	*Speedwell*	Thames	71′6″	7′1″	4′3″	20 B.H.P. 1 cyl. Bolinder				Canal Barge	Walker Bros
612.		Richard Farrell				20 B.H.P. 1 cyl. Bolinder				Barge	
613.	*Golden Fleece*					30 B.H.P. 2 cyl. Bolinder					
614.	*George*	Birmingham Canal	45′0″	6′0″	4′1½″	20 B.H.P. 1 cyl. Bolinder				Double Ended Tug	
615.		Elder Dempster				20 B.H.P. 1 cyl. Bolinder				Launch	
616.		Elder Dempster				20 B.H.P. 1 cyl. Bolinder				Launch	
617.		Elder Dempster				20 B.H.P. 1 cyl. Bolinder				Launch	
618.		Elder Dempster				20 B.H.P. 1 cyl. Bolinder				Launch	
619.		Elder Dempster				20 B.H.P. 1 cyl. Bolinder				Launch	
620.		Elder Dempster				20 B.H.P. 1 cyl. Bolinder				Launch	
621.	*Plover*	Fellows M&C	70′0″	7′0″	4′2″	15 B.H.P. 1 cyl. Bolinder					
622.	*Fort York*	Hudson Bay	80′9″	21′9″	9′1″	80 B.H.P. 2 cyl. Bolinder				Motor Lighter	Porthlevan
623.		Grand Canal C. Co.				15 B.H.P. 1 cyl. Bolinder				Narrow Boat	
624.		Grand Canal C. Co.				15 B.H.P. 1 cyl. Bolinder				Narrow Boat	
625.		Grand Canal C. Co.				15 B.H.P. 1 cyl. Bolinder				Narrow Boat	
626.		Grand Canal C. Co.				15 B.H.P. 1 cyl. Bolinder				Narrow Boat	
627.		Luftin				20 B.H.P. 1 cyl. Bolinder				Lighter	
628.	*Stella*					40 B.H.P. 2 cyl. Bolinder				Fishing Boat	
629.	*Aerotug II*		30′0″	8′0″	2′2″	16 B.H.P. 2 cyl. Bolinder				Aerial Propelled	
630.	*Felita*	Liverpool	103′0″	21′0″	10′6″	160 B.H.P. 2 cyl. Bolinder				Coaster	Abdela & Mitchell
631.	*St Dympna*		55′4″	16′0″	9′0″	40 B.H.P. 2 cyl. Bolinder				Fishing Boat	
632.		Chrome Co.				80 B.H.P. 2 cyl. Bolinder					
633.	*Aerotug I*		30′0″	8′0″	2′6″	15 B.H.P. 1 cyl. Bolinder				Aerial Propelled	
634.	*Lucy Mary*		53′9″		7′6″	40 B.H.P. 2 cyl. Bolinder				Fishing Boat	
635.	*Bird*					8 B.H.P. 1 cyl. Bolinder				Fishing Boat	
636.	*Bailey*		30′0″	6′10″	3′8″	16 B.H.P. 2 cyl. Bolinder				Pinnace	
637.	*Star of Mulroy*					65 B.H.P. 2 cyl. Bolinder				Fishing Boat	Pittenweem
						2 sets					
638.	*Mary Tavy*		96′0″	23′6″	11′6″	15″ 32″ 24″	15′0″	10′6″	140	Tug	
639.	*Elspeth*		35′0″	8′6″	2′3″	30 B.H.P. 2 cyl. Bolinder				Aerial Propelled	
640.		Baker & Startin	71′0″	22′0″	9′0″					Lighter	
641.		Elder Dempster				20 B.H.P. 1 cyl. Bolinder				Launch	
642.		Standard Oil Co.	96′0″	22′0″	5′6″	2 – 40 B.H.P. 2 cyl. Bolinders				Tanker	
643.	*Troth*		66′0″	18′0″	5′9″	50 B.H.P. 2 cyl. Bolinder				Fishing Boat	
644.	*Emperor*	Fellows M & C	70′0″	7′0″	4′2″	15 B.H.P. 1 cyl. Bolinder				Narrow Boat	

Ship No.	Name	Destination/Owner	Dimensions			Engines	Boiler			Type	Builder
			L	B	D	HP MP LP ST	DIA	LEN	LBS		
645.	*Raven*	Fellows M & C	70′0″	7′0″	4′2″	15 B.H.P. 1 cyl. Bolinder				Narrow Boat	
646.	*Rambler*	Fellows M & C	70′0″	7′0″	4′2″	15 B.H.P. 1 cyl. Bolinder				Narrow Boat	
647.	*Robin*	Fellows M & C	70′0″	7′0″	4′2″	15 B.H.P. 1 cyl. Bolinder				Narrow Boat	
648.	*Envoy*	Fellows M & C	70′0″	7′0″	4′2″	15 B.H.P. 1 cyl. Bolinder				Narrow Boat	
649.	*Rover*	Fellows M & C	70′0″	7′0″	4′2″	15 B.H.P. 1 cyl. Bolinder				Narrow Boat	
650.	*Venture*		30′0″	6′0″		16 B.H.P. 2 cyl. Bolinder				Launch	
651.	*Albert*		109′7″	25′1″	12′6″	120 B.H.P. 2 cyl. Bolinder				Ketch	
652.		HMS Fiscard				20 B.H.P. 1 cyl. Bolinder				Launch	
653.	*Industry*		62′0″	14′3″	6′0″	20 B.H.P. 1 cyl. Bolinder				Barge	
654.	*Tommy Atkins*		65′0″	15′6″	7′4″	80 B.H.P. 2 cyl. Bolinder				River Barge	
655.	*M 18*		170′0″	31′0″	12′2″	2 – 320 B.H.P. 4 cyl. Bolinders				Monitor	
656.	*Strathcona*		110′0″	24′0″	12′4″	80 B.H.P. 2 cyl. Bolinder				Aux Schooner	
657.	*HMS Indus*					30 B.H.P. 1 cyl. Bolinder					
658.	*Janus*		71′6″	7′1″	4′3″	15 B.H.P. 1 cyl. Bolinder					
659.	*Margaret*		36′0″	11′6″		12 B.H.P. 1 cyl. Bolinder				Fishing Boat	
660.	*Mary Fraser*					10 B.H.P. 1 cyl. Bolinder					
661.	*Attitete*					30 B.H.P. 2 cyl. Bolinder				Ferry Boat	
662.	*Atalanta*		123′0″	19′9″	8′4″	Supply of 120 B.H.P. 2 cyl. Bolinder				Motor Barge	
663.	*Indawgyi*					50 B.H.P. 2 cyl. Bolinder				Launch	
664.	*Cristo*		95′0″	19′0″	10′0″	120 B.H.P. 2 cyl. Bolinder				Coaster	Rennie Forrestt
665.	*M 19*		170′0″	31′0″	12′2″	Twin 320 B.H.P. Bolinders				Monitor	
666.	*M 20*		170′0″	31′0″	12′2″	Twin 320 B.H.P. Bolinders				Monitor	
667.	*M 23*		170′0″	31′0″	12′2″	Twin 320 B.H.P. Bolinders				Monitor	
668.	*M 26*		170′0″	31′0″	12′2″	Quad 120 B.H.P. Bolinders				Monitor	
669.	*M 27*		170′0″	31′0″	12′2″	Twin 160 + Twin 120 B.H.P. Bolinders				Monitor	
670.	*X 5*		105′6″	21′0″	7′6″	80 B.H.P. Bolinder				Lighter	Head Wrighton
671.	*X 6*		105′6″	21′0″	7′6″	40 B.H.P. Bolinder				Lighter	Head Wrighton
672.	*X 7*		105′6″	21′0″	7′6″	40 B.H.P. Bolinder				Lighter	Head Wrighton
673.	*X 199*		105′6″	21′0″	7′6″	40 B.H.P. Bolinder				Lighter	Head Wrighton
674.	*X 39*		105′6″	21′0″	7′6″	80 B.H.P. Bolinder				Lighter	Osbourne Graham
675.	*X 40*		105′6″	21′0″	7′6″	80 B.H.P. Bolinder				Lighter	
676.	*X 42*		105′6″	21′0″	7′6″	50 B.H.P. Bolinder				Lighter	Osbourne Graham
677.	*X 41*		105′6″	21′0″	7′6″	50 B.H.P. Bolinder				Lighter	
678.	*X 43*		105′6″	21′0″	7′6″	50 B.H.P. Bolinder				Lighter	
679.	*X 44*		105′6″	21′0″	7′6″	50 B.H.P. Bolinder				Lighter	
680.	*X 46*		105′6″	21′0″	7′6″	50 B.H.P. Bolinder				Lighter	Sunderland
681.	*X 45*		105′6″	21′0″	7′6″	50 B.H.P. Bolinder				Lighter	
682.	*X 47*		105′6″	21′0″	7′6″	50 B.H.P. Bolinder				Lighter	
683.	*X 59*		105′6″	21′0″	7′6″	Twin 30 B.H.P. Bolinder				Lighter	Sunderland S′Bld
684.	*X 60*		105′6″	21′0″	7′6″	Twin 30 B.H.P. Bolinders				Lighter	
685.	*X 61*		105′6″	21′0″	7′6″	Twin 30 B.H.P. Bolinders				Lighter	
686.	*X 62*		105′6″	21′0″	7′6″	Twin 30 B.H.P. Bolinders				Lighter	
687.	*X 63*		105′6″	21′0″	7′6″	Twin 30 B.H.P. Bolinders				Lighter	
688.	*X 64*		105′6″	21′0″	7′6″	Twin 30 B.H.P. Bolinders				Lighter	
689.	*M 25*		170′0″	31′0″	12′2″	Twin 320 B.H.P. Bolinders				Monitor	
690.	*M 28*		170′0″	31′0″	12′2″	Twin 320 B.H.P. Bolinders				Monitor	
691.	*Lynx*		65′8″	13′1″	7′8½″	120 B.H.P. Bolinder				Pilot Boat	
692.		D.E. Williams				15 B.H.P. Bolinder				Barge	

No.	Name	Owner	Length	Breadth	Depth	Engine	Type	Builder
[illegible]	[illegible]		[illegible]	[illegible]	[illegible]	[illegible]	[illegible]	
696.	*X 85*		105′6″	21′0″	7′6″	50 B.H.P. Skandia	Lighter	
697.	*X 82*		105′6″	21′0″	7′6″	60 B.H.P. Skandia	Lighter	
698.	*X 83*		105′6″	21′0″	7′6″	60 B.H.P. Skandia	Lighter	
699.	*X 84*		105′6″	21′0″	7′6″	60 B.H.P. Skandia	Lighter	
700.	*X 81*		105′6″	21′0″	7′6″	80 B.H.P. Skandia	Lighter	
701.	*X 89*		105′6″	21′0″	7′6″	50 B.H.P. Bolinder	Lighter	Caledon, Dundee
702.	*X 90*		105′6″	21′0″	7′6″	50 B.H.P. Bolinder	Lighter	
703.	*X 91*		105′6″	21′0″	7′6″	50 B.H.P. Bolinder	Lighter	
704.	*X 92*		105′6″	21′0″	7′6″	50 B.H.P. Bolinder	Lighter	
705.	*Lee Lee*		95′0″	19′0″	10′0″	120 B.H.P. 2 cyl. Bolinder	Coaster	Rennie, Richard + Newport
706.	*Chiman*		122′0″	21′0″	10′0″	160 B.H.P. 2 cyl. Bolinder	Coaster	Rennie Forrestt
707.		Asiatic Petroleum				20 B.H.P. 1 cyl. Bolinder	Launch	
708.		Asiatic Petroleum				20 B.H.P. 1 cyl. Bolinder	Launch	
709.	*High Flyer*		40′0″	9′0″	4′6″	40 B.H.P. 2 cyl. Bolinder	Launch	Tom Taylor
710.	*Shackleton*					15 B.H.P. 1 cyl. Bolinder		
711.	*Warita*		133′6″	23′6″	11′6″	320 B.H.P. 4 cyl. Bolinder	Coaster	Abdela & Mitchell
712.	*X 99*		105′6″	21′0″	7′6″	80 B.H.P. Bolinder	Lighter	Dobson
713.	*X 200*		105′6″	21′0″	7′6″	40 B.H.P. Bolinder	Lighter	Dobson
714.	*X 100*		105′6″	21′0″	7′6″	40 B.H.P. Bolinder	Lighter	Dobson
715.	*X 101*		105′6″	21′0″	7′6″	40 B.H.P. Bolinder	Lighter	Dobson
716.	*X 107*		105′6″	21′0″	7′0″	80 B.H.P. Bolinder	Lighter	Northumb. S′Bld
717.	*X 108*		105′6″	21′0″	7′6″	40 B.H.P. Bolinder	Lighter	
718.	*X 109*		105′6″	21′0″	7′6″	50 B.H.P. Bolinder	Lighter	
719.	*X 110*		105′6″	21′0″	7′6″	50 B.H.P. Bolinder	Lighter	
720.	*X 111*		105′6″	21′0″	7′6″	80 B.H.P. Bolinder	Lighter	Readhead, S. Shields
721.	*X 112*		105′6″	21′0″	7′6″	40 B.H.P. Bolinder	Lighter	
722.	*X 113*		105′6″	21′0″	7′6″	40 B.H.P. Bolinder	Lighter	
723.	*X 114*		105′6″	21′0″	7′6″	50 B.H.P. Bolinder	Lighter	
724.	*X 119*		105′6″	21′0″	7′6″	65 B.H.P. Bolinder	Lighter	Thompson, S′Land
725.	*X 120*		105′6″	21′0″	7′6″	65 B.H.P. Bolinder	Lighter	
726.	*X 121*		105′6″	21′0″	7′6″	65 B.H.P. Bolinder	Lighter	
727.	*X 122*		105′6″	21′0″	7′6″	65 B.H.P. Bolinder	Lighter	
728.	*X 123*		105′6″	21′0″	7′6″	65 B.H.P. Bolinder	Lighter	
729.	*X 118*		105′6″	21′0″	7′6″	80 B.H.P. Bolinder	Lighter	
730.	*X 179*		105′6″	21′0″	7′6″	Twin 40 B.H.P. Bolinders	Lighter	Brown, Greenock
731.	*X 180*		105′0″	21′0″	7′6″	Twin 40 B.H.P. Bolinders	Lighter	Brown
732.	*Z 16*		30′0″	8′9″	4′3″	30 B.H.P. Bolinder	Launch	Tom Taylor
733.	*Z 17*		30′0″	8′9″	4′3″	30 B.H.P. Bolinder	Launch	Tom Taylor
734.	*Z 1*		28′0″	8′9″	4′0″	20 B.H.P. Bolinder	Launch	Simpson Str.
735.	*Z 2*		28′0″	8′9″	4′0″	20 B.H.P. Bolinder	Launch	Simpson Str.
736.	*Z 7*		32′0″	8′9″	4′2″	20 B.H.P. Bolinder	Launch	Crichton, Saltney
737.	*Z 8*		32′0″	8′9″	4′2″	20 B.H.P. Bolinder	Launch	Crichton
738.	*Z 9*		32′0″	8′9″	4′2″	20 B.H.P. Bolinder	Launch	Crichton
739.	*Z 13*		30′0″	8′9″	4′3″	20 B.H.P. Bolinder	Launch	McGregor
740.	*Z 14*		30′0″	8′9″	4′3″	20 B.H.P. Bolinder	Launch	McGregor
741.	*Z 3*		30′0″	8′9″	4′3″	25 B.H.P. Bolinder	Launch	Steel
742.	*Z 4*		30′0″	8′9″	4′3″	25 B.H.P. Bolinder	Launch	Alley & McLellan
743.	*Z 5*		30′0″	8′9″	4′3″	25 B.H.P. Bolinder	Launch	McGregor
744.	*Z 6*		30′0″	8′9″	4′3″	25 B.H.P. Bolinder	Launch	McGregor
745.	*Theodor*		97′5″	27′2″	12′3″	80 B.H.P. 2 cyl. Bolinder	Sailing Ship	
746.		Brights P. Pulley				20 B.H.P. 1 cyl. Bolinder	Barge	
747.	*X 139*		105′6″	21′0″	7′6″	80 B.H.P. Bolinder	Lighter	Doxford

Ship No.	Name	Destination/Owner	Dimensions L	B	D	Engines HP MP LP ST	Boiler DIA	LEN	LBS	Type	Builder
748.	*X 140*		105′6″	21′0″	7′6″	80 B.H.P. Bolinder				Lighter	Doxford
749.	*X 141*		105′6″	21′0″	7′6″	80 B.H.P. Bolinder				Lighter	Doxford
750.	*X 166*		105′6″	21′0″	7′6″	40 B.H.P. Bolinder				Lighter	Beardmore
751.	*X 167*		105′6″	21′0″	7′6″	40 B.H.P. Bolinder				Lighter	Beardmore
752.	*X 168*		105′6″	21′0″	7′6″	40 B.H.P. Bolinder				Lighter	
753.	*X 169*		105′6″	21′0″	7′6″	40 B.H.P. Bolinder				Lighter	
754.	*X 170*		105′6″	21′0″	7′6″	40 B.H.P. Bolinder				Lighter	
755.	*X 171*		105′6″	21′0″	7′6″	40 B.H.P. Bolinder				Lighter	
756.	*X 172*		105′6″	21′0″	7′6″	40 B.H.P. Bolinder				Lighter	
757.	*X 173*		105′6″	21′0″	7′6″	40 B.H.P. Bolinder				Lighter	
758.	*X 174*		105′6″	21′0″	7′6″	40 B.H.P. Bolinder				Lighter	
759.	*X 175*		105′6″	21′0″	7′6″	50 B.H.P. Bolinder				Lighter	
760.	*X 165*		105′6″	21′0″	7′6″	40 B.H.P. Bolinder				Lighter	
761.	*X 181*		105′6″	21′0″	7′6″	80 B.H.P. Bolinder				Lighter	Blumer, Clyde
762.	*X 182*		105′6″	21′0″	7′6″	80 B.H.P. Bolinder				Lighter	
763.	*X 183*		105′6″	21′0″	7′6″	92 B.H.P. Avance				Lighter	
764.	*X 184*		105′6″	21′0″	7′6″	92 B.H.P. Avance				Lighter	
765.	*X 185*		105′6″	21′0″	7′6″	92 B.H.P. Avance				Lighter	
766.	*X 186*		105′6″	21′0″	7′6″	Twin 30 B.H.P. Bolinders				Lighter	Caird, Greenock
767.	*X 187*		105′6″	21′0″	7′6″	Twin 30 B.H.P. Bolinders				Lighter	
768.	*X 188*		105′6″	21′0″	7′6″	Twin 30 B.H.P. Bolinders				Lighter	
769.	*X 189*		105′6″	21′0″	7′6″	Twin 30 B.H.P. Bolinders				Lighter	
770.	*X 190*		105′6″	21′0″	7′6″	Twin 30 B.H.P. Bolinders				Lighter	Caird, Greenock
771.	*X 177*		105′6″	21′0″	7′6″	65 B.H.P. Bolinder				Lighter	Swan Hunter
772.	*X 178*		105′6″	21′0″	7′6″	Twin 30 B.H.P. Bolinders				Lighter	
773.	*X 191*		105′6″	21′0″	7′6″	80 B.H.P. Bolinder				Lighter	Thompson
774.	*X 192*		105′6″	21′0″	7′6″	80 B.H.P. Bolinder				Lighter	
775.	*X 193*		105′6″	21′0″	7′6″	80 B.H.P. Bolinder				Lighter	
776.	*X 194*		105′6″	21′0″	7′6″	Twin 30 B.H.P. Bolinders				Lighter	
777.	*X 195*		105′6″	21′0″	7′6″	Twin 30 B.H.P. Bolinders				Lighter	
778.	*X 196*		105′6″	21′0″	7′6″	Twin 40 B.H.P. Bolinders				Lighter	
779.	*X 198*		105′6″	21′0″	7′6″	Twin 40 B.H.P. Bolinders				Lighter	Ropnel
780.	*X 36*		105′6″	21′0″	7′6″	Twin 25 B.H.P. Bolinders				Lighter	Irvine
781.	*X 37*		105′6″	21′0″	7′6″	Twin 25 B.H.P. Bolinders				Lighter	Irvine
782.	*X 38*		105′6″	21′0″	7′6″	Twin 25 B.H.P. Bolinders				Lighter	Irvine
783.	*X 76*		105′6″	21′0″	7′6″	Twin 25 B.H.P. Bolinders				Lighter	Short, S'land
784.	*X 77*		105′6″	21′0″	7′6″	Twin 25 B.H.P. Bolinders				Lighter	
785.	*X 78*		105′6″	21′0″	7′6″	Twin 25 B.H.P. Bolinders				Lighter	
786.	*Z 10*		30′0″	8′9″	4′3″	20 B.H.P. Bolinder				Launch	Rowhedge
787.	*Z 11*		30′0″	8′9″	4′3″	20 B.H.P. Bolinder				Launch	
788.	*Z 12*		30′0″	8′9″	4′3″	20 B.H.P. Bolinder				Launch	
789.	*Bournville IV*		69′6″	6′11″	4′4″	15 B.H.P. Bolinder				Canal Barge	
790.	*Peacock*	Fellows M & C	70′0″	7′0″	4′2″	15 B.H.P. 1 cyl. Bolinder				Canal Barge	
791.	*X 93*		105′6″	21′0″	7′6″	40 B.H.P. Bolinder				Lighter	Ramage & Ferguson
792.		Edwards Bros				20 B.H.P. 2 cyl. Bolinder				Launch	
793.	*Z 15*		30′0″	8′9″	4′3″	20 B.H.P. Bolinder				Launch	Tom Taylor
794.	*X 142*		105′6″	21′0″	7′6″	80 B.H.P. Bolinder				Lighter	Doxford
795.	*X 143*		105′6″	21′0″	7′6″	80 B.H.P. Bolinder				Lighter	Doxford

797.	*X 145*		105′6″	21′0″	7′6″	80 B.H.P. Bolinder	Lighter	Doxford
798.	*X 146*		105′6″	21′0″	7′6″	80 B.H.P. Bolinder	Lighter	
799.		P.J. Hayden				15 B.H.P. Bolinder	Barge	
800.	*Indorita*		108′0″	22′0″	10′9″	160 B.H.P. Bolinder	Coaster	Abdela & M.
801.	*Eldorita*		108′0″	22′0″	10′9″	160 B.H.P. 2 cyl. Bolinder	Coaster	Abdela & M.
802.	*X 74*		105′6″	21′0″	7′6″	Twin 25 B.H.P. Bolinders	Lighter	Short
803.	*X 75*		105′6″	21′0″	7′6″	Twin 25 B.H.P. Bolinders	Lighter	Short
804.	*X 65*		105′6″	21′0″	7′6″	Twin 40 B.H.P. Skandia	Lighter	S'land S'Bld
805.	*X 66*		105′6″	21′0″	7′6″	Twin 40 B.H.P. Skandia	Lighter	
806.	*Fantome II*		167′9″	29′0″	16′3″	Twin 240 B.H.P. Bolinders	Yacht	
807.	*X 4*		105′6″	21′0″	7′6″	40 B.H.P. Bolinder	Lighter	Ropnel
808.	*X 3*		105′6″	21′0″	7′6″	40 B.H.P. Bolinder	Lighter	Ropnel
809.	*X 149*		105′6″	21′0″	7′6″	80 B.H.P. Bolinder	Lighter	Doxford
810.	*X 151*		105′6″	21′0″	7′6″	80 B.H.P. Bolilnder	Lighter	Doxford
811.	*X 50*		105′6″	21′0″	7′6″	80 B.H.P. Bolinder	Lighter	Richardson
812.	*X 51*		105′6″	21′0″	7′6″	80 B.H.P. Bolinder	Lighter	
813.	*X 52*		105′6″	21′0″	7′6″	80 B.H.P. Bolinder	Lighter	
814.	*X 53*		105′6″	21′0″	7′6″	80 B.H.P. Bolinder	Lighter	
815.	*X 98*		105′6″	21′0″	7′6″	50 B.H.P. Bolinder	Lighter	Dundee S'build
816.	*X 56*		105′6″	21′0″	7′6″	60 B.H.P. Skandia	Lighter	S'land S'build
817.	*X 57*		105′6″	21′0″	7′6″	60 B.H.P. Skandia	Lighter	
818.	*X 15*		105′6″	21′0″	7′6″	60 B.H.P. Skandia	Lighter	Austin, S'land
819.	*X 16*		105′6″	21′0″	7′6″	60 B.H.P. Skandia	Lighter	
820.	*X 17*		105′6″	21′0″	7′6″	60 B.H.P. Skandia	Lighter	
821.	*X 18*		105′6″	21′0″	7′6″	60 B.H.P. Skandia	Lighter	
822.	*X 87*		105′6″	21′0″	7′6″	60 B.H.P. Skandia	Lighter	Blyth S'build
823.	*X 88*		105′6″	21′0″	7′6″	60 B.H.P. Skandia	Lighter	
824.	*X 86*		105′6″	21′0″	7′6″	80 B.H.P. Skandia	Lighter	
825.	*X 129*		105′6″	21′0″	7′6″	50 B.H.P. Skandia	Lighter	Goole S'build
826.	*X 148*		105′6″	21′0″	7′6″	92 B.H.P. Avance	Lighter	Doxford
827.	*X 150*		105′6″	21′0″	7′6″	92 B.H.P. Avance	Lighter	
828.	*X 152*		105′6″	21′0″	7′6″	92 B.H.P. Avance	Lighter	
829.	*X 153*		105′6″	21′0″	7′6″	92 B.H.P. Avance	Lighter	
830.	*X 70*		105′6″	21′0″	7′6″	60 B.H.P. Avance	Lighter	Short
831.	*X 71*		105′6″	21′0″	7′6″	60 B.H.P. Avance	Lighter	
832.	*X 72*		105′6″	21′0″	7′6″	60 B.H.P. Avance	Lighter	
833.	*X 73*		105′6″	21′0″	7′6″	60 B.H.P. Avance	Lighter	
834.	*X 33*		105′6″	21′0″	7′6″	60 B.H.P. Avance	Lighter	Irvine
835.	*X 34*		105′6″	21′0″	7′6″	60 B.H.P. Avance	Lighter	
836.	*X 35*		105′6″	21′0″	7′6″	60 B.H.P. Avance	Lighter	
837.	*Seal*	Fellows M & C	70′0″	7′0″	4′2″	15 B.H.P. Bolinder	Narrow Boat	
838.	*Seagull*	Fellows M & C	70′0″	7′0″	4′2″	15 B.H.P. Bolinder	Narrow Boat	
839.	*Baron*	Fellows M & C	70′0″	7′0″	4′2″	15 B.H.P. Bolinder	Narrow Boat	
840.	*Grove Place*	London	55′0″	14′0″	8′0″	160 B.H.P. Bolinder	Tug	
841.	*Briton*	Fellows M & C	70′0″	7′0″	4′2″	15 B.H.P. 1 cyl. Bolinder	Narrow Boat	
842.		French Admiralty	32′0″	8′0″	4′6″	15 B.H.P. Dux Motor	Launch	Crichton
843.		HM Admiralty				Twin 320 B.H.P. Bolinders	Lighter	
844.		HM Admiralty				80 B.H.P. Bolinder	Lighter	
845.		HM Admiralty				30 B.H.P. Bolinder	Lighter	
846.		HM Admiralty				40 B.H.P. 2 cyl. Bolinder	Lighter	
847.	*Bethlehem*		142′3″	29′9″	13′6″	120 B.H.P. 2 cyl. Bolinder	Aux Motor Vessel	

	Ship No.	Name	Destination/Owner	Dimensions L	B	D	Engines HP MP LP ST	Boiler DIA	LEN	LBS	Type	Builder
	848.	*Record Reign*		112′2″	24′1″	9′5″	40 B.H.P. 1 cyl. Bolinder				Aux Motor Barge	
	849.	*Annie Stodden*		25′0″	8′5″		5 B.H.P. Bolinder				Fishing Vessel	
1916	850.	*Ellen*		27′0″	8′9″		5 B.H.P. Bolinder				Fishing Vessel	
	851.	*Daring*		27′0″	8′9″		5 B.H.P. Bolinder				Fishing Vessel	
	852.	*Enterprise*		109′5″	24′8″	10′3″	120 B.H.P. Bolinder				Aux Sailing Vessel	
	853.	*X 124*		105′6″	21′0″	7′6″	Twin 25 B.H.P. Bolinders				Lighter	
	854.	*X 209*		88′0″	20′0″	7′6″	Twin 80 B.H.P. Bolinders				Lighter	Robson
	855.	*X 210*		88′0″	20′0″	8′0″	Twin 80 B.H.P. Bolinders				Lighter	
	856.	*X 211*		88′0″	20′0″	8′0″	Twin 80 B.H.P. Bolinders				Lighter	
	857.	*X 216*		88′0″	20′0″	8′0″	Twin 80 B.H.P. Bolinders				Lighter	Osbourne Graham
	858.	*X 217*		88′0″	20′0″	8′0″	Twin 80 B.H.P. Bolinders				Lighter	
	859.	*X 222*		88′0″	20′0″	8′0″	Twin 80 B.H.P. Bolinders				Lighter	S'land S'build
	860.	*X 223*		88′0″	20′0″	8′0″	Twin 80 B.H.P. Bolinders				Lighter	S'land S'build
	861.	*X 224*		88′0″	20′0″	8′0″	80 B.H.P. Bolinders				Lighter	Tyne Iron S'bld
	862.	*X 225*		88′0″	20′0″	8′0″	80 B.H.P. Bolinders				Lighter	
	863.	*Hector*		61′0″	7′0″	4′0″	20 B.H.P. Bolinder				Motor Tug	
	864.	*Dudley*		40′0″	6′3″	4′1½″	20 B.H.P. Bolinder				Double Ended Tug	
	865.			40′0″	6′3″	4′1½″	20 B.H.P. Bolinder				Double Ended Tug	
	866.	*Tangaroa*		120′0″	25′0″	12′9″	80 B.H.P. Bolinder				Schooner	
	867.	*Sai Kwong*		80′0″	16′6″	4′6″	Twin 40 B.H.P. Bolinder				Lighter	
	868.	*Oakol*		220′0″	34′7½″	16′6″	Twin 320 B.H.P. Bolinders				Oil Tanker	W. Gray
	869.	*Palmol*		220′0″	34′7½″	16′6″	Twin 320 B.H.P. Bolinders				Oil Tanker	
	870.	*Juniata*		220′0″	34′7½″	16′6″	Twin 320 B.H.P. Bolinders				Oil Tanker	Short
	871.	*San Dario*		220′0″	34′7½″	16′6″	Twin 320 B.H.P. Bolinders				Oil Tanker	Short
	872.	*Timely*		78′0″	18′6″	8′6″	80 B.H.P. Bolinder				Herring Drifter	Oulton Broad
	873.	*Homely*		78′0″	18′6″	8′6″	80 B.H.P. Bolinder				Herring Drifter	
	874.	*Lerina*		78′0″	18′6″	8′6″	80 B.H.P. Bolinder				Herring Drifter	
	875.		French Admiralty	53′6″	11′9″	5′8″	80 B.H.P. Bolinder				Tug	
	876.		French Admiralty	53′6″	11′9″	5′8″	80 B.H.P. Bolinder				Tug	
	877.		French Admiralty	53′6″	11′9″	5′8″	80 B.H.P. Bolinder				Tug	
1917	878.		French Admiralty				50 B.H.P. Bolinder					
	879.		French Admiralty				50 B.H.P. Bolinder					
	880.		French Admiralty				50 B.H.P. Bolinder					
	881.		French Admiralty				50 B.H.P. Bolinder					
	882.		French Admiralty				50 B.H.P. Bolinder					
	883.		French Admiralty				50 B.H.P. Bolinder					
	884.		Cadbury Bros				15 B.H.P. Bolinder					
	885.			108′0″	23′9″	10′6″	Twin B.H.P. Bolinders				Wood Coaster	
	886.	*Lizzie*		43′6″	12′0″	5′0″	15 B.H.P. Bolinder				Pilot Boat	
	887.	*Lasca II*		118′6″	27′0″	14′5″	Twin 80 B.H.P. Bolinders				Yacht	
	888.	*Pioneer*		77′0″	21′6″	7′3″					Concrete Swim Barge	

	Ship No.	Name	Type	Builder	Dimensions LOA	LBP	BMLD	DMLD	DW	Engine	BHP	Destination	Launch Date	Delivery Date
1917	889.	*Molliette*	Concrete Coaster		131′0″	125′0″	25′0″	11′9″	300	Bolinder	120	London	11/1918	2/1919
	*890.									Bolinder	50	Bolinders N.Y.	Cancelled	
	891.	*Violette*	Concrete Coaster		131′0″	125′0″	25′0″	11′9″	300	Bolinder	120	London		8/1919
	*892		Land Engine							Bolinder	60			

1918	*896.	*Mountsfield*	Ketch		99′3″		23′5″	8′3″		Bolinder	50		
	*897.									Bolinder	50	Hanson Esq	
	*898.		Pump Set							Bolinder	5	James DT & T Co	
	899.	*Broiler*	Coaster	McGregor	75′9″		18′3″	9′6″		Bolinder	80		
	*900.	*Vega IV*	Coaster	McGregor						Bolinder	80		
	*901.	*Albion*	Stern Wheel Tug	Taylor	29′0″		8′0″	2′2″		Bolinder	16		
	*902.	*Florida*	Launch Tug		45′9″		9′0″	4′6″		Bolinder	40		
1919	*903.	*Stentor*	Canal Tug		61′0″		7′0″	4′0″		Bolinder	25		
	904.	*Ironside*	Swim Barge		72′6″		19′6″	6′6″	128			London	3/1920
	905.	*India*	Swim Barge		72′6″		19′6″	6′6″	128			London	3/1920
	*906.									Bolinders	2x25	Bristol PCM Co	
	*907.	*Marjory*	Sluice Pump										
	*908.		Swim Barge		90′0″		23′0″	8′5″					
	*909.									Bolinder	16	C.H. Bailey	
	910.	*Italy*	Swim Barge		72′6″		19′6″	6′6″	128			London	4/1920
	911.	*Inchcape*	Swim Barge		72′6″		19′6″	6′6″	128			London	4/1920
	*912.									Bolinder	20	H. Waite	
	*913.									Bolinder	20	H. Waite	
	*914.									Bolinder	20	M. Verstraeten	
	*915.	*Francis*								Bolinder	25		
	*916.	*Portugal*	Sailing Vessel							Petter Winch	13½		
	*917.	*Ann Elizabeth*								Bolinder	40		
	918.	*Shadwell*	Canal Barge			76′0″	14′1″	5′0″	80			London	5/1920
	919.	*Sheffield*	Canal Barge			76′0″	14′1″	5′0″	80			London	6/1920
	920.	*Skegness*	Canal Barge			76′0″	14′1″	5′0″	80			London	5/1920
	921.	*Southsea*	Canal Barge			76′0″	14′1″	5′0″	80			London	6/1920
	922.	*Pollack*	Ins Swim Barge		77′0″		20′0″	7′4″	150			London	10/1920
	923.	*Plaice*	Ins Swim Barge		77′0″		20′0″	7′4″	150			London	10/1920
	924.	Pilchard	Ins Swim Barge		77′0″		20′0″	7′4″	150			London	12/1920
	925.	*Pandora*	Ins Swim Barge		77′0″		20′0″	7′4″	150			London	12/1920
	*926.									Bolinder	25	A. Rutherford	
	927.		Land Engine							Bolinder	80	Eastern Smelting Co	
	*928.	*Rene*	Launch Tug							Bolinder	20		
	*929.									Hexa	6	Mr Nichols	
	930.	*Pelamid*	Ins Swim Barge		77′0″		20′0″	7′4″	150			London	2/1921
	931.	*Powam*	Ins Swim Barge		77′0″		20′0″	7′4″	150			London	2/1921
	*932.	*Kitanna*								Bolinder	80		
	933.	*Linton*	Coaster		135′0″	127′0″	23′6″	11′6″	360	Bolinder	320	London	5/1921
	934.	*Ben Truman*	Coaster		85′0″	80′0″	18′0″	8′9″	120	Bolinder	80	Chatham	1/1921
	*935.	*Sta Maria Magdelena*			118′1″		29′5″	9′8″		Bolinder	120		
	*936.	*San Martin*								Bolinder	2x160		
	*937.	*Georgita*	Lighter	Crichton	126′0″		16′9″	7′0″		Bolinder	2x50		
	*938.	*Wilita*	Lighter	Crichton	126′0″		16′9″	7′0″		Bolinder	2x50		
	939.	*Flanchford*	Tug		75′0″	70′0″	16′3″	9′0″		Bolinder	320	London	7/1921
	940.	*Rocott*	Tug		75′0″	70′0″	16′3″	9′0″		Bolinder	320	London	9/1921
	*941.		Canal Barge							Bolinder	15	Hildick & Hildick	
	*942.	*Mudsucker*	Hopper Barge		90′0″		26′0″	9′6″		Bolinder	2x80		
	*943.	*Britannia*	Barge		86′0″		16′0″			Bolinder	80		
	*944.	*Mermaid*	Canal Barge							Bolinder	20		
	*945.	*Ruby*	Canal Barge							Bolinder	15		
	*946.	*Benzedine*			57′6″		14′2″	6′2″		Bolinder	30		
	*947.									Bolinders	2x50	U E Singapore	

Ship No.		Name	Type	Builder	Dimensions LOA	LBP	BMLD	DMLD	DW	Engine	BHP	Destination	Launch Date	Delivery Date
	*948.	*Polita*	Lighter	Lytham	126′0″		16′9″	7′0″		Bolinders	2x50			
	*949.	*Dorita*	Lighter	Lytham	126′0″		16′9″	7′0″		Bolinders	2x50			
	*950.	*Marcita*	Lighter	Crichton	126′0″		16′9″	7′0″		Bolinders	2x50			
	*951.	*Carmentina*	Lighter	Lytham	126′0″		16′9″	7′0″		Bolinders	2x50			
	*952.	*Alita*	Lighter	Lytham	126′0″		16′9″	7′0″		Bolinder	2x50			
	*953.	*Jonita*	Lighter	Crichton	126′0″		16′9″	7′0″		Bolinder	2x50			
1920	*954.									Bolinder	15	Murphy Bros		
	*955.									Bolinder	160	Trikamjee Jivandas		
	*956.	*Acacia*								Bolinder	80			
	*957.									Bolinder	25	Leopold, Walford		
	*958.									Bolinder	50	Leopold, Walford		
	*959.									Bolinder	80	Leopold, Walford		
	*960.		Coal Whipping Barge		43′0″		15′0″	5′9″				Hudson & Co		
	*961.		Coal Whipping Barge		43′0″		15′0″	5′9″				Hudson & Co		
	*962.									Bolinder	25	J. Maxim		
	*963.									Bolinder	2x80	Argentine Sn Co		
	*964.									Bolinder	2x80	Argentine Sn Co		
	*965.									Bolinder	2x80			
	*966.									Bolinder	20	Richardson & Fletcher		
	*967.	*Fer*	Motor Barge	Crichton, Saltney	129′5″		16′4″	7′3″	151	Bolinder	125	Darwen & Mostyn, Flint		
	968.	*Witu*	Swim Barge		72′6″		19′6″	6′6″	110			London		2/1921
	969.	*Ximo*	Swim Barge		72′6″		19′6″	6′6″	110			London		2/1921
	*970.	*Arran Firth*	Coaster	Hepple	138′6″		23′3″	10′6″		Bolinder	320			
	*971.									Bolinder	160	Trikamjee Jivandas		
	*972.									Bolinder	16	Curtis Campbell		
	973.	*Ichabod*	Launch		32′0″	29′4″	8′9″	4′3″		Steam		W.Africa		4/1921
	*974.									Bolinder	40			
	*975.	*Pioneer*								Bolinder	80			
	976.	*William*	Swim Barge		71′0″		18′8½″	6′6″	105			London		4/1921
	977.	*John*	Swim Barge		71′0″		18′8½″	6′6″	105			London		4/1921
	978.	*Frank*	Swim Barge		71′0″		18′8½″	6′6″	105			London		5/1921
	979.	*Edea*	Launch		32′0″	29′4″	8′9″	4′3″		Bolinder	20	London		11/1921
	980.	*Faversham*	Swim Barge		78′9″		21′6″	7′0″	155			London		7/1921
	981.	*Walton*	Canal Barge		93′8″	86′0″	15′6″	5′9″	120			London		7/1921
	982.	*Watford*	Canal Barge		93′8″	86′0″	15′6″	5′9″	120			London		7/1921
	983.	*Westcliffe*	Canal Barge		93′8″	86′0″	15′6″	5′9″	120			London		7/1921
	984.	*Weybridge*	Canal Barge		93′8″	86′0″	15′6″	5′9″	120			London		7/1921
	985.	*Windsor*	Canal Barge		93′8″	86′0″	15′6″	5′9″	120			London		7/1921
	986.	*Woking*	Canal Barge		93′8″	86′0″	15′6″	5′9″	120			London		9/1921
	987.	*Somerville*	Launch		32′0″	29′4″	8′9″	4′3″		Bolinder	25	Penang		5/1923
1921	*988.	*Magheramorne*	Grab Dredger	G.Brown	91′0″		22′9″	7′6″		Bolinder	2x80			
	989.	*Arthur*	Swim Barge		71′0″		18′10″	6′6″	110			London		9/1921
	*990.									Bolinder	15	British Phosphate		
	*991.									Bolinder	15	British Phosphate		
	*992.	[illegible]		Philip & Son	71′0″		17′6″	10′0″		Engines 14″x30″x24″				

	*993.	*Minnie*	Swim Barge		71′0″	18′8½″	6′6″						
	994.	*Shandon*	Swim Barge		58′0″	15′10″	5′3″	50				London	9/1922
	995.	*Furley*	Swim Barge		58′0″		15′10″	5′3″	50			London	9/1922
	996.	*Thames*	Swim Barge		78′9″		21′6″	7′0″	150			London	4/1922
	*997.	*Ronaki*	Schooner							Bolinder	2x135	New Zealand	
1922	998.	*Raven*	Swim Barge		82′6″		21′6″	7′9″	190			London	7/1922
	999.	*Rook*	Swim Barge		82′6″		21′6″	7′9″	190			London	7/1922
	1000.	*Crow*	Swim Barge		82′6″		21′6″	7′9″	190			London	8/1922
	1001.	*Jackdaw*	Swim Barge		82′6″		21′6″	7′9″	190			London	8/1922
	1002.	*Jay*	Swim Barge		82′6″		21′6″	7′9″	190			London	10/1922
	1003.	*Magpie*	Swim Barge		82′6″		21′6″	7′9″	190			London	10/1922
	1004.	*London*	Swim Barge		78′9″		21′6″	7′0″	150			London	9/1922
	*1005.	*Genesta*								Bolinder	40		
	*1006.									Bolinder	100	Stockton & Co	
	*1007.									Bolinder	40	U E Singapore	
	*1008.	*Tetney*		Cook, W&G, Beverley						Bolinder	60		
	1009.	*Foch*	Tar Barge		83′0″		17′9″	5′6″	107			London	10/1922
	1010.	*Haig*	Tar Barge		83′0″		17′9″	5′6″	107			London	11/1922
	*1011.									Bolinder	20	U E Singapore	
	*1012.									Bolinder	25	Crosier	
	1013.	*Hotchkiss*	Shallow Draft Tug			40′0″	8′0″	2′6″		Bolinder	30	London	2/1923
	*1014.	*Enterprise*								Bolinder	40		
	1015.	*No.2*	Galvd Barge			50′0″	8′0″	3′3″	10			London	12/1922
	1016.	*Barlow*	Swim Barge		70′0″		20′3″	7′6″	150			London	12/1922
	1017.	*Membury*	Swim Barge		70′0″		20′3″	7′6″	150			London	12/1922
	1018.	*Finlass*	Swim Barge		70′0″		20′3″	7′6″	150			London	12/1922
	1019.	*Driffel*	Swim Barge		70′0″		20′3″	7′6″	150			London	12/1922
	1020.	*Webbel*	Swim Barge		70′0″		20′3″	7′6″	150			London	1/1923
	1021.	*Stockwell*	Swim Barge		70′0″		20′3″	7′6″	150			London	1/1923
	*1022.	*Adder*	Narrow Boat	Yarwood, Northwich						Bolinder	15	Fellows M&C	
	*1023.	*Avis*	Narrow Boat	Yarwood						Bolinder	15	Fellows M&C	
	*1024.	*Antelope*	Narrow Boat	Yarwood						Bolinder	15	Fellows M&C	
	*1025.	*Badger*	Narrow Boat	Yarwood						Bolinder	15	Fellows M&C	
	*1026.	*Bison*	Narrow Boat	Yarwood						Bolinder	15	Fellows M&C	
	*1027.	*Buffalo*	Narrow Boat	Yarwood						Bolinder	15	Fellows M&C	
	*1028.	*Camel*	Narrow Boat	Yarwood						Bolinder	15	Fellows M&C	
	*1029.	*Cormorant*	Narrow Boat	Yarwood						Bolinder	15	Fellows M&C	
	*1030.	*Crane*	Narrow Boat	Yarwood						Bolinder	15	Fellows M&C	
	*1031.	*Dolphin*	Narrow Boat	Yarwood						Bolinder	15	Fellows M&C	
	*1032.	*Dove*	Narrow Boat	Yarwood						Bolinder	15	Fellows M&C	
	*1033.	*Dragon*	Narrow Boat	Yarwood						Bolinder	15	Fellows M&C	
	1034.	*Marjory*	Swim Barge		78′9″		21′6″	7′0″	150			London	2/1923
	1035.	*Mary*	Swim Barge		78′9″		21′6″	7′0″	150			London	2/1923
	1036.	*Surrey*	Swim Barge		78′9″		21′6″	7′0″	150			London	2/1923
	1037.	*Munster*	Swim Barge		69′0″		17′0″	6′0″	96			London	2/1923
	1038.	*Leinster*	Swim Barge		69′0″		17′9″	6′0″	96			London	2/1923
	1039.		Wood Boat			18′0″	5′6″	2′1″				South Met Gas Co, London	
	1040.	*Amoy*	Swim Punt		55′0″		15′10¼″	5′0″	54			London	3/1923
	1041.	*Buma*	Swim Punt		55′0″		15′10¼″	5′0″	54			London	3/1923
	1042.	*Colon*	Swim Punt		55′0″		15′10¼″	5′0″	54			London	3/1923

Ship No.	Name	Type	Builder	Dimensions LOA	LBP	BMLD	DMLD	DW	Engine	BHP	Destination	Launch Date	Delivery Date
1043.	*Duala*	Swim Punt		55′0″		15′10¼″	5′0″	54			London		3/1923
*1044.	*Venapa*								Bolinder	50			
1045.	*Kennet*	Swim Barge		78′9″		21′4⅛″	7′6″	170			London		4/1923
1923 1046.	*Cissie*	Swim Barge		71′6″		18′0½″	6′6″	105			London		4/1923
1047.	*Maidstone*	Swim Barge		78′9″		21′4⅛″	7′6″	170			London		6/1923
1048.	*Peace*	Swim Barge		69′6″		18′0⅛″	6′6″	105			London		6/1923
1049.	*Victory*	Swim Barge		69′6″		18′0¼″	6′6″	105			London		6/1923
1050.	*Lionel*	Swim Barge		68′0″		17′3″	7′3″	110			London		5/1923
1051.	*Esme*	Swim Barge		68′0″		17′3″	7′3″	110			London		5/1923
*1052.	*South Sea Castle*	Wood Barge	Vosper	56′0″		13′6″	5′2¾″		Bolinder	40			
*1053.	*Rengam*		G. Brown						Bolinder	270			
*1054.	*Rompins*		G. Brown						Bolinder	270			
1055.	*Croindene*	Swim Barge		74′0″		20′4¼″	7′3″	140			London		8/1923
1056.	*Wandel*	Swim Barge		74′0″		20′4¼″	7′3″	140			London		8/1923
*1057.	*Dolphin*	Aux Brigantine	Garston	110′0″		22′0″	13′6″		Bolinder	2x100			
1058.	*Hannah*	Swim Barge		71′6″		18′0½″	6′6″	105			London		7/1923
1059.	*Beatrice*	Swim Barge		71′6″		18′0½″	6′6″	105			London		7/1923
1060.	*Lily*	Swim Barge		71′6″		18′0½″	6′6″	105			London		7/1923
1061.	*Maud*	Swim Barge		71′6″		18′0½″	6′6″	105			London		8/1923
1062.	*Grace*	Swim Barge		71′6″		18′0½″	6′6″	105			London		8/1923
1063.	*Ada*	Swim Barge		71′6″		18′0½″	6′6″	105			London		8/1923
1064.	*Macralph*	Steam Tug		65′0″	60′0″	15′3″	8′0″	45	Steam		London		11/1923
*1065.									Bolinder	80	U E Singapore		
1066.	*Melbourne*	Swim Barge		84′0″		24′0″	7′0″	195			Sittingbourne		11/1923
1067.	*Adelaide*	Swim Barge		84′0″		24′0″	7′0″	195			Sittingbourne		12/1923
1068.	*Sydney*	Swim Barge		84′0″		24′0″	7′0″	195			Sittingbourne		12/1923
1069.	*Medway*	Swim Barge		78′9″		21′4⅛″	7′6″	170			London		12/1923
1070.	*Wroxham*	Swim Barge		75′0″		201·″	7′6″	150			London		11/1923
1071.	*Breydon*	Swim Barge		75′0″		20′3″	7′6″	150			London		11/1923
*1072.									Bolinder	40	H.Wayte		
1073.	*Stourgate*	Tanker		90′0″	85′0″	19′0″	7′3″	110	Bollinder	135	London		4/1924
*1074.									Bolinder	15	British Phosphate		
1075.	*Kent*	Canal Barge		76′3″		14′1″	5′4″	80			London		1/1924
1076.	*Surrey*	Canal Barge		76′3″		14′1″	5′4″	80			London		1/1924
1077.	*Freemason*	Canal Barge		76′3″		14′1″	5′4″	80			London		1/1924
1078.	*Freebooter*	Canal Barge		76′3″		14′1″	5′4″	80			London		1/1924
1079.	*Sussex*	Canal Barge		76′3″		14′1″	5′4″	80			London		2/1924
1080.	*Essex*	Canal Barge		76′3″		14′1″	5′4″	80			London		2/1924
1081.	*Freeholder*	Canal Barge		76′3″		14′1″	5′4″	80			London		2/1924
1082.	*Freeman*	Canal Barge		76′3″		14′1″	5′4″	80			London		2/1924
1083.	*Lincoln*	Canal Barge		76′3″		14′1″	5′4″	80			London		3/1924
1084.	*Norfolk*	Canal Barge		76′3″		14′1″	5′4″	80			London		3/1924
1085.	*Freedom*	Canal Barge		76′3″		14′1″	5′4″	80			London		4/1924
1086.	*Freemartin*	Canal Barge		76′3″		14′1″	5′4″	80			London		4/1924
1087.	*British Maiden*	Coasting Tanker		94′0″	90′0″	19′3″	7′6″	140	Gardner	140	London		5/1924
1088.	*British Beagle*	Tank Barge		85′0″	79′0″	17′10″	6′0″	82			London		4/1924
*1089.									Bolinder	20	Brown Douglas		
1090.	*Edith*	Shallow Draft Tug			18′0″	7′0″	2′6″		Bolinder	12	London		6/1924

	*1094.	*Ulco*	Barge Tug	Cran, Leith	77′6″		21′6″	12′3″		Engines 14″x21½″x35″x24″ Boiler 13′6″x14′0″x150			
	*1095.									Bolinder	24	Burns Philp	
	1096.	*Garrison*	Swim Barge		69′6″		18′0¼″	6′6″	105			London	6/1924
	1097.	*Vedette*	Swim Barge		69′6″		18′0¼″	6′6″	105			London	6/1924
	1098.	*Privateer*	Swim Barge		69′6″		18′0¼″	6′6″	105			London	6/1924
	1099.	*Renown*	Swim Barge		69′6″		18′0¼″	6′6″	105			London	6/1924
	1100.	*Coronet*	Swim Barge		69′6″		18′0¼″	6′6″	105			London	6/1924
	1101.	*Convoy*	Swim Barge		69′6″		18′0¼″	6′6″	105			London	6/1924
	*1102.	*McGraph*								Bolinder	24		
	*1103.	*Endymion*	Yacht	Camper & Nicholson						Bolinder	2x270		
	*1104.	*Presidente Ospina*	Suction & Grab Dredger			110′0″	27′0″	6′0″		Steam		Colombia	12/1924
	1105.	*Jamaica*	Canal Barge		77′6″		14′5″	5′6″	90			London	7/1924
	1106.	*Madeira*	Canal Barge		77′6″		14′5″	5′6″	90			London	7/1924
	1107.	*Havana*	Canal Barge		77′6″		14′5″	5′6″	90			London	8/1924
	1108.	*Sumatra*	Canal Barge		77′6″		14′5″	5′6″	90			London	8/1924
1924	*1109.	*Buffalo*	Narrow Boat							Bolinder	15	Fellows M&C	
	*1110.	*Captain*	Narrow Boat	F M&C						Bolinder	15	Fellows M&C	
	*1111.	*Colonel*	Narrow Boat							Bolinder	15	Fellows M&C	
	*1112.	*Duteous*	Narrow Boat							Bolinder	15	Fellows M&C	
	*1113.	*General*	Narrow Boat							Bolinder	15	Fellows M&C	
	*1114.	*Hecla*	Narrow Boat							Bolinder	15	Fellows M&C	
	*1115.	*Sultan*	Narrow Boat							Bolinder	15	Fellows M&C	
	*1116.	*Monarch*	Narrow Boat							Bolinder	15	Fellows M&C	
	*1117.	*Pilot*	Narrow Boat							Bolinder	15	Fellows M&C	
	*1118.	*Marquis*	Narrow Boat							Bolinder	15	Fellows M&C	
	*1119.	*The King*	Narrow Boat							Bolinder	15	Fellows M&C	
	*1120.	*Count*	Narrow Boat							Bolinder	15	Fellows M&C	
	*1121.	*Swallow*	Narrow Boat							Bolinder	15	Fellows M&C	
	*1122.	*Swift*	Narrow Boat							Bolinder	15	Fellows M&C	
	*1123.	*Prince*	Narrow Boat							Bolinder	15	Fellows M&C	
	*1124.	*Admiral*	Narrow Boat							Bolinder	15	Fellows M&C	
	*1125.	*President*	Narrow Boat							Bolinder	15	Fellows M&C	
	*1126.	*Viceroy*	Narrow Boat							Bolinder	15	Fellows M&C	
	*1127.	*Vulcan*	Narrow Boat							Bolinder	15	Fellows M&C	
	*1128.	*Wembley*	Swim Barge		82′0″		21′7″	8′6″	220			London	6/1924
	*1130.	*Muspratt*	Coaster							Bolinder	60		
	1131.	*Caupolican*	Tug		69′0″	59′0″	13′2″	6′10″		Steam		Chile	11/1924
	*1132.									Bolinder	40	Brown Douglas	
	1133.	*Pulai*	Launch		32′0″	29′4″	8′9″	4′3″		Bolinder	25	Malay States	8/1924
	*1134.	*Inde*		Crichton	105′0″		29′0″	7′0″		Bolinder	2x100		
	*1135.									Bolinder	30	Canadian Kraft	
	*1136.	*Enid Blanche*			78′0″		20′0″	11′4½″		Engines 14″x22.1/16″x36¼″ Boiler 13′0″x10′0″x185			
	1137.	*Rosehaugh*	Tunnel Launch			60′0″	16′0″	4′6″		Bolinder	80	Dar es Salaam	10/1924
	*1138.									Bolinder	2x40	Brown & Douglas	
	*1139.									Bolinder	80	Gill Prop Co	
	1140.	*Rodeo*	Tug		60′8″	55′11¼″	14′6″	6′6″		Gardner	120	Union Lighterage	12/1924
	*1141.									Bolinder	60	Brown Douglas	

Ship No.	Name	Type	Builder	Dimensions LOA	LBP	BMLD	DMLD	DW	Engine	BHP	Destination	Launch Date	Delivery Date
1142.	*Privateer*	Swim Barge		69'6"		18'0"	6'6"	105			London		10/1924
1143.	*Remand*	Swim Barge		69'6"		18'0"	6'6"	105			London		10/1924
1144.	*Coronet*	Swim Barge		69'6"		18'0"	6'6"	105			London		10/1924
1145.	*Gauntlet*	Swim Barge		69'6"		18'0"	6'6"	105			London		10/1924
1146.	*Sentinel*	Swim Barge		69'6"		18'0"	6'6"	105			London		10/1924
1147.	*Pabiol*	Swim Barge		69'6"		18'0"	6'6"	105			London		10/1924
*1148.									Bolinder	60	Brown Douglas		
*1149.									Bolinder	40	U E Bangkok		
1150.	*Martin*	Swim Barge		75'4"		15'7½"	5'4"	80			London		12/1924
1151.	*Parrot*	Swim Barge		75'4"		15'7½"	5'4"	80			London		12/1924
*1152.									Bolinder	50	W.J.Stewart		
*1153.									Bolinder	2x80	Asiatic Petroleum		
*1154.									Bolinder	20	Brown Douglas		
*1155.									Bolinder	30	Brown Douglas		
*1156.									Bolinder	40	Asiatic Petroleum		
1157.	*Croydon*	Swim Barge		78'9"		21'4⅛"	7'6"	170			London		12/1924
1158.	*Lady Dorman*	Launch		31'6"	29'4"	8'9"	4'3"		Pollock	40	Egypt	9/1925	10/1925
1159.	*Jolly Tar*	Tug		60'0"	55'0"	14'0"	7'4"		Bolinder	135	London	5/1926	7/1926
1160.	*Bickley*	Swim Barge		78'0"		20'9"	7'6"	166			London	2/1925	3/1925
1161.	*Cranley*	Swim Barge		78'0"		20'9"	7'6"	166			London	2/1925	3/1925
1162.	*Filey*	Swim Barge		78'0"	7'6"	166					London	2/1925	3/1925
1163.	*Horley*	Swim Barge		78'0"		20'9"	7'6"	166			London	2/1925	3/1925
1164.	*Kenley*	Swim Barge		78'0"		20'9"	7'6"	166			London	3/1925	4/1925
1165.	*Netley*	Swim Barge		78'0"		20'9"	7'6"	166			London	3/1925	4/1925
1166.	*Purley*	Swim Barge		78'0"		20'9"	7'6"	166			London	6/1925	7/1925
1167.	*Shirley*	Swim Barge		78'0"		20'9"	7'6"	166			London	6/1925	7/1925
1168.	*Swanley*	Swim Barge		78'0"		20'9"	7'6"	166			London		7/1925
1169.	*Wembley*	Swim Barge		78'0"		20'9"	7'6"	166			London		7/1925
1170.	*Pearl*	Canal Barge			76'0"	14'1"	5'0"	85			London	1/1925	2/1925
1171.	*Ruby*	Canal Barge			76'0"	14'1"	5'0"	85			London	1/1925	2/1925
1172.	*Diamond*	Canal Barge			76'0"	14'1"	5'0"	85			London	2/1925	2/1925
1173.	*Emerald*	Canal Barge			76'0"	14'1"	5'0"	85			London	2/1925	2/1925
1174.	*Patrol*	Swim Barge		69'6"		18'0"	6'6"	105			London	3/1925	4/1925
1175.	*Coronet*	Swim Barge		69'6"		18'0"	6'6"	105			London		6/1925
1176.	*Briton*	Swim Barge		69'6"		18'0"	6'6"	105			London	4/1925	4/1925
1177.	*Gauntlet*	Swim Barge		69'6"		18'0"	6'6"	105			London	4/1925	4/1925
1178.	*Sentinel*	Swim Barge		69'6"		18'0"	6'6"	105			London		4/1925
1179.	*Rambler*	Swim Barge		69'6"		18'0"	6'6"	105			London		4/1925
1180.	*Northward*	Tank Swim Barge		87'6"		21'9"	8'0"	185			London	4/1925	5/1925
1181.	*Southward*	Tank Swim Barge		87'6"		21'9"	8'0"	185			London	4/1925	5/1925
1182.	*Eastward*	Tank Swim Barge		87'6"		21'9"	8'0"	185			London	5/1925	6/1925
1183.	*Westward*	Tank Swim Barge		87'6"		21'9"	8'0"	185			London	5/1925	6/1925
1184.	*Windward*	Tank Swim Barge		87'6"		21'9"	8'0"	185			London	6/1925	7/1925
1185.	*Leeward*	Tank Swim Barge		87'6"		21'9"	8'0"	185			London	5/1925	7/1925
1925 1186.	*Mersham*	Dredging Pontoon			30'0"	14'0"	3'6"				South Merstham	5/1925	7/1925
1187.	*Roberts*	Tar Barge		83'0"		17'9"	5'6"	80			London	7/1925	7/1925
1188.	*Kitchener*	Tar Barge		83'0"		17'9"	5'6"	80			London	7/1925	7/1925
1189.	[illegible]	Swim Punt		55'0"		16'0"	5'0"				Faversham	8/1925	8/1925

	*1193.	*Isabel*	Canal Barge	74′0″		10′9″	5′0″		Bolinder	20			
	1194.	*Lido*	Tanker	98′0″	9″′6″	21′3″	8′9″	170	Gardner	150	London	4/1926	7/1926
	1195.	*Janet*	Swim Barge	73′0″		17′10½″	6′6″	110			London	8/1925	8/1925
	1196.	*Madge*	Swim Barge	73′0″		17′10½″	6′6″	110			London	8/1925	8/1925
	1197.	*Elsie*	Swim Barge	73′0″		17′10½″	6′6″	110			London	8/1925	8/1925
	1198.	*Maimunah*	Passenger & Cargo Vessel	140′0″	130′0″	25′0″	10′0″	50	Bolinder	350	Sarawak	10/1925	12/1925
	1199.	*Robin Redbreast*	Tug	66′6″	62′0″	16′0″	6′9″		Bolinder	120	London	9/1925	
	*1200.								Bolinder	10	Bushel Bros		
	1201.	*Trylite*	Swim Barge	77′6″		19′11″	7′6″	165			London	12/1925	1/1926
	1202.	*Venetian*	Swim Barge	64′6″		17′11¼″	6′0″	80			London	12/1925	1/1926
	1203.	*Reg*	Swim Barge	85′0″		22′6″	8′3″	220			London	12/1925	2/1926
	1204.	*Horace*	Swim Barge	85′0″		22′6″	8′3″	220			London	12/1925	2/1926
	1205.	*Oak*	Canal Barge	76′0″		14′0″	5′0″	80				11/1925	12/1925
	1206.	*Fir*	Canal Barge	76′0″		14′0″	5′0″	80				11/1925	12/1925
	1207.	*Pine*	Canal Barge	76′0″		14′0″	5′0″	80				11/1925	1/1926
	1208.	*Elm*	Canal Barge	76′0″		14′0″	5′0″	80				11/1925	1/1926
	1209.	*Yew*	Canal Barge	76′0″		14′0″	5′0″	80				12/1925	1/1926
	1210.	*Teak*	Canal Barge	76′0″		14′0″	5′0″	80				1/1926	1/1926
	*1211.	*Advance*	Canal Boat	70′0″		7′0″	3′6″		Bolinder	15			
	*1212.	*Albert*	Monkey Barge						Bolinder	20			
	*1213.	*Harry*	Monkey Barge						Bolinder	20			
	*1214.								Bolinder	25			
	*1215.	*Sweden*							Bolinder	10			
	1216.	*Noni*	Tug	54′0″	50′0″	13′0″	6′0″		Bolinder	100	Faversham	2/1926	3/1926
	*1217.		Tanker	92′6″		22′0″	8′9″						
	*1218.	*Arthur*	Tug	48′0″		10′6″			Bolinder	50			
	*1219.								Bolinder	150	Turner & Co		
	1220.	*Leader*	Launch	31′10″	29′4″	8′9″	4′3″		Bolinder	25	Corinto	12/1927	12/1927
	1221.	*British Boy*	Tank Barge		66′0″	13′9″	4′6″				Manchester	4/1926	5/1926
	1222.		Tunnel Launch		60′0″	16′0″	4′0″		Kelvin	60	Colombia	4/1926	
	*1223.	*Ilen*	Aux Sailing Vessel						Bolinder	24	Falklands		
	*1224.	*Eagle*	Narrow Boat						Bolinder	15	Fellows M&C		
	*1225.	*Elk*	Narrow Boat						Bolinder	15	Fellows M&C		
	*1226.	*Emu*	Narrow Boat						Bolinder	15	Fellows M&C		
	*1227.	*Falcon*	Narrow Boat						Bolinder	15	Fellows M&C		
	*1228.	*Ferret*	Narrow Boat						Bolinder	15	Fellows M&C		
	*1229.	*Fox*	Narrow Boat						Bolinder	15	Fellows M&C		
	*1230.	*Greyhound*	Narrow Boat						Bolinder	15	Fellows M&C		
	*1231.	*Hare*	Narrow Boat						Bolinder	15	Fellows M&C		
	*1232.	*Hawk*	Narrow Boat						Bolinder	15	Fellows M&C		
	*1233.	*Ibex*	Narrow Boat						Bolinder	15	Fellows M&C		
	*1234.	*Jackal*	Narrow Boat						Bolinder	15	Fellows M&C		
	*1235.	*Jaguar*	Narrow Boat						Bolinder	15	Fellows M&C		
	*1236.								Bolinder	20	Kempson & Co		
1926	1237.		Towing Barge	72′6″		20′0″	5′6″	100			Columbia		5/1926
	1238.		Towing Barge	72′6″		20′0″	5′6″	100			Columbia		6/1926
	1239.	*Pasto*	Tug	60′0″	55′0″	14′0″	6′3″		Bolinder	120	Columbia	6/1926	9/1926
	1240.		Tunnel Launch		60′0″	16′0″	4′0″		Kelvin	60	Columbia		7/1926
	1241.		Tunnel Launch		60′0″	16′0″	4′0″		Kelvin	60	Columbia		7/1926
	1242.	*Dorothy*	Swim Barge	78′9″		21′4″	7′2″	160			London	5/1926	6/1926

Ship No.	Name	Type	Builder	Dimensions LOA	LBP	BMLD	DMLD	DW	Engine	BHP	Destination	Launch Date	Delivery Date
1243.	*Alert*	Hopper			45′0″	11′0″	5′0″	30			Margate	6/1926	6/1926
*1244.									Bolinder	24	U E Singapore		
*1245.									Bolinder	24	British Guinea		
											Devt Co		
1246.	*Milne Watson*	Tank Barge			76′3″	18′6″	6′6″	107			London	8/1926	8/1926
1247.	*Eastwick*	Tug		47′3″	44′0″	11′0″	5′9″			Allen	80	6/1935	
1248.	*Dart*	Tug		54′0″	50′0″	13′0″	6′0″		Bolinder	120	Balfour Beatty		
											London	11/1927	1/1928
*1249.									Bolinder	40	U E Singapore		
1250.	*Yarmouth*	Tank Swim Barge		88′6″		22′0″	7′9″	150			London	1/1927	2/1927
1251.	*Portsmouth*	Tank Swim Barge		88′6″		22′0″	7′9″	150			London	1/1927	2/1927
1252.	*Tynemouth*	Tank Swim Barge		88′6″		22′0″	7′9″	150			London	2/1927	3/1927
1253.	*Grangemouth*	Tank Swim Barge		88′6″		22′0″	7′9″	150			London	3/1927	4/1927
1254.	*Nine*	Swim Barge		72′6″		19′0″	7′0″	126			London	5/1927	5/1927
1255.	*Ten*	Swim Barge		61′0″		18′0″	6′1″	80			London	4/1927	5/1927
*1256.									Bolinder	40	U E Bangkok		
1257.	*Senchi*	Passenger Launch			70′0″	13′0″	5′6″		Twin Bolinder	50	W.Africa	4/1927	9/1927
1258.	*Medway*	Canal Barge			72′6″	14′0″	6′0″				London	4/1927	5/1927
*1259.	*Accretion*	Canal Tug		50′6″		7′8″	3′0″		Bolinder	50			
1260.	*Upas*	Swim Barge		85′0″		21′8″	8′6″	213			London	5/1927	6/1927
1261.	*Vine*	Swim Barge		85′0″		21′8″	8′6″	213			London	5/1927	6/1927
1262.	*Willow*	Swim Barge		85′0″		21′8″	8′6″	213			London	5/1927	6/1927
*1263.	*Mafia*	Surf Boat		45′0″		10′0″	5′0″		Bolinder	30			
1264.		Towing Barge		100′0″		22′0″	5′10″				Dorman Long, Egypt		11/1926
1265.		Towing Barge		100′0″		22′0″	5′10″				Dorman Long, Egypt		11/1926
1266.	*General III*	Tug		75′0″	70′0″	17′6″	9′3″		Ruston Hornsby	310	London		
*1267.	Lilias	Trawler		115′0″		22′0″	13′0″		Bolinder	350	Grimsby		
1268.	*Ferrocrete*	Coaster		104′0″	99′0″	21′6″	8′6″	215	Bolinder	135	London	9/1927	11/1927
*1269.	*Colne*	Canal Boat		71′6″		7′0″	4′1″		Bolinder	20			
1270.	*Scottie*	Tug		70′0″	65′3″	16′0″	8′5″		Bolinder	270	London	6/1930	1/1933
*1271.		Canal Barge		61′0″		12′11″	5′6″		Bolinder	20	Patric Farrell		
*1272.	*Hauturu*	Aux Barge	G. Brown	130′0″		27′4″	9′6″		Bolinder	2x150			
*1273.	*Normana*	Launch							Bolinder	20			
*1274.	*Lerwick*	Fishing Boat		26′2″		8′0″	3′6″		Beta	6/7			
1275.	*Ridham*	Swim Barge		84′11″		23′11″	7′9″	167			Sittingbourne	6/1927	8/1927
1276.	*Kemsley*	Swim Barge		84′11″		23′11″	7′9″	167			Sittingbourne	7/1927	8/1927
1277.	*Grovehurst*	Swim Barge		84′11″		23′11″	7′9″	167			Sittingbourne	8/1927	8/1927
1278.	*Don Lorenzo*	Coaster		80′0″	75′0″	18′0″	8′0″	118	Bolinder	120	Venezuela	7/1927	10/1927
*1279.	*Blue Circle*	Steam Tug	Lytham	77′6″		21′6″	11′4″		Engines 14″x22″x35/24				
									Boiler 13′6″x10′0″x180				
1280.	*Uxbridge*	Canal Barge			77′0″	13′11″	4′6″		Bolinder	30	Upnor		5/1927
*1281.		Narrow Boat							Bolinder	15	Fellows M&C		
*1282.									Bolinder	24	Burns Philp		
1283.	*Vulture*	Launch Tug		48′6″	45′0″	11′0″	5′6″		Widdop	85	Sierra Leone	7/1927	10/1927
1927 1284.		Hopper Barge			45′0″	15′0″	5′0″	10			Crown Agents,		
											Sierra Leone	7/1927	11/1927
1285.		Hopper Barge			45′0″	15′0″	5′0″	10			Crown Agents,		

	1288.		Barge			90′0″	20′0″	4′3½″				Sudan		12/1927
	1289.		Barge			90′0″	20′0″	4′3½″				Sudan		12/1927
	*1290.	*Ipacary*	Tug		46′6″		13′0″	6′0″		Bolinder	120			
	*1291.	*Isiry*	Tug		46′6″		13′0″	6′0″		Bolinder	120			
	*1292.		Canal Barge							Bolinder	20	Walker Bros		
	*1293.	*Banco*	Steam Tug	Cochrane	77′6″		21′6″	12′3″		Engines 14″x21½″x35/24 Boiler 13′6″x10′0″x200				
	1294.	*Bolford*	Canal Barge		77′0″	73′0″	13′11″	5′0″	58	Bolinder	90	APCM, London	10/1927	11/1927
	1295.	*Patricia*	Motor Barge		60′0″	56′0″	13′6″	6′1′	36	Bolinder	70	Fernando PO	11/1927	1/1928
	1298.	*Ilo No 1*	Motor Barge		64′0″	60′0″	14′6″	6′0″	46	Bolinder	50	London	6/1929	6/1929
	*1297.	*Cromford*	Canal Barge	Yare Dry Dock	73′0″		13′11″	5′0″		Kromhout	100			
	*1298.	*Toa*		Auckland, NZ	106′0″		26′0″	8′0″		Bolinder	2x90			
	*1299.	*Quitador*	Tug	Crichton	100′0″		21′0″	10′0″		Bolinder	2x300	R. Plate		
	*1300.	*Jersey*	Tug	Robb, Leith	40′0″		11′9″	5′11″		Bolinder	90			
	1301.	*Bee*	Coaster		79′6″	75′0″	16′6″	6′9″	100	Twin Bolinder	40	Shephard, Cowes, IOW	12/1927	1/1928
	*1302.	*Sri Mukah*			88′0″		22′6″	8′6″		Bolinder	180			
	*1303.	*Lindfar*	Fishing Vessel		56′0″		17′9″			Bolinder	60	Lowestoft		
	1304.	*Barking*	Tug		54′0″	50′0″	13′0″	6′0″		Bolinder	120	Gas Light & Coke Co London	6/1928	7/1928
	1305.		Barge		70′0″		15′0″	4′3½″				Sudan		4/1928
	1306.	*Ina Rose*	Tug		54′0″	50′0″	13′0″	6′0″		Allen	120	London	7/1935	8/1935
	1307.		Launch		31′10″	29′4″	8′9″	4′3″		Bolinder	25	Payne & Wardlaw, Balboa	4/1928	5/1928
	1308.	*Andagoya*	Salvage Buoy Tug		98′6″	92′6″	20′0″	10′8″	33	Bolinder	300	Columbia	5/1928	7/1928
1928	1309.	*Lagopet I*	Motor Barge		70′0″	66′0″	15′0″	5′0″		Twin Bolinder	30	Venezuela	12/1928	1/1929
	1310.	*Lagopet II*	Motor Barge		70′0″	66′0″	15′0″	5′0″		Twin Bolinder	30	Venezuela	12/1928	1/1929
	1311.	*Fortune*	Launch		31′10″	29′4″	8′9″	4′3″		Bolinder	50	Humphrey & Grey, London	7/1928	9/1928
	1312.	*Rodney*	Launch		31′10″	29′4″	8′9″	4′3″		Bolinder	30	London	9/1928	10/1928
	*1313.	*Kwaibo*	Coaster	Crichton	157′6″		26′0″	10′0″		Bolinder	2x180			
	1314.	*Shamrock*	Stern Wheeler		114′0″	100′0″	21′0″	4′0″	22	Steam		Singapore		7/1928
	1315.	*Buena Ventura*	Medical Launch		43′0″	40′0″	10′0″	4′9″		Bolinder	50		8/1928	9/1928
	1316.	*Cartagena*	Medical Launch		43′0″	40′0″	10′0″	4′9″		Bolinder	50		9/1928	10/1928
	1317.	*Santa Marta*	Medical Launch		43′0″	40′0″	10′0″	4′9″		Bolinder	50		9/1928	9/1928
	1318.	*Tumaco*	Medical Launch		43′0″	40′0″	10′0″	4′9″		Bolinder	50		10/1928	10/1928
	1319.	*Peer*	Swim Barge		88′0″		22′0″	8′3″	200			London	11/1928	12/1928
	1320.	*Premier*	Swim Barge		88′0″		22′0″	8′3″	200			London	11/1929	12/1929
	1321.	*Courtier*	Swim Barge		88′0″		22′0″	8′3″	200			London	11/1928	2/1929
	1322.	*Noble*	Swim Barge		88′0″		22′0″	8′3″	200			London	12/1928	2/1929
	1323.	*Lord*	Swim Barge		88′0″		22′0″	8′3″	200			London	1/1929	3/1929
	1324.	*Squire*	Swim Barge		88′0″		22′0″	8′3″	200			London	2/1929	3/1929
	*1325.	*Cormooring*	Salvage Vessel		65′0″		16′3″	9′0″		Engines 8″x18″x14″ Boiler 7′0″x8′0″x140				
	1326.	*Cub*	Launch		31′10″	29′4″	8′9″	4′3″		Widdop	30	London	7/1935	7/1935
	1327.	*Metro Two*	Launch		31′10″	29′4″	8′9″	4′3″		Bolinder	40	London	4/1930	4/1930
	1328.	*Jason*	Barge		85′0″		21′8″	8′6″	200			London	2/1919	4/1929
	1329.	*Krishna*	Barge		85′0″		21′8″	8′6″	200			London	2/1929	4/1929
	1330.	*Luna*	Barge		85′0″		21′8″	8′6″	200			London	3/1929	4/1929
	1331.	*Mercury*	Barge		85′0″		21′8″	8′6″	200			London	3/1929	10/1929
	1332.	*Spring*	Barge		85′0″		21′8″	200				London	4/1929	10/1929

	Ship No.	Name	Type	Builder	Dimensions LOA	LBP	BMLD	DMLD	DW	Engine	BHP	Destination	Launch Date	Delivery Date
	1333.	*Geoffrey Stanley*	Barge Type Coaster		95'6"	90'0"	18'0"	7'0"	113	Plenty	90	WD & HR Mitchell, London	3/1929	5/1929
	1334.	*Carbonang III*	Barge		96'0"		23'0"	7'0"	250			Lobito Bay	3/1929	3/1929
	1335.	*Carbonang IV*	Barge		96'0"		23'0"	7'0"	250			Lobito Bay	4/1929	4/1929
1929	1336.	*Bakura*	Launch		64'0"	63'6"	16'0"	4'6"		Twin Bolinder	40	Red Sea	5/1929	7/1929
	1337.	*Lagopet MB3*	Motor Barge		70'0"	66'0"	15'0"	5'0"		Twin Bolinder	30	Venezuela	4/1929	4/1929
	1338.	*Lagopet MB4*	Motor Barge		70'0"	66'0"	15'0"	5'0"		Twin Bolinder	30	Venezuela	5/1929	7/1929
	1339.	*Lagopet MB5*	Motor Barge		70'0"	66'0"	15'0"	5'0"		Twin Bolinder	30	Venezuela	8/1929	8/1929
	1340.	*Isla Dorada*	Barge			100'0"	28'0"	6'0"	200			Argentine	6/1929	6/1929
	1341.	*Isla Flores*	Barge			100'0"	28'0"	6'0"	200			Argentine	6/1929	6/1929
	1342.	*Isla Linda*	Barge			100'0"	28'0"	6'0"	200			Argentine	7/1929	7/1929
	1343.	*Isla Perdida*	Barge			100'0"	28'0"	6'0"	200			Argentine	7/1929	8/1929
	1344.	*Goorkha*	Swim Barge		95'9"		22'0"	9'0"	290			London	7/1929	8/1929
	1345.	*Gotha*	Swim Barge		95'9"		22'0"	9'0"	290			London	9/1929	9/1929
	1346.	*Gondola*	Swim Barge		95'9"		22'0"	9'0"	290			London	9/1929	9/1929
	1347.	*Gomera*	Swim Barge		95'9"		22'0"	9'0"	290			London	9/1929	10/1929
	1348.	*Gondia*	Swim Barge		95'9"		22'0"	9'0"	290			London	10/1929	10/1929
	1349.	*Goleta*	Swim Barge		95'9"		22'0"	9'0"	290			London	10/1929	10/1929
	1350.	*Magdalena*	Cattle Barge			85'0"	17'0"	6'0"				London	10/1929	
	1351.	*Linda*	Launch			30'0"	8'0"	4'0"		Widdop	24			
	1352.	*Goldace*	Coaster		104'0"	99'0"	21'6"	8'6"	228	Bolinder	150	London	3/1931	5/1931
	1353.	*Tat*	Tug		70'0"	65'3"	16'0"	8'5"		Bolinder	270	London	2/1930	3/1930
	1354.	*Grito de Ascencio*	Tunnel Tug			60'0"	17'0"	5'6"		Twin Bolinder	120	Montevideo	8/1930	12/1930
1930	1355.	*D.H. No.10*	Hopper Barge			90'0"	22'0"	8'6"	225			Dover	4/1930	5/1930
	*1356.	*Lilac*	Launch		39'6"		10'6"	5'6"						
	*1357.		Swim Barge		78'9"		21'5"	7'2"						
	*1358.		Swim Barge		78'9"		21'5"	7'2"						
	1359.	*Effingham*	Swim Barge		78'0"		20'11"	7'6"	160			London	4/1930	5/1930
	1360.	*Guildford*	Swim Barge		78'0"		20'11"	7'6"	160			London	4/1930	5/1930
	1361.	*Godalming*	Swim Barge		78'0"		20'11"	7'6"	160			London	5/1930	5/1930
	1362.	*Haselmere*	Swim Barge		78'0"		20'11"	7'6"	160			London	5/1930	6/1930
	1363.	*Petersfield*	Swim Barge		78'0"		20'11"	7'6"	160			London	6/1930	9/1930
	1364.	*Midhurst*	Swim Barge		78'0"		20'11"	7'6"	160			London	7/1930	9/1930
	1365.	*Balham*	Swim Barge		55'0"		15'11⅛"	5'5"	50			London	5/1930	5/1930
	1366.	*Purley*	Swim Barge		55'0"		15'11⅛"	5'5"	50			London	5/1930	5/1930
	1367.	*Redhill*	Swim Barge		55'0"		15'11⅛"	5'5"	50			London	5/1930	6/1930
	1368.	*Reigate*	Swim Barge		55'0"		15'11⅛"	5'5"	50			London	5/1930	6/1930
	1369.	*Godstone*	Swim Barge		55'0"		15'11⅛"	5'5"	50			London	6/1930	7/1930
	1370.	*Horley*	Swim Barge		55'0"		15'11⅛"	5'5"	50			London	6/1930	7/1930
	1371.	*Atlantis*	Swim Barge		120'0"		24'9"	7'3"	250			London	6/1930	7/1930
	1372.	*Awunaga*	Launch			70'0"	14'0"	5'6"		Twin Bolinder	50	Ada	9/1930	10/1930
	1373.	*T.I.S.1*	Canal Barge			72'10"	13'9"	5'6"	75			London	7/1930	7/1930
	1374.	*T.I.S.2*	Canal Barge			72'10"	13'9"	5'6"	75			London	7/1930	7/1930
	1375.	*T.I.S.3*	Canal Barge			72'10"	13'9"	5'6"	75			London	7/1930	7/1930
	1376.	*T.I.S.4*	Canal Barge			72'10"	13'9"	5'6"	75			London	7/1930	7/1930
	1377.	*T.I.S.5*	Canal Barge			72'10"	13'9"	5'6"	75			London	7/1930	8/1930
	1378.	*T.I.S.6*	Canal Barge			72'10"	13'9"	5'6"	75			London	7/1930	8/1930
	[illegible]	[illegible]	[illegible]			72'10"	13'9"	5'6"	75			London	8/1930	8/1930

	[illegible]		[illegible]			72′10″	13′9″	5′6″	75			London	8/1930	9/1930
	1382.	*T.I.S.10*	Canal Barge			72′10″	13′9″	5′6″	75			London	8/1930	9/1930
	1383.	*T.I.S.11*	Canal Barge			72′10″	13′9″	5′6″	75			London	8/1930	9/1930
	1384.	*T.I.S.12*	Canal Barge			72′10″	13′9″	5′6″	75			London	9/1930	9/1930
	1385.	*El Motahir*	Launch		55′0″		13′0″	5′6″		Atlantic	30/38	Alexandria	8/1930	9/1930
	1386.	*Itaca III*	Tank Barge		91′0″	85′10″	18′0″	7′8″	74	Bolinder	120	Buenos Aires	10/1930	11/1930
	1387.	*Colorcrete*	Motor Barge		78′2″	74′0″	14′3⅝″	5′9″	60	Kromhout	150	Northfleet	12/1930	1/1931
	1388.	*Beatty*	Tank Swim Barge		83′0″		20′3″	6′9″	150			London	11/1930	11/1930
	1389.	*Sturdee*	Tank Swim Barge		83′0″		20′3″	6′9″	150			London	11/1930	11/1930
	1390.	*Kennet*	Launch Tug		35′0½″	32′6″	9′0″	4′6″		Gardner	54	London	3/1931	4/1931
	1391.	*Anak*	Swim Barge		100′0″		25′0″	9′6″	370			London	3/1931	5/1931
	*1392.	*Thrive On*	Fishing Vessel	Marstrand	61′0″					Bolinder				
	1393.	*Ann*	Swim Punt		55′0″		15′11¼″	5′5″	50			London	6/1931	5/1931
	1394.	*Mollie*	Swim Punt		55′0″		15′11¼″	5′5″	50			London	6/1931	5/1931
1931	1395.	*Indigo*	Canal Barge		78′0″		14′4⅝″	6′0″				London	7/1931	7/1931
	1396.	*Jade*	Canal Barge		78′0″		14′4⅝″	6′0″				London	7/1931	7/1931
	1397.	*Khaki*	Canal Barge		78′0″		14′4⅝″	6′0″				London	7/1931	8/1931
	1398.	*Lilac*	Canal Barge		78′0″		14′4⅝″	6′0″				London	7/1931	8/1931
	1399.	*Henry*	Canal Barge		71′6″		6′11″	4′10½″		Bolinder	20	Assoc Canal Carriers		
												London	8/1931	10/1931
	1400.	*Prince*	Canal Barge		71′6″		6′11″	4′10½″		Bolinder	20	Assoc Canal Carriers		
												London	8/1931	10/1931
	1401.	*Bying*	Tar Barge		85′0″		20′3″	6′9″	135			London	10/1931	10/1931
	1402.	No.7	Crane Pontoon		70′1″	68′0″	13′9″	4′6″				London	11/1931	1/1932
	1403.	*No.19*	Hopper Barge		72′0″		12′6″	5′0″	75			London	12/1931	1/1932
	1404.	*No.20*	Hopper Barge		72′0″		12′6″	5′0″	75			London	12/1931	1/1932
	1405.	*Forth II*	Swim Barge		62′6″		16′6″	5′10″				London	12/1931	12/1931
	1406.	*Goldbell*	Motor Barge			93′6″	22′6″	9′3″	255	Twin Bolinder	50	London	6/1932	7/1932
	1407.	*Goldcrown*	Motor Barge			93′6″	22′6″	9′3″	255	Twin Bolinder	50	London	7/1932	8/1932
	1408.	*Golddrift*	Motor Barge			93′6″	22′6″	9′3″	255	Twin Bolinder	50	London	8/1932	9/1932
	1409.	*Goldeve*	Motor Barge			93′6″	22′6″	9′3″	255	Twin Bolinder	50	London	9/1932	11/1932
	1410.	*Crowstone*	Tug		70′0″	66′0″	16′9″	8′1⅝″		Mirrless Bickerton & Day	275	London	6/1932	10/1932
1932	1411.	*Starboardwatch*	Tank Swim Barge		85′0″		22′9″	8′0″	197			London	11/1932	12/1932
	1412.	*Portwatch*	Tank Swim Barge		85′0″		22′9″	8′0″	197			London	11/1932	12/1932
	1413.	*Dogwatch*	Tank Swim Barge		85′0″		22′9″	8′0″	197			London	11/1932	12/1932
	1414.	*Middlewatch*	Tank Swim Barge		85′0″		22′9″	8′0″	197			London	11/1932	12/1932
	1415.	*Morningwatch*	Swim Barge		85′0″		22′9″	8′0″	197			London	1/1933	3/1933
	1416.	*Nightwatch*	Tank Swim Barge		85′0″		22′9″	8′0″	197			London	1/1933	3/1933
	1417.	*Horwood*	Tank Swim Barge		85′0″		21′0″	6′9″	140			London	9/1932	9/1932
	1418.	*Angus*	Swim Barge		81′0″		20′11″	7′6″	160			London	12/1932	1/1933
	1419.	*Fife*	Swim Barge		81′0″		20′11″	7′6″	160			London	12/1932	1/1933
	1420.	No.9	Dredger		68′3″		13′8⅞″	4′6″				London	12/1932	1/1932
	1421.	*Basket*	Swim Barge		78′6″		21′0″	8′6″	190			London	3/1933	3/1933
	1422.	*Packet*	Swim Barge		78′6″		21′0″	8′6″	190			London	3/1933	3/1933
	1423.	Coquet	Swim Barge		90′0″		20′10″	9′0″	240			London	6/1933	7/1933
	1424.	*Conway*	Swim Barge		90′0″		20′10″	9′0″	240			London	6/1933	7/1933
	1425.	*Colne*	Swim Barge		90′0″		20′10″	9′0″	240			London	6/1933	7/1933
	1426.	*Chelmar*	Swim Barge		90′0″		20′10″	9′0″	240			London	7/1933	7/1933
	1427.	*Cherwell*	Swim Barge		90′0″		20′10″	9′0″	240			London	7/1933	7/1933
	1428.	*Clare*	Swim Barge		90′0″		20′10″	9′0″	240			London	7/1933	8/1933
	1429.	*Ching*	Swim Barge		90′0″		20′10″	240				London	8/1933	8/1933
	1430.	*Cuckmere*	Swim Barge		90′0″		20′10″	9⅞″	240			London	9/1933	9/1933

	Ship No.	Name	Type	Builder	Dimensions LOA	LBP	BMLD	DMLD	DW	Engine	BHP	Destination	Launch Date	Delivery Date
	1431.	*Culm*	Swim Barge		90'0"		20'10"	9'0"	240			London	9/1933	9/1933
	1432.	*Cray*	Swim Barge		90'0"		20'10"	9'0"	240			London	9/1933	9/1933
	1433.	*Graveny*	Tank Swim Barge		95'0"		20'10"	8'6"	200			London	4/1933	5/1933
1933	1434.	*Springwell*	Tank Swim Barge		58'0"		17'0"	5'9"	64			London	6/1933	6/1933
	1435.	*Gulliver*	Swim Barge		120'0"		24'9"	7'3"	300			London	9/1933	10/1933
	1436.	*Arctic II*	Swim Barge		62'6"		18'0"	6'6"				London	10/1933	10/1933
	1437.	*Lady Sheila*	Coaster		104'10½"	99'0"	23'6"	9'3"	275	Twin Allen	160	Watson, London	7/1934	3/1935
	1438.	*Kara*	Tug		70'0"	65'3"	16'0"	8'5"		Allen	370	London	3/1935	5/1935
	1439.	*Albany*	Swim Barge		78'0"		20'11"	7'6"	160			London	3/1934	3/1934
	1440.	*Orama*	Swim Barge		78'0"		20'11"	7'6"	160			London	3/1934	3/1934
	1441.	*Avetta*	Swim Barge		78'6"		21'2"	8'6"				London	11/1933	12/1933
	1442.	*Gotette*	Swim Barge		78'6"		21'2"	8'6"				London	11/1933	12/1933
	1443.	*Gaur*	Swim Barge		81'0"		21'6"	8'0"	185			London	1/1934	2/1934
	1444.	*Gayel*	Swim Barge		81'0"		21'6"	8'0"	185			London	1/1934	2/1934
	1445.	*Rodney*	Swim Barge		81'0"		21'6"	8'0"	185			London	3/1934	3/1934
	1446.	*Wroxham*	Swim Barge		81'0"		21'6"	8'0"	185			London	3/1934	3/1934
	1447.	*Strategy*	Swim Barge		81'0"		21'6"	8'0"	185			London	1/1934	1/1934
	1448.	*Stratagem*	Swim Barge		81'0"		21'6"	8'0"	185			London	1/1934	1/1934
	1449.	*Kawara*	Tug		70'3"	65'0"	17'6"	9'11"		Atlas Polar	455	Rochester	7/1934	11/1934
	1450.	*St Botolph*	Swim Barge		81'0"		21'1½"	8'0"				London	3/1934	3/1934
	1451.	*St Clements*	Swim Barge		81'0"		21'1½"	8'0"				London	3/1934	3/1934
	1452.	*Cyclops*	Swim Barge		120'0"		24'9"	7'3"	250			London	2/1934	3/1934
	1453.	*No.50*	Canal Hopper			72'0"	9'0"	4'10"	55			London	2/1934	2/1934
	1454.	*No.51*	Canal Hopper			72'0"	9'0"	4'10"	55			London	2/1934	2/1934
	1455.	*No.52*	Canal Hopper			72'0"	9'0"	4'10"	55			London	2/1934	2/1934
	1456.	*No.53*	Canal Hopper			72'0"	9'0"	4'10"	55			London	2/1934	2/1934
	1457.	*Friday*	Canal Barge		79'6"		14'4"	5'1"	90			London	4/1934	4/1934
	1458.	*Saturday*	Canal Barge		79'6"		14'4"	5'1"	90			London	4/1934	4/1934
	1459.	*Sunday*	Canal Barge		79'6"		14'4"	5'1"	90			London	4/1934	4/1934
	1460.	*Birthday*	Canal Barge		79'6"		14'4"	5'1"	90			London	4/1934	5/1934
	1461.	*Holiday*	Canal Barge		79'6"		14'4"	5'1"	90			London	4/1934	5/1934
	1462.	*Payday*	Canal Barge		79'6"		14'4"	5'1"	90			London	4/1934	5/1934
1934	1463.	*Greenwich*	Swim Barge		72'8"		17'10"	6'6"	105			London	5/1934	6/1934
	1464.	Poplar	Swim Barge		72'8"		17'10"	6'6"	105			London	5/1934	6/1934
	1465.	*Camroux I*	Coaster		136'0"	130'0"	25'0"	10'9"		Deutz	300	Newcastle Shipping London	10/1934	12/1934
	1466.	*Camroux II*	Coaster		136'0"	130'0"	25'0"	10'9"		Deutz	300	Newcastle Shipping London	11/1934	1/1935
	1467.	*Truro*	Swim Barge		78'0"		20'11"	7'6"	160			London	5/1934	6/1934
	1468.	*Trelawney*	Swim Barge		78'0"		20'11"	7'6"	160			London	5/1934	6/1934
	1469.	*Tintagel*	Swim Barge		78'0"		20'11"	7'6"	160			London	5/1934	6/1934
	1470.	*Tregenna*	Swim Barge		78'0"		20'11"	7'6"	160			London	5/1934	6/1934
	1471.	*Baroda*	Swim Barge		82'0"		21'4"	8'6"				London	7/1934	8/1934
	1472.	*Benares*	Swim Barge		82'0"		21'4"	8'6"				London	7/1934	8/1934
	1473.	*Bhopal*	Swim Barge		82'0"		21'4"	8'6"				London	8/1934	9/1934
	1474.	*Burdwan*	Swim Barge		82'0"		21'4"	8'6"				London	8/1934	9/1934
	1475.	*Mersey*	Swim Barge		72'8"		17'10"	6⅜"	110			London	6/1934	6/1934
	[illegible]	[illegible]	[illegible]		[illegible]		17'10"	[illegible]	110			London	6/1934	6/1934

Year	No.	Name	Type						Engine	HP	Owner		
	1479.	*Rosebriar*	Canal Barge	78′2¾″	76′8¼″	14′1.4/20″	5′6″				London	10/1934	11/1934
	1480.	*Rosebourne*	Canal Barge	78′2¾″	76′8¼″	14′1.4/20″	5′6″				London	12/1934	1/1935
	1481.	*Rosethorne*	Canal Barge	78′2¾″	76′8¼″	14′1.4/20″	5′6″				London	12/1934	1/1935
	1482.	*Rosewell*	Canal Barge	78′2¾″	76′8¼″	14′1.4/20″	5′6″				London	1/1935	2/1935
	1483.	*Rosehall*	Canal Barge	78′2¾″	76′8¼″	14′1.4/20″	5′6″				London	1/1935	2/1935
	1484.	*Lemnos*	Swim Barge	82′0″		22′6″	8′0″	200			London	9/1934	10/1934
	1485.	*Samos*	Swim Barge	82′0″		22′6″	8′0″	200			London	9/1934	10/1934
	1486.	*Achieve*	Swim Barge	78′0″		20′11″	7′6″	160			London	9/1934	11/1934
	1487.	*Attempt*	Swim Barge	78′0″		20′11″	7′6″	160			London	9/1934	11/1934
	1488.	*Buddy*	Swim Barge	78′0″		20′11″	7′6″	160			London	2/1935	3/1935
	1489.	*Brisk*	Swim Barge	78′0″		20′11″	7′6″	160			London	2/1935	3/1935
	1490.	*No.14*	Dredger	70′2″	70′0″	13′10″	4′6″				London	10/1935	11/1935
	1491.	*Didcot*	Swim Barge	105′0″		24′9″	6′9″	220			London	10/1934	11/1934
	1492.	*Eaton*	Swim Barge	105′0″		24′9″	6′9″	220			London	11/1934	12/1934
	1493.	*Fowey*	Swim Barge	105′0″		24′9″	6′9″	220			London	11/1934	1/1935
	1494.	*Cowie*	Swim Barge	91′8″		20′10″	9′0″	250			London	12/1934	12/1934
	1495.	*Connon*	Swim Barge	91′8″		20′10″	9′0″	250			London	12/1934	12/1934
	1496.	*Teign*	Canal Barge	72′9⅞″	72′6″	14′0″	5′6″				London	12/1934	2/1935
	1497.	*Tone*	Canal Barge	72′9⅞″	72′6″	14′0″	5′6″				London	12/1934	2/1935
	1498.	*Masters 4*	Swim Barge	80′0″		16′10⅛″	6′6″	120			London	2/1935	3/1935
	1499.	*Armadale*	Swim Barge	86′4⅞″		23′10″	8′3″	250			London	4/1935	4/1935
	1500.	*Birkdale*	Swim Barge	86′4⅞″		23′10″	8′3″	250			London	4/1935	4/1935
	1501.	*Colindale*	Swim Barge	86′4⅞″		23′10″	8′3″	250			London	4/1935	6/1935
	1502.	*Dovedale*	Swim Barge	86′4⅞″		23′10″	8′3″	250			London	4/1935	6/1935
	1503.	*Eskdale*	Swim Barge	86′4⅞″		23′10″	8′3″	250			London	6/1935	6/1935
	1504.	*Ferndale*	Swim Barge	86′4⅞″		23′10″	8′3″	250			London	6/1935	6/1935
	1505.	*Phoebe II*	Launch Tug	41′2⅜″	37′3″	11′0″	5′5″		Gleniffer	80	London	3/1935	4/1935
	1506.	*Clytha*	Swim Barge	72′8″		17′10″	6′6″	105			London	5/1935	5/1935
	1507.	*Bigswear*	Swim Barge	72′8″		17′10″	6′6″	105			London	5/1935	5/1935
	1508.	*Castleton*	Swim Barge	72′8″		17′10″	6′6″	105			London	5/1935	5/1935
	1509.	*Holmhurst*	Swim Barge	72′8″		17′10″	6′6″	105			London	5/1935	5/1935
	1510.	*Tana*	Swim Barge	72′8″		17′10″	6′6″	105			London	5/1935	6/1935
	1511.	*Tanrec*	Swim Barge	72′8″		17′10″	6′6″	105			London	5/1935	6/1935
1935	1512.	*Widdop*	Launch Tug	41′0″	38′0″	10′6″	5′3″		Widdop	60	London	7/1935	7/1935
	1513.	*Stratum*	Swim Barge	82′0″		22′6″	8′0″	200			London	7/1935	7/1935
	1514.	*Stratus*	Swim Barge	82′0″		22′6″	8′0″	200			London	7/1935	7/1935
	1515.	*Lady Stella*	Coaster	104′10½″	99′0″	23′6″	9′3″	270	Twin Allen	160	Watson, London	11/1935	1/1936
	1516.		Dummy Pontoon		50′0″	20′0″	3′6″				Medway Conservancy, London	6/1935	7/1935
	1517.	*Astra*	Swim Barge	78′0″		20′11″	7′6″	160			London	8/1935	8/1935
	1518.	*Candida*	Swim Barge	78′0″		20′11″	7′6″	160			London	8/1935	8/1935
	1519.	*Monkwood*	Swim Barge	81′0″		21′6″	8′0″	185			London	7/1935	8/1935
	1520.	*Ringwood*	Swim Barge	81′0″		21′6″	8′0″	185			London	7/1935	8/1935
	1521.	*Olivine*	Swim Barge	82′0″		22′6″	8′0″	200			London	9/1935	10/1935
	1522.	*Olivory*	Swim Barge	82′0″		22′6″	8′0″	200			London	9/1935	10/1935
	1523.		Ferry Pontoon	22′0″		9′6″	3′0″				London		11/1935
	1524.	*Drone*	Swim Punt	55′0″		15′11¼″	5′5″	50			London	8/1935	9/1935
	1525.	*Weevil*	Swim Punt	55′0″		15′11¼″	5′5″	50			London	8/1935	9/1935
	1526.	*Westwick*	Launch Tug	46′0″	43′0″	12′0″	5′7″		Allen	80	R.G. Odell, London	10/1935	11/1935
	1527.	*Jaymar*	Launch Tug	41′0″	38′0″	10′6″	5′3″		Widdop	60	London	9/1935	10/1935
	1528.	*Swift*	Launch Tug	41′0″	38′0″	10′6″	5′3″		Widdop	60	London	4/1936	5/1936

	Ship No.	Name	Type	Builder	Dimensions LOA	LBP	BMLD	DMLD	DW	Engine	BHP	Destination	Launch Date	Delivery Date
	1529.	*Olivale*	Swim Barge		78′0″		20′11″	7′6″	160			London	10/1935	10/1935
	1530.	*Oliventure*	Swim Barge		78′0″		20′11″	7′6″	160			London	10/1935	10/1935
	1531.	*Velsheda*	Swim Barge		78′0″		20′11″	7′6″	160			London	10/1935	10/1935
	1532.	*Norada*	Swim Barge		78′0″		20′11″	7′6″	160			London	10/1935	10/1935
	1533.	*Nyria*	Swim Barge		78′0″		20′11″	7′6″	160			London	10/1935	10/1935
	1534.	*Mariska*	Swim Barge		78′0″		20′11″	7′6″	160			London	10/1935	10/1935
	1535.	*Ormonde*	Swim Barge		78′0″		20′11″	7′6″	160			London	12/1935	1/1936
	1536.	*Orford*	Swim Barge		78′0″		20′11″	7′6″	160			London	12/1935	1/1936
	1537.	*Oronsay*	Swim Barge		78′0″		20′11″	7′6″	160			London	1/1936	1/1936
	1538.	*Orsova*	Swim Barge		78′0″		20′11″	7′6″	160			London	1/1936	1/1936
	1539.	*Nobby*	Swim Punt		55′0′		15′11¼″	5′5″	50			London	1/1936	2/1936
	1540.	*Bungie*	Swim Punt		55′0″		15′11¼″	5′5″	50			London	1/1936	2/1936
	1541.	*Tresco*	Swim Barge		78′0″		20′11″	7′6″	160			London	1/1936	2/1936
	1542.	*Trevose*	Swim Barge		78′0″		20′11″	7′6″	160			London	1/1936	2/1936
	1543.	*Misbourne*	Canal Barge			71′6″	13′10¼″	5′6″	86			London	2/1936	3/1936
	1544.	*Clun*	Canal Barge			71′6″	13′10¼″	5′6″	86			London	2/1936	3/1936
	1545.	*Abundance*	Swim Barge		78′0″		20′11″	7′6″	160			London	2/1936	3/1936
	1546.	*Ayli*	Swim Barge		78′0″		20′11″	7′6″	160			London	2/1936	3/1936
	1547.	*Cerovim*	Swim Barge		78′0″		20′11″	7′6″	160			London	3/1936	3/1936
	1548.	*London Pride*	Swim Barge		78′0″		20′11″	7′6″	160			London	3/1936	3/1936
	1549.	*Korvit*	Swim Barge		78′0″		20′11″	7′6″	160			London	3/1936	4/1936
	1550.	*Banzai*	Swim Barge		78′0″		20′11″	7′6″	160			London	3/1936	4/1936
1936	1551.	*Tresmeer*	Swim Barge		78′0″		20′11″	7′6″	160			London	4/1936	4/1936
	1552.	*Treween*	Swim Barge		78′0″		20′11″	7′6″	160			London	4/1936	4/1936
	1553.	*Trelowarren*	Swim Barge		78′0″		20′11″	7′6″	160			London	4/1936	4/1936
	1554.	*Tresillian*	Swim Barge		78′0″		20′11″	7′6″	160			London	4/1936	4/1936
	1555.	*Heyford*	Swim Barge		72′8″		18′10″	7′0″	120			London	5/1936	6/1936
	1556.	*Washford*	Swim Barge		72′8″		18′10″	7′0″	120			London	5/1936	6/1936
	1557.	*Burford*	Swim Barge		72′8″		18′10″	7′0″	120			London	5/1936	6/1936
	1558.	*Dornford*	Swim Barge		72′8″		18′10″	7′0″	120			London	5/1936	5/1936
	1559.	*Shamley*	Swim Barge		78′0″		20′11″	7′6″	160			London	4/1936	5/1936
	1560.	*Sunbridge*	Swim Barge		78′0″		20′11″	7′6″	160			London	4/1936	5/1936
	1561.	*Chancellor*	Swim Barge		78′0″		20′11″	7′6″	160			London	5/1936	6/1936
	1562.	*Lord Nelson*	Swim Barge		78′0″		20′11″	7′6″	160			London	5/1936	6/1936
	1563.	*Adventure*	Swim Barge		78′0″		20′11″	7′6″	160			London	6/1936	6/1936
	1564.	*Alltransport*	Swim Barge		78′0″		20′11″	7′6″	160			London	6/1936	6/1936
	1565.	*Acid*	Tar Barge		87′2″	86′2″	16′4½″	5′6″	115			London	7/1936	8/1936
	1566.	*Jaywick*	Swim Barge		72′8″		17′10″	6′6″	105			London	6/1936	7/1936
	1567.	*Crantock*	Swim Barge		72′8″		17′10″	6′6″	105			London	6/1936	7/1936
	1568.	*Angles*	Swim Barge		72′8″		17′10″	6′6″	105			London	6/1936	7/1936
	1569.	*Compton*	Swim Barge		72′8″		17′10″	6′6″	105			London	6/1936	7/1936
	1570.	*Oakley*	Swim Barge		85′0″		22′6″	8′0″	210			London	10/1936	10/1936
	1571.	*Hailey*	Swim Barge		85′0″		22′6″	8′0″	210			London	10/1936	10/1936
	1572.	*Beckenham*	Swim Barge		72′8″		17′10″	6′6″	105			London	6/1936	7/1936
	1573.	*West Ham*	Swim Barge		72′8″		17′10″	6′6″	105			London	6/1936	7/1936
	1574.		Open Lighter		72′6″		20′0″	5′9″	130			Aden		8/1936
	1575.	*Effra*	Swim Barge		78′0″		20′11″	7′6″	160			London	7/1936	7/1936

1577.	*Clutha*	Swim Barge	78′0″		20′11″	7′6″	160			London	7/1936	8/1936
1578.	*Beck*	Swim Barge	78′0″		20′11″	7′6″	160			London	7/1936	8/1936
1579.	*Ruislip*	Canal Tug	31′6″	30′3″	6′9″	4′3″		Widdop	24	London	8/1936	9/1936
1580.	*Nancy Lee*	Launch Tug	47′0″	43′9″	13′0″	4′9½″		Bolinder	70	London	9/1936	10/1936
1581.	*Varlet*	Launch Tug	41′0″	38′0″	10′6″	5′3″		Widdop	60	London	4/1937	5/1937
1582.	*Arthur*	Swim Barge	78′0″		20′11″	7′6″	160			Rochester	9/1936	9/1936
1583.	*John*	Swim Barge	78′0″		20′11″	7′6″	160			Rochester	9/1936	9/1936
1584.	*Peter*	Swim Barge	78′0″		20′11″	7′6″	160			Rochester	9/1936	9/1936
1585.	*Foster*	Swim Barge	78′0″		20′11″	7′6″	160			London	9/1936	10/1936
1586.	*Instow*	Swim Barge	105′0″		24′9″	6′9″	220			London	7/1936	8/1936
1587.	*Jarrow*	Swim Barge	105′0″		24′9″	6′9″	220			London	7/1936	8/1936
1588.	*Castle*	Swim Barge	72′8″		17′10″	6′6″	105			London	9/1936	9/1936
1589.	*Contract*	Swim Barge	72′8″		17′10″	6′6″	105			London	9/1936	9/1936
1590.	*Olivhithe*	Swim Barge	78′0″		20′11″	7′6″	160			London	10/1936	10/1936
1591.	*Olivex*	Swim Barge	78′0″		20′11″	7′6″	160			London	10/1936	10/1936
1592.	*David*	Swim Barge	78′0″		20′11″	7′6″	160			Rochester	10/1936	11/1936
1593.	*Dennis*	Swim Barge	78′0″		20′11″	7′6″	160			Rochester	10/1936	11/1936
1594.	*Dermbach*	Swim Barge	72′8″		17′10″	6′6″	105			London	2/1937	2/1937
1595.	*Greatbentley*	Swim Barge	72′8″		17′10″	6′6″	105			London	2/1937	2/1937
1596.	*Nub*	Swim Punt	55′0″		15′11¼″	5′5″	50			London	4/1937	5/1937
1597.	*Dub*	Swim Punt	55′0″		15′11¼″	5′5″	50			London	4/1937	5/1937
1598.	*Midlothian*	Swim Barge	81′0″		20′10″	7′6″	160			London	11/1936	11/1936
1599.	*Kirkcudbright*	Swim Barge	81′0″		20′10″	7′6″	160			London	11/1936	11/1936
1600.	*Lednock*	Swim Barge	84′9″		20′10″	8′5″	200			London	12/1936	12/1936
1601.	*Leadon*	Swim Barge	84′9″		20′10″	8′5″	200			London	12/1936	12/1936
1602.	*Lambourne*	Swim Barge	84′9″		20′10″	8′5″	200			London	12/1936	12/1936
1603.	*Lambroath*	Swim Barge	84′9″		20′10″	8′5″	200			London	12/1936	12/1936
1604.	*Ditchley*	Swim Barge	85′0″		22′6″	8′0″	200			London	3/1937	4/1937
1605.	*Iffley*	Swim Barge	85′0″		22′6″	8′0″	200			London	3/1937	4/1937
1606.	*Dereck*	Swim Barge	78′0″		20′11″	7′6″	160			Rochester	12/1936	1/1937
1607.	*Donald*	Swim Barge	78′0″		20′11″	7′6″	160			Rochester	12/1936	1/1937
1608.	*Dudley*	Swim Barge	78′0″		20′11″	7′6″	160			Rochester	1/1937	1/1937
1609.	*Duncan*	Swim Barge	78′0″		20′11″	7′6″	160			Rochester	1/1937	1/1937
1610.	*Garsdale*	Swim Barge	86′0″		24′0″	8′3″	250			London	1/1937	2/1937
1611.	*Iredale*	Swim Barge	86′0″		24′0″	8′3″	250			London	1/1937	2/1937
1612.	*Hamdale*	Swim Barge	86′0″		24′0″	8′3″	250			London	2/1937	2/1937
1613.	*Jendale*	Swim Barge	86′0″		24′0″	8′3″	250			London	2/1937	2/1937
1614.	*Tring*	Canal Tug	46′6″	44′11″	11′6″	4′10″		Widdop	80	London	2/1937	3/1937
1615.	*Quarterday*	Canal Barge	79′3¼″	78′6″	14′4⅝″	5′1⅞″	100			London	7/1937	8/1937
1616.	*Halfday*	Canal Barge	79′3¼″	78′6″	14′4⅝″	5′1⅞″	100			London	7/1937	8/1937
1617.	*Fullday*	Canal Barge	79′3¼″	78′6″	14′4⅝″	5′1⅞″	100			London	7/1937	8/1937
1618.	*Easterday*	Canal Barge	79′3¼″	78′6″	14′4⅝″	5′1⅞″	100			London	7/1937	8/1937
1619.	*Xmasday*	Canal Barge	79′3¼″	78′6″	14′4⅝″	5′1⅞″	100			London	7/1937	8/1937
1620.	*Joyday*	Canal Barge	79′3¼″	78′6″	14′4⅝″	5′1⅞″	100			London	7/1937	8/1937
1621.	*Ben Lui*	Canal Barge	78′0″	77′4″″	14′1″	5′3″	100			London	3/1937	4/1937
1622.	*Ben More*	Canal Barge	78′0″	77′4½″	14′1″	5′3″	100			London	3/1937	4/1937
1623.	*Ben Nevis*	Canal Barge	78′0″	77′4½″	14′1″	5′3″	100			London	3/1937	4/1937
1624.	*Ben Vorlich*	Canal Barge	78′0″	77′4½″	14′1″	5′3″	100			London	3/1937	4/1937
1625.	*Felda*	Swim Barge	78′0″		20′11″	7′6″	160			London	2/1937	3/1937
1626.	*Lake Rise*	Swim Barge	78′0″		20′11″	7′6″	160			London	2/1937	3/1937
1627.	*Daffodil*	Swim Barge	78′0″		20′11″	7′6″	160			London	3/1937	4/1937

Ship No.	Name	Type	Builder	Dimensions LOA	LBP	BMLD	DMLD	DW	Engine	BHP	Destination	Launch Date	Delivery Date
1528.	*Stratstone*	Swim Barge		78'0"		20'11"	7'6"	160			London	3/1937	4/1937
1529.	*Stratwood*	Swim Barge		78'0"		20'11"	7'6"	160			London	4/1937	4/1937
1530.	*Stratland*	Swim Barge		78'0"		20'11"	7'6"	160			London	4/1937	4/1937
1531.	*Roc 1*	Tank Launch		49'6"	46'6"	10'0"	5'6"	9	Allen	66	Sharjah	8/1937	10/1937
1532.	*Roc 2*	Tank Launch		49'6"	46'6"	10'0"	5'6"	9	Allen	66	Sharjah	9/1937	12/1937
1533.	*Roc 3*	Tank Launch		49'6"	46'6"	10'0"	5'6"	9	Allen	66	Sharjah	11/1937	12/1937
1634.	*Trusty*	Swim Barge		105'0'		24'9"	6'9"	220			London	5/1937	6/1937
1635.	*Prompt*	Swim Barge		105'0"		24'9"	6'9"	220			London	5/1937	6/1937
1636.	*Royal Oak*	Swim Barge		105'0"		24'9"	9'6"	381			London	6/1937	6/1937
1637.	*Royal Sovereign*	Swim Barge		105'0"		24'9"	9'6"	381			London	6/1937	7/1937
1638.	*Welfare*	Swim Barge		105'0"		24'9"	9'6"	381			London	6/1937	7/1937
1639.	*Velocity*	Swim Barge		105'0"		24'9"	9'6"	381			London	7/1937	7/1937
1640.	*Newton*	Swim Barge		105'0"		24'9"	9'6"	381			London	5/1937	5/1937
1641.	*Alfred Robertson*	Medical Launch		54'3"	51'3"	12'0"	6'6"		Gardner	136	London	5/1938	5/1938
1937 1642.	*Turville*	Swim Barge		76'0"		17'10"	7'0"	130			London	7/1937	8/1937
1643.	*Fingest*	Swim Barge		76'0"		17'10"	7'0"	130			London	7/1937	8/1937
1644.	*Skirmett*	Swim Barge		76'0"		17'10"	7'0"	130			London	8/1937	8/1937
1645.	*Frieth*	Swim Barge		76'0"		17'10"	7'0"	130			London	8/1937	8/1937
1646.	*Hambleden*	Swim Barge		76'0"		17'10"	7'0"	130			London	8/1937	9/1937
1647.	*Millend*	Swim Barge		76'0"		17'10"	7'0"	130			London	8/1937	9/1937
1648.	*Swallow*	Launch Tug		41'0"	38'0"	10'6"	5'3"		Widdop	60	London	11/1937	12/1937
1649.	*Lady Sophia*	Coaster		110'6"	105'0"	23'6"	9'6"	27	Atlas Polar	210	Watson Rochester	8/1938	10/1938
1650.		River Lighter			125'0"	25'0"	6'6"	220			Abadan		2/1938
1651.		River Lighter			125'0"	25'0"	6'6"	220			Abadan		3/1938
1652.	*Tideway*	Swim Barge		78'0"		20'11"	7'6"	160			London	8/1937	9/1937
1653.	*Causeway*	Swim Barge		78'0"		20'11"	7'6"	160			London	8/1937	9/1937
1654.	*Highway*	Swim Barge		78'0"		20'11"	7'6"	160			London	9/1937	9/1937
1655.	*Headway*	Swim Barge		78'0"		20'11"	7'6"	160			London	9/1937	9/1937
1656.	*Foneus*	Swim Barge		78'0"		20'11"	7'6"	160			London	9/1937	9/1937
1657.	*Korlus*	Swim Barge		78'0"		20'11"	7'6"	160			London	9/1937	9/1937
1658.	*Abele*	Swim Barge		78'0"		20'11"	7'6"	160			London	10/1937	10/1937
1659.	*Abies*	Swim Barge		78'0"		20'11"	7'6"	160			London	10/1937	10/1937
1660.	*C 40*	Swim Barge		85'0"		22'6"	8'0"	200			Sheernees	7/1937	7/1938
1661.	*Piper 4*	Swim Barge		78'0"		20'11"	7'6"	160			London	9/1937	10/1937
1662.	*Piper 5*	Swim Barge		78'0"		20'11"	7'6"	160			London	9/1937	10/1937
1663.	*Emily Jane*	Swim Barge		78'0"		20'11"	7'6"	160			London	10/1937	10/1937
1664.	*Peter T*	Swim Barge		78'0"		20'11"	7'6"	160			London	10/1937	10/1937
1665.		Open Lighter		72'6"		20'0"	5'9"	130			Aden		3/1938
1666.		Open Lighter		72'6"		20'0"	5'9"	130			Aden		3/1938
1667.	*Cornflower*	Swim Barge		85'0"		22'6"	8'0"	200			London	12/1937	1/1938
1668.	*Oliver*	Swim Barge		85'0"		22'6"	8'0"	200			London	12/1937	1/1938
1669.	*Kenwyn*	Swim Barge		78'0"		20'11"	7'6"	160			London	10/1937	10/1938
1670.	*Anker*	Swim Barge		78'0"		20'11"	7'6"	160			London	11/1937	11/1938
1671.	*Etherbabe*	Swim Barge		78'0"		20'11"	7'6"	160			London	11/1937	12/1937
1672.	*Ethermite*	Swim Barge		78'0"		20'0"	7'6"	160			London	11/1937	12/1937
1673.		Open Lighter		72'6"		20'0"	5'9"	130			Aden		3/1938
1674.	*C 38*	Swim Barge		85'0"		22'6"	8'0"	200			Sheerness	5/1938	5/1938

	1678.	*Olivetree*	Swim Barge	78′0″		20′11″	7′6″	160			London	2/1938	2/1938
	1679.	*Chess*	Swim Barge	78′0″		20′11″	7′6″	160			London	2/1938	2/1938
	1680.	*Orcades*	Swim Barge	78′0″		20′11″	7′6″	160			London	3/1938	3/1938
	1681.	*Orontes*	Swim Barge	78′0″		20′11″	7′6″	160			London	3/1938	3/1938
	1682.	*Deborah*	Swim Barge	78′0″		20′11″	7′6″	160			Rochester	4/1938	4/1938
	1683.	*Delilah*	Swim Barge	78′0″		20′11″	7′6″	160			Rochester	4/1938	4/1938
	1684.	*Vassal*	Launch Tug	41′0″	38′0″	10′6″	5′3″		Widdop	60	London	6/1938	7/1938
	1685.	*Tommy Lee*	Launch Tug	49′6″	46′3″	13′0″	4′9½″		Crossley	100	London	8/1938	8/1938
	1686.	*Duckett*	Launch Tug	49′6″	46′3″	13′0″	4′9½″		Crossley	100	London	8/1938	9/1938
	1687.	*Seaford*	Swim Barge	78′0″		20′11″	7′6″	160			London	5/1938	5/1938
	1688.	*Ethergate*	Swim Barge	78′0″		20′11″	7′6″	160			London	5/1938	5/1938
	1689.	*Dorcas*	Swim Barge	78′0″		20′11″	7′6″	160			Rochester	5/1938	5/1938
	1690.	*Dornia*	Swim Barge	78′0″		20′11″	7′6″	160			Rochester	5/1938	5/1938
	1691.	*Olivegrove*	Swim Barge	78′0″		20′11″	7′6″	160			London	8/1938	9/1938
	1692.	*Oliveco*	Swim Barge	78′0″		20′11″	7′6″	160			London	8/1938	9/1938
1938	1693.	*Dolores*	Swim Barge	78′0″		20′11″	7′6″	160			Rochester	8/1938	9/1938
	1694.	*Doris*	Swim Barge	78′0″		20′11″	7′6″	160			Rochester	8/1938	9/1938
	1695.	*Dulcie*	Swim Barge	78′0″		20′11″	7′6″	160			Rochester	9/1938	9/1938
	1696.	*Deirdre*	Swim Barge	78′0″		20′11″	7′6″	160			Rochester	9/1938	9/1938
	1697.	*Tunnel*	Swim Barge	105′0″		24′9″	6′9″	250			London	9/1938	11/1938
	1698.	*Tunnelite*	Swim Barge	105′0″		24′9″	6′9″	250			London	9/1938	11/1938
	1699.	*Adeline*	Swim Barge	105′0″		24′9″	9′6″	381			London	11/1938	11/1938
	1700.	*Emilene*	Swim Barge	105′0″		24′9″	9′6″	381			London	11/1938	12/1938
	1701.	*Jesamine*	Swim Barge	105′0″		24′9″	9′6″	381			London	11/1938	12/1938
	1702.	*Albertine*	Swim Barge	105′0″		24′9″	9′6″	381			London	11/1938	12/1938
	1703.	*Lucine*	Swim Barge	105′0″		24′9″	9′6″	381			London	12/1938	1/1940
	1704.	*Rosine*	Swim Barge	105′0″		24′9″	9′6″	381			London	12/1938	1/1940
	1705.	*C 41*	Swim Barge	85′0″		22′6″	8′0″	200			Sheerness	7/1938	8/1938
	1706.	*C 76*	Swim Barge	85′0″		22′6″	8′0″	200			Sheerness	7/1938	8/1938
	1707.	*St Hugh*	Swim Barge	78′0″		20′11″	7′6″	160			London	9/1938	10/1938
	1708.	*Meadway*	Swim Barge	78′0″		20′11″	7′6″	160			London	9/1938	10/1938
	1709.	*Samaden*	Launch Tug	41′0″	38′0″	10′6″	5′3″		Widdop	60		7/1939	7/1940
	1710.	*St Olaf*	Swim Barge	78′0″		20′11″	7′6″	160			London	10/1938	11/1938
	1711.	*St Kitts*	Swim Barge	78′0″		20′11″	7′6″	160			London	10/1938	11/1938
	1712.	*Talland*	Swim Barge	78′0″		20′11″	7′6″	160			London	1/1939	1/1939
	1713.	*Bantry Bay*	Swim Barge	78′0″		20′11″	7′6″	160			London	1/1939	1/1939
	1714.	*Howcott*	Swim Barge	78′0″		20′11″	7′6″	160			London	2/1939	3/1939
	1715.	*Howstan*	Swim Barge	78′0″		20′11″	7′6″	160			London	2/1939	3/1939
1939	1716.	*Daru*	Swim Barge	85′0″		22′6″	8′0″	200			London	6/1939	6/1939
	1717.	*Kissy*	Swim Barge	85′0″		22′6″	8′0″	200			London	6/1939	6/1939
	1718.	*Tuscan*	Swim Barge	78′0″		20′11″	7′6″	160			London	1/1939	1/1939
	1719.	*Talisman*	Swim Barge	78′0″		20′11″	7′6″	160			London	1/1939	1/1939
	1720.	*Hoopoo*	Swim Barge	78′0″		20′11″	7′6″	160			London	1/1939	2/1939
	1721.	*Hornbill*	Swim Barge	78′0″		20′11″	7′6″	160			London	1/1939	2/1939
	1722.	*Demdima*	Swim Barge	78′0″		20′11″	7′6″	160			London	2/1939	3/1939
	1723.	*Darjeeling*	Swim Barge	78′0″		20′11″	7′6″	160			London	2/1939	3/1939
	1724.	*Luka*	Launch Tug	41′0″	38′0″	10′6″	5′3″		Widdop	60	Leopoldville	1/1941	2/1940
	1725.	*Silverdash*	Launch Tug	43′9″	40′0″	12′0″	12′0″	5′9″	Crossley	100	London	2/1940	4/1940
	1726.	*Dominence*	Coaster	118′6″	113′0″	24′6″	9′6″	300	Atlas Polar	250	Rochester	1/1940	4/1940
	1727.		Swim Barge	72′8″		18′0″	6′6″	105			Chatham		8/1940
	1728.	*Cob*	Swim Barge	72′8″		18′0″	6′6″	105			London		5/1948

Ship No.	Name	Type	Builder	Dimensions LOA	LBP	BMLD	DMLD	DW	Engine	BHP	Destination	Launch Date	Delivery Date
1729.	*Ludo*	Swim Barge		78'0"		20'11"	7'6"	160			London	4/1939	4/1939
1730.	*Listo*	Swim Barge		78'0"		20'11"	7'6"	160			London	4/1939	4/1939
1731.	*Morecambe Bay*	Swim Barge		78'0"		20'11"	7'6"	160			London	4/1939	5/1939
1732.	*Poole Bay*	Swim Barge		78'0"		20'11"	7'6"	160			London	4/1939	5/1939
1733.	*Barle*	Swim Barge		78'0"		20'11"	7'6"	160			London	12/1939	12/1939
1734.	*Beane*	Swim Barge		78'0"		20'11"	7'6"	160			London	12/1939	12/1939
1735.	*Tetrach*	Swim Barge		78'0"		20'11"	7'6"	160			London	9/1939	9/1939
1736.	*Seraskier*	Swim Barge		78'0"		20'11"	7'6"	160			London	9/1939	9/1939
1737.	*Silverdot*	Launch Tug		43'9"	40'0"	12'0"	5'9"		Crossley	100	London	3/1939	4/1939
1738.	*Craftsman*	Swim Barge		80'0"		22'4"	6'6"	180			London	5/1939	5/1939
1739.	*Cragsman*	Swim Barge		80'0"		22'4"	6'6"	180			London	5/1939	5/1939
1740.	*Etherbeam*	Swim Barge		78'0"		20'11"	7'6"	160			London	8/1939	8/1939
1741.	*Etherbird*	Swim Barge		78'0"		20'11"	7'6"	160			London	8/1939	8/1939
1742.	*Barvie*	Swim Barge		78'0"		20'11"	7'6"	160			London	12/1939	12/1939
1743.	*Brue*	Swim Barge		78'0"		20'11"	7'6"	160			London	12/1939	12/1939
1744.	*Millgate*	Swim Barge		76'0"		17'10"	7'0"	130			London	9/1939	9/1939
1745.	*Lane End*	Swim Barge		76'0"		17'10"	7'0"	130			London	9/1939	9/1939
1746.	*Spurgrove*	Swim Barge		76'0"		17'10"	7'0"	130			London	10/1939	10/1939
1747.	*Shogmore*	Swim Barge		76'0"		17'10"	7'0"	130			London	10/1939	10/1939
1748.	*Cadmore*	Swim Barge		76'0"		17'10"	7'0"	130			London	10/1939	10/1939
1749.	*Moorend*	Swim Barge		76'0"		17'10"	7'0"	130			London	10/1939	11/1939
1750.	*Brora*	Swim Barge		78'0"		20'11"	7'6"	160			London	12/1939	1/1940
1751.	*Meavey*	Swim Barge		78'0"		20'11"	7'6"	160			London	12/1939	1/1940
1752.	*Irwell*	Swim Barge		78'0"		20'11"	7'6"	170			London	2/1940	2/1940
1753.	*C 42*	Swim Barge		78'0"		20'11"	7'6"	160			Queenborough	3/1940	6/1940
1754.	*C 91*	Swim Barge		78'0"		20'11"	7'6"	160			Queenborough	3/1940	6/1940
1755.	*Falcon Brook*	Launch Tug		35'0"	32'6"	10'6"	4'6"		Bolinder	40	London	11/1939	12/1939
1756.	*Mexshell II*	Tank Launch		49'5½"	46'0"	10'0"	5'0"		Widdop	36	Southampton	12/1939	1/1940
1757.	*E 25*	Swim Barge		85'0"		22'6"	8'0"	200			Faversham	4/1940	4/1940
1758.	*E 26*	Swim Barge		85'0"		22'6"	8'0"	200			Faversham	4/1940	4/1940
1759.	*C 92*	Swim Barge		85'0"		22'6"	8'0"	200			Queenborough	6/1940	7/1940
1760.	*C 88*	Swim Barge		86'0"		23'0"	9'0"	250			Chatham	2/1941	4/1941
1761.	*C 89*	Swim Barge		86'0"		23'0"	9'0"	250			Chatham	3/1941	5/1941
1762.	*C 90*	Swim Barge		86'0"		23'0"	9'0"	250			Chatham	3/1941	5/1941
1763.	*C 43*	Swim Barge		89'0"		24'9"	9'6"	300			Sheerness	11/1940	11/1940
1764.	*C 162*	Swim Barge		89'0"		24'9"	9'6"	300			Sheerness	11/1940	11/1940
1765.	*Min 1*	Swim Barge		78'0"		20'11"	7'6"	160			Faversham	12/1940	3/1941
1766.	*Min 2*	Swim Barge		78'0"		20'11"	7'6"	160			Faversham	12/1940	3/1941
1767.	*Min 3*	Swim Barge		78'0"		20'11"	7'6"	160			Faversham	4/1941	5/1941
1768.	*Min 4*	Swim Barge		78'0"		20'11"	7'6"	160			Faversham	4/1941	5/1941
1769.	*Min 5*	Swim Barge		78'0"		20'11"	7'6"	160			Faversham	5/1941	6/1941
1770.	*Min 6*	Swim Barge		78'0"		20'11"	7'6"	160			Faversham	5/1941	6/1941
1771.	*N A 159*	Swim Barge		85'0"		22'6"	8'0"	200			Faversham	8/1940	11/1941
1772.	*N A 160*	Swim Barge		85'0"		22'6"	8'0"	200			Faversham	9/1940	11/1941
1783.	*Engadine*	Tug		54'0"	50'0"	13'0"	6'0"		Widdop	150	London	8/1940	10/1941
1774.	*No 7*	Pontoon		35'9"		24'0"	6'7"				Chatham		1/1940
1775.	*No 8*	Pontoon		35'9"		24'0"	6'7"				Chatham		2/1940
[illegible]	[illegible]	[illegible]		126'0"	130'0"	25'0"	10'9"	400	Crossley	330	London	1/1941	4/1941

1779.	*Min 19*	Swim Barge	78′0″		20′11″	7′6″	160			Sheerness		12/1941
1780.	*Y C 75*	Dumb Barge		100′0″	22′0″	9′0″	270			Chatham	8/1941	12/1941
1781.	*Isin*	Coaster	119′6″	110′0″	24′0″	9′0″	181	Crossley	360	Turkey	4/1942	7/1942
1782.	*N A 161*	Swim Barge	85′0″		22′6″	8′0″	200			Faversham	5/1942	7/1942
1783.	*N A 162*	Swim Barge	85′0″		22′6″	8′0″	200			Faversham	5/1942	8/1942
1784.	*Bar Survey 2*	Survey Launch	54′0″	50′0″	11′6″	5′4½″		Widdop	90	Maracaibo	1/1942	5/1942
1785.	*Bar Survey 4*	Survey Launch	54′0″	50′0″	11′6″	5′4½″		Widdop	90	Maracaibo	4/1942	7/1942
1786.	*Bar Survey 1*	Pilot Launch	54′0″	50′0″	11′6″	5′4½″		Widdop	90	Maracaibo	9/1941	1/1942
1787.	*Bar Survey 3*	Pilot Launch	54′0″	50′0″	11′6″	5′4½″		Widdop	90	Maracaibo	10/1941	3/1942
1788.		Torpedo Targets	28′0″		8′0″	3′6″				Singapore		12/1940
1789.		Torpedo Targets	28′0″		8′0″	3′6″				Singapore		12/1940
1790.		Torpedo Targets	28′0″		8′0″	3′6″				Singapore		12/1940
1791.		Torpedo Targets	28′0″		8′0″	3′6″				Singapore		12/1940
1792.		Torpedo Targets	28′0″		8′0″	3′6″				Singapore		12/1940
1793.	*Mayshell*	Tank Launch	49′5½″	46′0″	10′0″	5′0″	8	Widdop	36	London		4/1941
1794.	*RN Air 1A*	FAASP Lighter	132′0″	120′0″	24′0″	9′0″		Widdop	300	Lee on Solent	1/1942	11/1942
1795.	*Mercury*	Tank Launch	49′5½″	46′0″	10′0″	5′0″	8	Widdop	36	W.Africa		11/1941
1796.	*TLC 148*	Landing Vessel	158′10½″	143′0″	30′0″	8′9½″		3 Power Napier Sealions	350 each	London	12/1941	3/1942
1797.	*Tafo*	Launch Tug	41′0″	38′0″	10′6″	5′3″		Widdop	60	London		1/1944
1798.	*Min 20*	Swim Barge	78′0″		20′11″	7′6″	160			Faversham		5/1944
1799.	*Min 21*	Swim Barge	78′0″		20′11″	7′6″	160			Faversham		5/1944
1800.	*HO 711*	Open Lighter	72′6″		20′0″	5′9″	130			London	2/1942	2/1942
1801.	*HO 712*	Open Lighter	72′6″		20′0″	5′9″	130			London	2/1942	2/1942
1802.	*HO 713*	Open Lighter	72′6″		20′0″	5′9″	130			London	5/1942	6/1942
1803.	*HO 714*	Open Lighter	72′6″		20′0″	5′9″	130			London	5/1942	7/1944
1804.	*C 615*	Naval Store Vessel	105′6″	99′6″	21′6″	8′6″	189	Widdop	180	Sheerness		4/1943
1805.	*C 616*	Naval Store Vessel	105′6″	99′0″	21′6″	8′6″	185	Widdop	180	Chatham		6/1943
1806.	*C 617*	Naval Store Vessel	105′6″	99′0″	21′6″	8′6″	185	Widdop	180	Chatham		7/1943
1807.	*1050*	RAF Refueller	45′9″		10′0″	6′3″	9	Twin Scammell	54 each	Dumbarton		2/1943
1808.	*1051*	RAF Refueller	45′9″		10′0″	6′3″	9	Twin Scammell	54 each	Dumbarton		10/1942
1809.	*1052*	RAF Refueller	45′9″		10′0″	6′3″	9	Twin Scammell	54 each	Dumbarton	10/1942	11/1942
1810.	*1053*	RAF Refueller	45′9″		10′0″	6′3″	9	Twin Scammell	54 each	Dumbarton	8/1942	9/1942
1811.	*1054*	RAF Refueller	45′9″		10′0″	6′3″	9	Twin Scammell	54 each	Dumbarton		4/1943
1812.	*1055*	RAF Refueller	45′9″		10′0″	6′3″	9	Twin Scammell	54 each	Dumbarton		1/1943
1813.	*1056*	RAF Refueller	45′9″		10′0″	6′3″	9	Twin Scammell	54 each	Dumbarton		5/1943
1814.	*1057*	RAF Refueller	45′9″		10′0″	6′3″	9	Twin Scammell	54 each	Tewkesbury		8/1943
1815.		Water Barge	95′1½″		21′0″	8′0″	210			Takoradi		9/1942
1816.	*Min 8*	Swim Barge	85′0″		22′6″	8′0″	200			Faversham	8/1942	9/1942
1817.	*Min 7*	Swim Barge	85′0″		22′6″	8′0″	200			Faversham	8/1942	9/1942
1818.	*Min 10*	Swim Barge	85′0″		22′6″	8′0″	200			Faversham	8/1942	9/1942
1819.	*Min 9*	Swim Barge	85′0″		22′6″	8′0″	200			Faversham	9/1942	9/1942
1820.	*Min 11*	Swim Barge	85′0″		22′6″	8′0″	200			Faversham	9/1942	1/1943
1821.	*Min 12*	Swim Barge	85′0″		22′6″	8′0″	200			Faversham		1/1943
1822.	*Mortar*	N A Vessel	103′1½″	95′0″	20′8″	9′0″	167	Petter	250	Upnor		12/1943
1823.	*Howitzer*	N A Vessel	103′1½″	95′0″	20′8″	9′0″	167	Petter	250	Chatham		2/1944
1824.	*Min 22*	Swim Barge	85′0″		22′6″	8′0″	200			Faversham		6/1943
1825.	*Min 23*	Swim Barge	85′0″		22′6″	8′0″	200			Faversham		6/1943
1826.	*Min 24*	Swim Barge	85′0″		22′6″	8′0″	200			Faversham		7/1943
1827.	*Min 25*	Swim Barge	85′0″		22′6″	8′0″	200			Faversham		7/1943
1828.	*501*	Dumb Lighter	180′6″	174′0″	27′11″	7′0″	500			Belgian Congo		7/1943
1829.	*502*	Dumb Lighter	180′6″	174′0″	27′11″	7′0″	500			Belgian Congo		8/1943

	Ship No.	Name	Type	Builder	Dimensions LOA	LBP	BMLD	DMLD	DW	Engine	BHP	Destination	Launch Date	Delivery Date
	1830.	*503*	Dumb Lighter		180′6″	174′0″	27′11″	7′0″	500			Belgian Congo		10/1943
1942	1831.	*C 620*	Naval Store Vessel		105′6″	99′0″	21′6″	8′6″	185	Widdop	180	Rochester		4/1944
	1832.	*C 621*	Naval Store Vessel		105′6″	99′0″	21′6″	8′6″	185	Widdop	180	Rochester		5/1944
	1833.	*TLC 350*	TLC Vessel		195′6″	175′0⅝″	30′0″	8′9½″		Twin Davey Paxmen	500 each			11/1942
	1834.	*Min 26*	Swim Barge		85′0″		22′6″	8′0″	200			Faversham		4/1944
	1835.	*Min 27*	Swim Barge		85′0″		22′6″	8′0″	200			Faversham		4/1944
1943	1836.	*701*	Dumb Lighter		216′8″	210′0″	32′0″	8′0″	700			Belgian Congo		9/1944
	1837.	*702*	Dumb Lighter		216′8″	210′0″	32′0″	8′0″	700			Belgian Congo		5/1944
	1838.	*Ripon*	Twin Screw Ferry		172′2″	160′0″	30′0″	18′0″		Twin Crossley	480 each			9/1945
	1839.	*Seafox*	Twin Screwferry		172′2″	160′0″	30′0″	18′0″		Twin Crossley (Engine: Crabtree, Lowestoft) (Boiler: Cochran)	480 each			11/1946
	1840.	*Vic 56*	Coastal Lighter		85′0″	80′0″	20′0″	9′6″	166	Steam	140 ihp			1945
	1841.	*Vic 57*	Coastal Lighter		85′0″	80′0″	20′0″	9′6″	166	Steam	140 ihp			6/1946
	1842.	*Nervo*	Coastal Lighter		85′0″	80′0″	20′0″	9′6″	180	Kelvin	60	Rochester		12/48
	1843.	*Knox*	Coastal Lighter		85′0″	80′0″	20′0″	9′6″	180	Kelvin	60	Rochester		5/1949
1844.	1844	*Goldhind*	Motor Coaster		180′6″	165′5″	30′0′	11′0″	580	Crossley	480	London		4/1949
	1845.	*Goldlynx*	Motor Coaster		180′6″	165′5″	30′0″	11′0″	580	Crossley	576	London		2/1950
	1846.		Dumb Oil Barge			52′6″	10′6″	4′0″	20			Belgian Congo		3/1945
	1847.	*C 647*	Naval Store Vessel		105′6″	99′0″	21′6″	8′6″	185	Widdop	180	Sheerness		11/1948
	1848.	*C 648*	Naval Store Vessel		105′6″	99′0″	21′6″	8′6″	185	Widdop	180	Sheerness		6/1949
	1849.													
	1850.													
	1351.		Dumb Lighter		72′6″		20′0″	5′9″	90			Venezuela		4/1946
	1352.		Dumb Lighter		72′6″		20′0″	5′9″	90			Venezuela		4/1946
	1353.		Dumb Lighter		72′6″		20′0″	5′9″	90			Venezuela		5/1946
	1354.	*Stanza*	Swim Barge		85′0″		22′6″	8′0″	200			Rochester		5/1947
	1355.	*Replacer*	Swim Barge		85′0″		22′6″	8′0″	200			London		6/1947
	1356.	*Langham*	Swim Barge		85′0″		22′6″	8′0″	200			London		7/1947
	1357.	*Marconi*	Swim Barge		85′0″		22′6″	8′0″	200			London		7/1947
	1358.	*Everest*	Swim Barge		85′0″		22′6″	8′0″	200			London		7/1947
	1359.	*Steve*	Swim Barge		85′0″		22′6″	8′0″	200			London		8/1947
	1360.	*Ern*	Swim Barge		85′0″		22′6″	8′0″	200			London		10/1947
	1361.	*Empire Miller*	Swim Barge		85′0″		22′6″	8′0″	200			London		12/1947
	1362.	*Taurus*	Swim Barge		85′0″		22′6″	8′0″	200			London		3/1948
	1363.	*Duke of York*	Swim Barge		85′0″		22′6″	8′0″	200			London		2/1948
	1364.	*Angus*	Swim Barge		85′0″		22′6″	8′0″	200			London		3/1948
	1365.	*Anson*	Swim Barge		85′0″		22′6″	8′0″	200			London		4/1948
1945	1866.	*George Pickering*	Motor Barge		88′0″	82′0″	18′6″	7′6″	85	Widdop	120	Freetown		7/1947
	1867.	*Nigretia*	Motor Tug		54′0″	50′0″	13′0″	6′0″		Widdop	120	Lagos		10/1947
	1868.	*Soeanggi*	Motor Tug		54′0″	50′0″	12′0″	5′4½″		Widdop	90	Batavia		1/1948
	1869.	*Soebang*	Motor Tug		54′0″	50′0″	12′0″	5′4½″		Widdop	90	Balik Papan		2/1948
	1870.	*Mercedes*	Motor Tug		70′0″	66′0″	17′6″	8′6″		Crossley	480	London		7/1953
1946	1871.	*Royal Ash*	Swim Barge		105′0″		24′9″	9′6″	381			London		10/1947
	1872.	*Royal Oak*	Swim Barge		105′0″		24′9″	9′6″	381			London		12/1947
	1873.	*Royal Beech*	Swim Barge		105′0″		24′9″	9′6″	381			London		12/1947
	1874.	*Lucine*	Swim Barge		105′0″		24′9″	9′6″	381			London		1/1948

	1879.	*Hayhow*	Swim Barge	78′0″		20′11″	7′6″	160			Rochester	5/1948
	1880.	*Rayner*	Swim Barge	78′0″		20′11″	7′6″	160			Rochester	6/1948
	1881.	*Watson*	Swim Barge	78′0″		20′11″	7′6″	160			Rochester	1/1949
	1882.	*Wright*	Swim Barge	78′0″		20′11″	7′6″	160			Rochester	4/1949
	1883.	*Rands*	Swim Barge	78′0″		20′11″	7′6″	160			Rochester	6/1949
	1884.	*Smy*	Swim Barge	78′0″		20′11″	7′6″	160			Rochester	6/1949
	1885.		Open Lighter		92′0″	26′0″	7′0″	200			Burutu	2/1948
	1886.		Open Lighter		92′0″	26′0″	7′0″	200			Burutu	2/1948
	1887.	*Atap*	Motor Tug	54′0″	50′0″	13′0″	6′0″		Widdop	150	Sapele	6/1949
	1888.	*Garnock*	Swim Barge	78′0″		20′11′	7′6″	160			London	9/1950
	1889.	*Eskin*	Swim Barge	78′0″		20′11″	7′6″	160			London	9/1950
	1890.	*Mark*	Swim Barge	78′0″		20′11″	7′6″	160			London	1/1951
	1891.	*Madrid*	Swim Barge	78′0″		20′11″	7′6″	160			London	5/1951
	1892.	*Alkali*	Tank Barge	87′2″	86′2″	16′4½″	5′6″	115			London	8/1948
1947	1893.	*Sir Frederick*	Twin Screw Barge		75′0″	13′0″	4′6″	40	Twin 2 cyl McLaren	44 each	Demerara	9/1950
	1894.	*Wiramia*	Dumb Lighter		75′0″	13′0″	4′6″	50			Demerara	12/1949
	1895.	*Wampari*	Dumb Lighter		75′0″	13′0″	4′6″	50			Demerara	1/1950
	1896.		Dumb Barge	216′8″	210′0″	32′0″	8′0″	700			Belgian Congo	10/1950
	1897.		Dumb Barge	216′8″	210′0″	32′0″	8′0″	700			Belgian Congo	1/1951
	1898.		Dumb Barge	216′8″	210′0″	32′0″	8′0″	700			Belgian Congo	4/1951
	1899.		Dumb Barge	216′8″	210′0″	32′0″	8′0″	700			Belgian Congo	8/1951
	1900.	*Cresta*	Motor Tug	54′0″	50′0″	13′0″	6′0″		Widdop	150	Sapele	8/1949
	1901.		Open Lighter		92′0″	26′0″	7′0″	200			Burutu	6/1949
	1902.		Open Lighter		92′0″	26′0″	7′0″	200			Burutu	7/1949
	1903.	*Gwalior*	Swim Barge	85′0″		22′6″	8′0″	200			London	7/1949
	1904.	*Lyon*	Swim Barge	85′0″		22′6″	8′0″	200			London	11/1949
	1905.	*St Hugh*	Swim Barge	85′0″		22′6″	8′0″	200			London	12/1949
	1906.	*Fontwell*	Swim Barge	85′0″		22′6″	8′0″	200			London	10/1950
	1907.	*Foster*	Swim Barge	85′0″		22′6″	8′0″	200			London	4/1951
	1908.	*Almond*	Swim Barge	85′0″		22′6″	8′0″	200			London	5/1951
	1909.	*Frederick Peters*	Launch Tug	41′0″	38′0″	10′6″	5′3″		Widdop	60	Takoradi	10/1948
	1910.	*Vigo*	Swim Barge	78′0″		20′11″	7′6″	160			London	6/1951
	1911.	*Manilla*	Swim Barge	78′0″		20′11″	7′6″	160			London	6/1951
	1912.	*Rom*	Swim Barge	85′0″		22′6″	8′0″	200			London	5/1951
	1913.	*Singleton*	Swim Barge	85′0″		22′6″	8′0″	200			London	8/1951
	1914.	*Storrington*	Swim Barge	85′0″		22′6″	8′0″	200			London	8/1951
	1915.	*Silverbelle*	Swim Barge	85′0″		22′6″	8′0″	200			London	10/1951
	1916.	*Goldband*	Swim Barge	85′0″		22′6″	8′0″	200			London	10/1951
	1917.	*Persil*	Swim Barge	85′0″		22′6″	8′0″	200			London	9/1951
	1918.		Dumb Lighter	72′6″		22′0″	5′9″	130			Aden	10/1949
	1919.		Dumb Lighter	72′6″		22′0″	5′9″	130			Aden	10/1949
	1920.	*Marina*	Swim Barge	78′0″		20′11″	7′6″	160			London	1/1952
	1921.	*Stronghold*	Swim Barge	78′0″		20′11″	7′6″	160			London	1/1952
	1922.	*Guinea Gold*	Swim Barge	78′0″		20′11″	7′6″	160			London	2/1952
	1923.	*Seraflo*	Swim Barge	78′0″		20′11″	7′6″	160			London	2/1952
	1924.	*Silverdial*	Motor Tug	83′7½″	77′6″	21′0″	9′6″		Atlas Polar	605	London	7/1950
	1925.	*Silverbeam*	Motor Tug	83′7½″	77′6″	21′0″	9′6″		Atlas Polar	605	London	3/1951
1948	1926.	*Kwami*	Launch Tug	41′0″	38′0″	10′6″	5′3″		Widdop	60	Takoradi	5/1950
	1927.		Steel Unicraft	60′0″		12′0″	4′3″				Nigeria	6/1950
	1928.		Steel Unicraft	60′0″		12′0″	4′3″				Nigeria	6/1950
	1929.		Steel Unicraft	60′0″		12′0″	4′3″				Nigeria	7/1950

	Ship No.	Name	Type	Builder	Dimensions LOA	LBP	BMLD	DMLD	DW	Engine	BHP	Destination	Launch Date	Delivery Date
	1930.		Steel Unicraft		60'0"		12'0"	4'3"				Nigeria		7/1950
	1931.	*H O 745*	Open Lighter			72'6"	20'0"	5'9"	130			Takoradi		11/1950
	1932.	*H O 746*	Open Lighter			72'6"	20'0"	5'9"	130			Takoradi		11/1950
	1933.	*H O 747*	Open Lighter			72'6"	20'0"	5'9"	130			Takoradi		2/1951
	1934.	*H O 748*	Open Lighter			72'6"	20'0"	5'9"	130			Takoradi		1/1951
	1935.	*H O 749*	Open Lighter			71'6"	20'0"	5'9"	130			Takoradi		4/1951
	1936.	*H O 750*	Open Lighter			72'6"	20'0"	5'9"	130			Takoradi		4/1951
	1937.	*Kofi*	Launch Tug		41'0"	38'0"	10'6"	5'3"		Widdop	60	Takoradi		5/1950
	1938.	*Barlight No.3*	Dumb Lighter		72'6"		20'0"	5'9"	130			Lagos		12/1950
	1939.	*Barlight No.4*	Dumb Lighter		72'6"		20'0"	5'9"	130			Lagos		12/1950
1949	1940.	*Placate*	Motor Tug		54'4½"	50'0"	13'0"	6'0"		Crossley	150	London		5/1951
	1941.	*Plashy*	Motor Tug		45'2½"	41'6"	12'6"	5'10½"		Crossley	90	London		8/1951
	1942.	*Plaudit*	Motor Tug		45'2½"	41'6"	12'6"	5'10½"		Crossley	90	London		10/1951
1950	1943.	*Wisk*	Swim Barge		85'0"		22'6"	8'0"	200			London		9/1951
	1944.	*Alamein*	Swim Barge		85'0"		22'6"	8'0"	200			London		12/1951
	1945.	*Abo*	Swim Barge		85'0"		22'6"	8'0"	200			London		1/1952
	1946.	*Asmara*	Swim Barge		85'0"		22'6"	8'0"	200			London		1/1952
	1947.	*Panda*	Launch Tug		41'6"	38'0"	10'6"	5'3"		Widdop	60	Lagos		2/1953
	1948.	*Panko*	Launch Tug		41'6"	38'0"	10'6"	5'3"		Widdop	60	Lagos		2/1953
	1949.	*Medusa*	Motor Tug		50'0"	46'0"	14'0"	6'6"		Crossley	150	London		3/1953
	1950.	*Daren*	Swim Barge		78'0"		20'11"	7'6"	160			London		4/1952
	1951.	*St Abbs*	Swim Barge		78'0"		20'11"	7'6"	160			London		3/1952
	1952.	*St Kitts*	Swim Barge		78'0"		20'11"	7'6"	160			London		3/1952
1951	1953.	*Balcombe*	Swim Barge		78'0"		20'11"	7'6"	160			London		4/1952
	1954.	*Brede*	Swim Barge		78'0"		20'11"	7'6"	160			London		4/1952
	1955.	*Chartwell*	Swim Barge		78'0"		20'11"	7'6"	160			London		9/1952
	1956.	*Cooden*	Swim Barge		78'0"		20'11"	7'6"	160			London		9/1952
	1957.	*Ifield*	Swim Barge		78'0"		20'11"	7'6"	160			London		10/1952
	1958.	*Sidley*	Swim Barge		78'0"		20'11"	7'6"	160			London		10/1952
	1959.	*Armenia*	Swim Barge		85'0"		22'6"	8'0"	200			London		6/1952
	1960.	*Akyab*	Swim Barge		85'0"		22'6"	8'0"	200			London		7/1952
	1961.	*Aleppo*	Swim Barge		85'0"		22'6"	8'0"	200			London		7/1952
	1962.	*Ararat*	Swim Barge		85'0"		22'6"	8'0"	200			London		6/1952
	1963.	*Dunedin*	Swim Barge		85'0"		22'6"	8'0"	200			London		6/1953
	1964.	*Gisborne*	Swim Barge		85'0"		22'6"	8'0"	200			London		7/1953
	1965.	*Quex*	Swim Barge		85'0"		22'6"	8'0"	200			London		8/1953
	1966.	*Byland*	Swim Barge		86'0"		23'0"	9'0"	250			London		15/1/53
	1967.	*Kirkham*	Swim Barge		86'0"		23'0"	9'0"	250			London		20/2/53
	1968.	*Thornton*	Swim Barge		86'0"		23'0"	9'0"	250			London		11/3/53
	1969.	*Tintern*	Swim Barge		86'0"		23'0"	9'0"	250			London		10/4/53
	1970.	*Stratonic*	Swim Barge		86'0"		23'0"	9'0"	250			London		6/7/53
	1971.	*Stratoshere*	Swim Barge		86'0"		23'0"	9'0"	250			London		16/7/53
	1972.	*Acre*	Swim Barge		86'0"		23'0"	9'0"	250			London		16/9/53
	1973.	*Adept*	Swim Barge		86'0"		23'0"	9'0"	250			London		13/10/53
	1974.	*Agile*	Swim Barge		86'0"		23'0"	9'0"	250			London		25/11/53
	1975.	*Aide*	Swim Barge		86'0"		23'0"	9'0"	250			London		7/12/53
	1976.	*Lobe*	Motor Tug		68'6"	63'0"	17'0"	7'3"		Twin Widdop	120 each	Lagos		30/10/52
	1977.	*Bluff*	Swim Barge		85'0"		22'6"	8'0"	200			London		16/12/53
					[illegible]		22'6"	8'0"	200			London		16/12/53

	1981.	*Stratover*	Swim Barge	85′0″	22′6″	8′0″	200	London	22/3/54
	1982.	*Strathithe*	Swim Barge	85′0″	22′6″	8′0″	200	London	22/3/54
	1983.	*Christchurch*	Swim Barge	85′0″	22′6″	8′0″	200	London	11/6/54
	1984.	*Lyttelton*	Swim Barge	85′0″	22′6″	8′0″	200	London	11/6/54
	1985.	*Invercargill*	Swim Barge	85′0″	22′6″	8′0″	200	London	12/7/54
	1986.	*Rotorua*	Swim Barge	85′0″	22′6″	8′0″	200	London	12/7/54
	1987.	*Westport*	Swim Barge	85′0″	22′6″	8′0″	200	London	26/11/54
	1988.	*Wanganui*	Swim Barge	85′0′	22′6″	8′0″	200	London	26/11/54
	1989.	*Kuwait*	Tank Barge	85′0″	23′6″	8′0″	185	London	29/2/54
	1990.	*Tampico*	Tank Barge	85′0″	23′6″	8′0″	185	London	5/1/55
	1991.	*Stanlow*	Tank Barge	85′0″	23′6″	8′0″	185	London	21/1/55
	1992.	*Eccles*	Tank Barge	85′0″	23′6″	8′0″	185	London	9/3/55
	1993.	*Saltend*	Tank Barge	85′0″	23′6″	8′0″	185	London	18/3/55
	1994.	*Miri*	Tank Barge	85′0″	23′6″	8′0″	185	London	12/4/55
	1995.	*Lingdale*	Swim Barge	87′0″	22′6″	8′0″	220	London	1/3/54
	1996.	*Teesdale*	Swim Barge	87′0″	22′6″	8′0″	220	London	30/4/54
	1997.	*Garsdale*	Swim Barge	87′0″	22′6″	8′0″	220	London	30/4/54
	1998.	*Bedale*	Swim Barge	87′0″	22′6″	8′0″	220	London	29/3/54
1952	1999.	*Rank*	Swim Barge	78′0″	20′11″	7′6″	160	London	13/5/54
	2000.	*Robinson*	Swim Barge	78′0″	20′11″	7′6″	160	London	13/5/54
	2001.	*Happy*	Swim Barge	78′0″	20′11″	7′6″	160	Rochester	12/8/54
	2002.	*Dopey*	Swim Barge	78′0″	20′11″	7′6″	160	Rochester	12/8/54
	2003.	*Grumpy*	Swim Barge	78′0″	20′11″	7′6″	160	Rochester	11/10/54
	2004.	*Sleepy*	Swim Barge	78′0″	20′11″	7′6″	160	Rochester	11/10/54
	2005.	*Sneezy*	Swim Barge	78′0″	20′11″	7′6″	160	Rochester	28/12/54
	2006.	*Bashful*	Swim Barge	78′0″	20′11″	7′6″	160	Rochester	24/1/55
	2007.	*Taylor*	Swim Barge	78′0″	20′11″	7′6″	160	London	8/6/55
	2008.	*Gaze*	Swim Barge	78′0″	20′11″	7′6″	160	London	8/6/55
	2009.	*Kidd*	Swim Barge	78′0″	20′11″	7′6″	160	London	4/7/55
	2010.	*Mumford*	Swim Barge	78′0″	20′11″	7′6″	160	London	4/7/55
	2011.	*Sentinel*	Swim Barge	78′0″	20′11″	7′6″	160	Rochester	17/8/56
	2012.	*Spark*	Swim Barge	78′0″	20′11″	7′6″	160	Rochester	17/8/56
	2013.	*Stygian*	Swim Barge	78′0″	20′11″	7′6″	160	Rochester	24/10/56
	2014.	*Snapper*	Swim Barge	78′0″	20′11″	7′6″	160	Rochester	19/12/56
	2015.	*Storm*	Swim Barge	78′0″	20′11″	7′6″	160	Rochester	19/12/56
	2016.	*Sturdy*	Swim Barge	78′0″	20′11″	7′6″	160	Rochester	15/1/57
	2017.	*Fishbourne*	Swim Barge	78′0″	20′11″	7′6″	160	London	27/7/62
	2018.	*Calbourne*	Swim Barge	78′0″	20′11″	7′6″	160	London	27/7/62
	2019.	*Hamper M1*	Hopper Barge	100′0″	24′10″	8′7″	300	London	6/11/61
	2020.	*Howler MG*	Hopper Barge	100′0″	24′10″	8′7″	300	London	30/1/62
	2021.		Swim Barge	78′0″	20′11″	7′6″	160		
	2022.		Swim Barge	78′0″	20′11″	7′6″	160		
	2023.	*Ashey*	Swim Barge	78′0″	20′11″	7′6″	160	London	7/2/58
	2024.	*Alverstone*	Swim Barge	78′0″	20′11″	7′6″	160	London	7/2/58
	2025.	*Odiam*	Swim Barge	78′0″	20′11″	7′6″	160	London	25/7/60
	2026.	*Ironshaft*	Swim Barge	78′0″	20′11″	7′6″	160	London	14/12/60
	2027.	*Oporto*	Swim Barge	78′0″	20′11″	7′6″	160	London	25/7/60
	2028.	*Ironflint*	Swim Barge	78′0″	20′11″	7′6″	160	London	28/3/61
	2029.	*Earn*	Swim Barge	78′0″	20′11″	7′6″	160	London	24/7/62
	2030.		Swim Barge	78′0″	20′11″	7′6″	160	London	7/1962
	2031.	*South Stoke*	Swim Barge	86′0″	23′0″	9′0″	250	London	18/4/62

	Ship No.	Name	Type	Builder	Dimensions LOA	LBP	BMLD	DMLD	DW	Engine	BHP	Destination	Launch Date	Delivery Date
	2032.		Swim Barge		78′0″		20′11″	7′6″	160			London		4/1962
	2033.		Swim Barge		78′0″		20′11″	7′6″	160					
	2034.		Swim Barge		78′0″		20′11″	7′6″	160					
	2035.	*Wasp*	Motor Tug		65′0″	60′5″	15′6″	7′0″		Widdop	180	Freetown		17/5/53
	2036.	*Panpo*	Launch Tug		43′6″	40′6″	10′6″	5′3″		Widdop	90	Lagos		22/4/54
	2037.	*Panya*	Launch Tug		43′6″	40′6″	10′6″	5′3″		Widdop	90	Lagos		22/4/54
1953	2038.	*Kwasi*	Launch Tug		43′6″	40′6″	10′6″	5′3″		Widdop	90	Takoradi		10/11/54
	2039.	*Yapton*	Swim Barge		86′0″		23′0″	9′0″	250			London		3/7/59
	2040.	*Caprice*	Swim Barge		85′0″		23′6″	8′0″	220			London		14/3/61
	2041.	*Cardiff*	Swim Barge		85′0″		23′6″	8′0″	220			London		14/3/61
	2042.	*Dale Park*	Swim Barge		86′0″		23′0″	9′0″	250			London		7/4/60
	2043.	*Anyako*	Motor Launch			24′0″	6′6″	3′6″		Lister	20	Takoradi		19/6/59
	2044.	*Mayhew*	Swim Barge		85′0″		22′6″	8′0″	200			London		21/10/54
	2045.	*Bit*	Swim Barge		85′0″		22′6″	8′0″	200			London		21/10/54
	2046.	*Charles Carter*	Swim Barge		78′0″		20′11″	7′6″	160			London		13/8/55
	2047.	*Sunmill*	Swim Barge		78′0″		20′11″	7′6″	160			London		13/8/55
	2048.	*Bembridge*	Swim Barge		78′0″		20′11″	7′6″	160			London		6/10/55
	2049.	*Bonchurch*	Swim Barge		78′0″		20′11″	7′6″	160			London		6/10/55
	2050.	*Chale*	Swim Barge		78′0″		20′11″	7′6″	160			London		29/11/55
	2051.	*Osborne*	Swim Barge		78′0″		20′11″	7′6″	160			London		29/11/55
	2052.	*Trust*	Swim Barge		78′0″		20′11″	7′6″	160			London		27/3/57
	2053.	*Triumph*	Swim Barge		78′0″		20′11″	7′6″	160			London		27/3/57
	2054.	*Leadenhall*	Swim Barge		85′0″		23′6″	8′0″	220			London		10/10/58
	2055.	*Phillpot*	Swim Barge		85′0″		23′6″	8′0″	220			London		10/10/58
	2056.	*Eastcheap*	Swim Barge		85′0″		23′6″	8′0″	220			London		10/10/58
	2057.	*Crosswall*	Swim Barge		85′0″		23′6″	8′0″	220			London		24/3/59
	2058.	*Prescot*	Swim Barge		85′0″		23′6″	8′0″	220			London		24/3/59
	2059.	*Cullum*	Swim Barge		85′0″		23′6″	8′0″	220			London		24/3/59
	2060.	*B P Haulier*	River Tanker		148′0″	140′0″	27′6″	8′6″	300	Blackstone	242	Faversham		31/8/55
	2061.		Steel Pontoon		40′0″		16′0½″	3′0″				Rochester		2/3/54
1954	2062.	*Lightship*	Swim Barge		86′0″		23′0″	9′0″	250			London		24/5/55
	2063.	*Lordship*	Swim Barge		86′0″		23′0″	9′0″	250			London		24/5/55
	2064.	*Kingship*	Swim Barge		86′0″		23′0″	9′0″	250			London		20/7/55
	2065.	*Worship*	Swim Barge		86′0″		23′0″	9′0″	250			London		20/7/55
	2066.	*Township*	Swim Barge		86′0″		23′0″	9′0″	250			London		15/9/55
	2067.	*Hardship*	Swim Barge		86′0″		23′0″	9′0″	250			London		15/9/55
	2068.	*Akaroa*	Swim Barge		85′0″		22′6″	8′0″	200			London		18/1/56
	2069.	*Ashurton*	Swim Barge		85′0″		22′6″	8′0″	200			London		18/1/56
	2070.	*Burwood*	Swim Barge		85′0″		22′6″	8′0″	200			London		8/3/56
	2071.	*Greytown*	Swim Barge		85′0′		22′6″	8′0″	200			London		8/3/56
	2072.	*Longburn*	Swim Barge		85′0″		22′6″	8′0″	200			London		9/4/56
	2073.	*Picton*	Swim Barge		85′0″		22′6″	8′0″	200			London		9/4/56
	2074.	*Jumbo*	Mooring Vessel			70′0″	24′0″	9′6″				Rochester		23/7/56
	2075.	*Lastholme*	Motor Barge			94′0″	20′0″	6′0″	95	Twin Harbourmaster	60 each	Conyer		11/1/56
	2076.	*Headsail*	Tank Barge		105′0″		24′9″	9′6″	300			London		9/1/56
	2077.	*Lugsail*	Tank Barge		105′0″		24′9″	9′6″	300			London		27/1/56
	2078.	*Staysail*	Tank Barge		105′0″		24′9″	9′6″	300			London		19/4/56
	2079.	*Topsail*	Tank Barge		105′0″		24′9″	9′6″	300			London		19/4/56
			[illegible]		105′0″		24′9″	9′6″	300			London		26/7/56

	2083.												
	2084.												
	2085.												
	2086.												
	2087.												
	2088.	*Nightwatch*	Tank Barge	85'0"		22'9"	8'0"	220			London		30/11/56
	2089.	*Calshot*	Swim Barge	85'0"		22'9"	8'0"	200			London		30/11/56
	2090.												
1955	2091.		Tank Barge	48'0"		14'6"	5'6"				Sapele		1/7/55
	2092.	Soundbarrier	Swim Barge	86'0"		23'0"	9'0"	250			London		7/11/56
	2093.	*Supersonic*	Swim Barge	86'0"		23'0"	9'0"	250			London		7/11/56
	2094.	*Obeche*	Canal Barge	86'0"		18'6"	5'8"	120			London		8/10/56
	2095.	*Abura*	Canal Barge	86'0"		18'6"	5'8"	120			London		8/10/56
	2096.	*Agba*	Canal Barge	86'0"		18'6"	5'6"	120			London		21/11/56
	2097.	*Wawa*	Canal Barge	86'0"		18'6"	5'8"	120			London		21/11/56
	2098.	*Stonechurch*	Tank Barge	86'0"		23'6"	8'0"	150			Erith		18/3/57
	2099.	*Stonecourt*	Tank Barge	85'0"		23'6"	8'0"	150			Erith		4/6/57
	2100.	*Stonecrest*	Tank Barge	85'0"		23'6"	8'0"	150			Erith		28/6/57
	2101.		Dummy Pier	50'0"		20'0"	3'6"				Rochester		28/2/57
	2102.	*H.G. Bloomfield*	Swim Barge	90'0"		24'10"	8'6"	275			London		8/11/57
	2103.	*J.S. Graham*	Swim Barge	90'0"		24'10"	8'6"	275			London		8/11/57
	2104.	*Daniellia*	Motor Barge		96'0"	20'6"	6'6"		AEC Marine	100	Sapele		16/7/56
1956	2105.	*Ulco*	Motor Tanker	162'6"	33'0"	10'6"			Deutz	500	London		21/5/58
	2106.	*Irongate*	Swim Barge	87'0"		22'6"	8'0"	220			London		6/3/58
	2107.	*Ironduke*	Swim Barge	87'0"		22'6"	8'0"	220			London		6/3/58
	2108.	*SHB Seahorse*	Maintenance Tender		80'0"	26'0"	10'0"		Twin Gardner	152 each	Southampton		26/11/58
	2109.	*Ket*	Swim Barge	98'11"		20'10"	9'0"	260			London		23/6/58
	2110.	*Killure*	Swim Barge	98'11"		20'10"	9'0"	260			London		23/6/58
	2111.	*Nore*	Swim Barge	78'0"		20'11"	7'6"	160			London		29/7/58
	2112.	*Kent Swale*	Hatched Lighter	78'0"		19'0"	5'0"	75			Faversham		31/7/58
	2113.	*Brading*	Swim Barge	78'0"		20'11"	7'6"	160			London		29/7/58
1957	2114.		Dumb Barge	30'0"		10'0"	4'6"				Sudan		5/11/58
	2115.	*Lord Devonport*	Motor Tug		77'0"	21'0"	11'6"		British Polar	935	London		10/7/59
	2116.	*Lord Ritchie*	Motor Tug		77'0"	21'0"	11'6"		British Polar	935	London		19/1/60
	2117.	*Lord Waverley*	Motor Tug		77'0"	21'0"	11'6"		British Polar	935	London		17/5/61
	2118.	*P.L.A. No 18184*	Reclamation Vessel		130'0"	38'0"	13'6"		Polar	1960	London		18/1/61
	2119.	*Wakefield*	Motor Tanker	92'4"	88'0"	17'9"	7'0"	100	Gardner	152	London		7/11/59
1959	2120.	*Toledo*	Steel Sailing Yacht	35'0"		9'0"	7'6"		Albin	10			
	2121.	*Alice*	Swim Barge	68'0"		18'0"	6'9"				London		1/2/60
	2122.	*Cosray 25*	Motor Tug	70'0"	65'0"	18'6"	8'0"		Twin Crossley	274 each			18/6/60
1960	2123.	*Danby Cross*	Motor Tug	87'0"	80'0"	23'6"	11'0"		Crossley	750	River Tees		3/8/61
	2124.	*Humphrey Morris*	M O Cutter	97'4"	87'0"	21'0"	9'6"		Ruston	655	London		26/2/62
	2125.		Ferry		15'0"	10'0"	2'6"				Sudan		18/8/60
	2126.		Ferry		15'0"	10'0"	2'6"				Sudan		18/8/60
	2127.	*Sun XXIV*	Motor Tug		82'6"	22'6"	11'0"		Mirrless	720	London	12/61	29/5/62
	2128.	*The Duchess*	Motor Coaster	170'3"	160'0"	28'0"	11'6"	530	Newbury	400	London		28/3/63
	2129.	*Capacity*	Motor Coaster	170'3"	160'0"	28'0"	11'6"	530	Newbury	400	London		24/10/63
1961	2130.		Pier Pontoon	30'0¾"		12'1"	3'6"				Rochester		24/11/61
	2131.	*James P*	Motor Barge	111'9"	106'4"	22'0"	9'6"	300	Skandia	150	London		5/12/63
	2132.	*Curlew*	Harbour Launch	40'0"	37'4½"	12'0"	6'0"		Caterpillar	150	Freetown		11/6/63
	2133.	*Broadness*	Salvage Vessel		100'0"	28'0"	11'0"		Twin Diesel Electric	265 each	London		9/3/65

Ship No.	Name	Type	Builder	Dimensions LOA	LBP	BMLD	DMLD	DW	Engine	BHP	Destination	Launch Date	Delivery Date
2134.	*Stoneness*	Salvage Vessel			100′0″	28′0″	11′0″		Twin Diesel Electric	265	London		15/12/65
2135.	*Victor Allcard*	M O Launch		59′3″	51′0″	14′0″	7′0″		Gardner	230	London		21/1/65
2136.	*Binsted*	Swim Barge		86′0″		24′0″	9′0″	265			London		1/8/64
2137.	*Burpham*	Swim Barge		86′0″		24′0″	9′0″	265			London		21/3/65
2138.	*Sun III*	Motor Tug		93′8½″	86′0″	24′0″	12′3″		Mirrless	1340	London		22/4/66
2139.	*Kurra-Falls*	Passenger Launch		3517″		11′0″	6′0″		Kelvin	150	Lagos		1/7/66
2140.	*Eileen*	Swim Barge		78′0″		20′11″	7′6″	160			London		5/7/66
2141	*Angmering*	Swim Barge		86′0″		24′0″	9′0″	285			London		10/11/66
2142	*Ashington*	Swim Barge		86′0″		24′0″	9′0″	285			London		29/11/66
2143	*Ashurst*	Swim Barge		86′0″		24′0″	9′0″	285			London		21/12/66
2144	*Sun XXVII*	Motor Tug		115′0″	105′0″	28′0″	13′3″		Mirrless	2100	London		12/1968
	Nicholas	Swim Barge											1966
	Greybear	Welded Swim Barge											
	Greyfox	Welded Swim Barge											
	Denton	Personnel Launch										After closure	Begun 1969

Footnotes
1. Ship No. is Pollocks assigned Ship Number.
2. All dimensions are given in feet and inches.
3. Builder given where known, if not Pollocks.
   * on list from Ship Number 889 indicates vessel not built at Faversham.

Abbreviations used

L	length
B	breadth
D	depth of hold
HP	high pressure cylinder
MP	medium pressure cylinder
LP	low pressure cylinder
ST	stroke
LOA	length over all
LBP	length between perpendiculars
BMLD	breadth moulded
DMLD	depth moulded
DW	dry weight/tonnage

Changes of Name

Ship No. 190 *Ember* — formerly *Crane*
Ship No. 192 *Halo* — formerly *Blake*

Ship No. 217 *Guida* — formerly *Dunree*

Ship No. 264 *Adur II* — formerly *Radiant*
Ship No. 270 *Fortaleza* — later *Comet*
Ship No. 296 *Catita* — formerly *Cerebus*
Ship No. 297 *Rachel* — formerly *Cervate*

Ship No. 312 *Travers* — later *Crudoleo*
Ship No. 321 *Beluga* — formerly *Restorer*
Ship No. 322 *Helvetia* — formerly *Resource*

Ship No. 450 *Enid* — formerly *Suprema*

Ship No. 485 *Clovis* — formerly *Esplendour*
Ship No. 499 *Lady Sybil* — formerly *Anne*

Ship No. 527 *Ben Johnson* — formerly Ialine

Ship No. 566 *Bunga* — formerly *Miri*
Ship No. 576 *The Miller* — later *Arthur Gamman*
Ship No. 580 *Brighstone* — formerly *Eliza Holt*

Ship No. 630 *Felita* — formerly *Sir William*

Ship No. 638 *Mary Tavy* — formerly *New Collector*
Ship No. 648 *Envoy* — formerly *Empress*
Ship No. 680 *X 46* — later *Nigel* and to Bristol

Ship No. 705 *Lee Lee* — later *Annuity* owned Everards
Ship No. 706 *Chiman* — formerly *Lutona*
Ship No. 714 *X 100* — later *British Toiler* owned B.P.

Ship No. 806 *Fantome II* — formerly *Belem*

Ship No. 841 *Briton* — formerly *Baroness*

Ship No. 870 *Juniata* — formerly *Sprucol*
Ship No. 871 *San Dario* — formerly *Teakol*
Ship No. 899 *Broiler* formerly *Innisbeg*

Ship No. 933 *Linton* formerly *Admiral Vernon*

Ship No. 967 *Fer* a wartime order. Sold by Darwen & Mostyn at Appledore for Anglo African Trading
It is not clear when the engine was supplied for *Buffalo*

Ship No. 1073 *Stourgate* later *Harriet Spearing*

Ship No. 1110 *Captain* formerly *Countess*
Ship No. 1117 *Pilot* formerly *Princess*

Ship No. 1194 *Lido* later *Ann M*
Ship No. 1199 *Robin Redbreast* later *Sangay*

Ship No. 1247 *Eastwick* formerly *Laybay*
Ship No. 1266 *General III* formerly *Leneh*

Ship No. 1304 *Barking* formerly *Lonie*

Ship No. 1325 *Cormooring* later *Aldous*

Ship No. 1408 *Golddrift* later *Suleskjaer*
Ship No. 1409 *Goldeve* later *Leaspray*
Ship No. 1437 *Lady Sheila* formerly *Lanada*
Ship No. 1438 *Kara* formerly *Landay*

Ship No. 1465 *Camroux I* later *The Marquis*
Ship No. 1466 *Camroux II* later *The Marchioness*

Ship No. 1510 *Tana* later *Angles*
Ship No. 1511 *Tanrec* later *Compton*
Ship No. 1512 *Widdop* launched as *Jubilee*
Ship No. 1515 *Lady Stella* later *Glas Island*

Ship No. 1776 *Empire Creek* later *Milborne*
Ship No. 1777 *Empire Crag* later *Colne Trader* later *Spithead Trader*
Ship No. 1778 *Isin* later *Imla Layteri*
Ship No. 1794 *RN Air 1A* later *Signa*

Ship No. 1832 *C621* later *Maureen Brush*

Ship No. 1842 *Nervo* originally intended as a *Vic*
Ship No. 1844 *Goldhind* later *Tawai*
Ship No. 1845 *Goldlynx* later *Ballyedward*
Ship No. 1866 *George Pickering* formerly *Kite*

Ship No. 2122 *Cosray 25* later *Grainthorpe*
Ship No. 2138 *Sun III* later *Fabian's Bay* and to Swansea

Ship No. 1306 *Ina Rose* was fitted out on the East side of the creek alongside Standard Wharf. The sheds behind remain much the same today.

Ship No. 1216 *Noni*, a tug built for use on Faversham Creek, towing a lighter down past Standard Wharf and the Big Building.

MAIN INDEX

Ship No. 1838 *Ripon*. The launch gang included Charlie Carter, George Ledner, Percy Dadson, Clarence Fowle, N. Trigg, Wilf Carter, Percy Read and Charlie Dane.

Ship No. 2060 *B.P. Haulier* was a regular visitor to the oil depot at the South end of Standard Wharf until it closed in the mid 1970s. This was one of her last trips.

Ship No. 1848 *C 648*, a Naval Store Vessel, one of a pair built in 1948, destined for Sheerness.

One of Marshall Pollock's investments in the 1940s was the Ferry Inn on the Isle of Sheppey. During the floods in 1953 supplies were delivered using a DUKW.

INDEX OF SHIPS

Index of ships mentioned in the text. The primary name of the ship is given with a previous or subsequent name in brackets.